# THE BANKNOTE YEARBOOK

# THE
# BANKNOTE
# YEARBOOK
## —FIFTH EDITION

*Edited by*
James Mackay, MA, DLitt
John W. Mussell, FRGS
and
the Editorial Team of BANKNOTE NEWS

*Consultant Editors*
Barry Boswell
Laurence Pope, LL.B Solicitor
Martin Mac Devitt

ISBN 10: 1870192796
ISBN 13: 9781870192798

Published by
TOKEN PUBLISHING LIMITED
Orchard House, Heathpark, Honiton, Devon EX14 1YD, UK
Telephone: 01404 46972   Fax: 01404 44788
e-mail: info@tokenpublishing.com   Website: www.tokenpublishing.com

Printed and bound in England by J. H. Haynes & Co. Ltd., Sparkford

# Bonhams 1793
## inc. Glendinings

Glendining's, a division of Bonhams, has been selling banknotes, coins and medals at auction since the turn of the last century. Recent results have reflected the current buoyancy of the market, with high prices being achieved for quality items.

For information about buying or selling at Bonhams please contact John Millensted on +44 (0) 20 7393 3914

Illustrated:
A Collumpton & Devonshire Bank £5 for 1809, featured in our recent sale.

**Bonhams**
Montpelier Street
Knightsbridge
London SW7 1HH
+44 (0) 20 7393 3900
+44 (0) 20 7393 3905 fax
www.bonhams.com/coins

# CONTENTS

# PREFACE

THE fifth edition of the BANKNOTE YEARBOOK, like its predecessor, has been two years in the making—perhaps we should re-title it the *Banknote Biannual*. The catalogue has been substantially expanded and English notes are now listed in three grades of condition. It is hoped to extend this feature to the notes of the Scottish and Irish banks in due course.

Another major improvement is the listing of errors and constant varieties in addition to the normal notes, and for this reason we are also including a feature describing the various errors and the technical problems from which they arise. This has been set out in a concise manner, classifying the different types of error which may be encountered, enabling the collector to recognise them and understand how they were created. We feel that this easily studied survey will prove a considerable boon to the eagle-eyed error-spotter. It will be an eye-opener to discover the level of interest in errors as reflected in the market prices quoted in this edition.

Apart from the survey of recent banknote design and a resume of the events over the period from the beginning of 2005 till the end of 2006, we have taken the opportunity to revise and update other existing features of permanent reference value.

In the previous edition we commented on the introduction of the European single currency, arguably the most important event in the entire history of paper money. Since then the Euro has extended to some of the countries which swelled the number of members in 2005–6, and even to some which, like Montenegro, are not in the European Union but which nevertheless have found it convenient to embrace the common currency.

Unlike the Euro coins, where each country has its own distinctive obverse motifs, the Euro notes have uniform designs on both sides and their origin can only be identified by the prefix letters. Although well designed and printed, there is an undeniable monotony about the Euro notes and this may well explain the curious phenomenon in Germany where "regios" are all the rage. This term has been coined to denote pieces of paper money which are apparently legal tender in a particular region of the country.

This originated in the town of Prien am Chiemsee, in Bavaria, hence the term "Chiemgauer" (something from the Chiem district). These notes were the dreamchild of a high school teacher, Christian Gelleri in 2003 as a means of stimulating the local economy. What began as a project for his students, with an initial production run of just 20 notes, has steadily expanded and more recent issues have run to as many as 2,000.

One suspects that these issues were mainly aimed at collectors and already they have quite a following in their native country, but if this takes off and spreads to other parts of Europe the market will undoubtedly harden. "Global money is wonderful for international trade and tourism," states Gelleri, "but regional money strengthens local business cycles and the culture in the region." Well, this remains to be seen, but he may well be right. After all, the precedent of Notgeld immediately springs to mind.

Certainly this development even has the Bundesbank sitting up and taking note, but a recent report from the German federal bank concludes that this local currency does not pose any threat to the national economy, far less a serious threat to the Euro.

Already "Chiemgauer" has evolved as a generic term for this local currency, although the dozen or so local authorities that have jumped on the band wagon have agreed that "regio" is preferable.

And now there are even regiocards, debit cards which function in the new-fangled local currencies. At the time of writing, 15 other districts in Germany have followed suit. The regios are traded at a modest discount which goes to local charities. Interestingly, the secret of their success is a general distrust of the Euro and a rise in national or regional pride. Perhaps the latter explains why the Scottish banks have so fiercely protected their note-issuing privileges.

At the other end of the scale we note that the latest attempt by the United States Treasury to dispense with the dollar bill and replace it with a coin has met with formidable hostility.

The USA generally has an image of innovative and forward thinking, but in the matter of its currency people are incredibly conservative. Twice before, attempts to introduce circulating dollar coins, featuring Susan B. Anthony and Sacagawea respectively, failed miserably for the simple reason that the dollar bill was not phased out.

In Scotland, pound coins were conspicuous by their absence so long as the three note-issuing banks continued to produce pound notes, and it is only since the demise of the last of the Royal Bank pounds that pound and two-pound coins have circulated freely. The Presidential series of dollar coins, planned for release every three months until all dead presidents have been portrayed—an exercise which will take ten years—represents a determined effort by the US authorities to get dollar coins into general circulation, but it is doomed to failure so long as the Father of His Country continues to adorn the dollar bill, a piece of paper currently worth about 50p or €1 with an average life of only a few weeks.

Interestingly, the Governing Council of the European Central Bank briefly considered the introduction of €1 and €2 notes late in 2004 but decided against such a move on the grounds that this would be bad for the retail sector in general and the vending machine industry in particular, not to mention the relatively high cost of printing and processing low-denomination notes. These are all sound arguments which have militated against notes of minimal value in most countries, and yet the United States has continued to ignore them.

Meanwhile, in West Africa, states bordering Nigeria have apparently been accepting ten-shilling and five-pound notes issued in 1967–68 by the erstwhile breakaway state of Biafra. These notes have even circulated to some extent in eastern Nigeria itself, although they were declared illegal 40 years ago!

The paper money market has remained remarkably buoyant during the past two years, and saleroom results reveal that records are constantly been broken. In this period we have witnessed the first prices for individual notes pass the million-pound mark (admittedly these seven-figure results occurred in the USA and actually surpassed $2 million). With the mighty dollar continuing to waver—at the time of writing it has come perilously close to two to the pound sterling—perhaps American notaphilists are finding greater security in the Treasury notes of past eras rather than the depreciated currency of the present day.

Of course these headline-grabbing results are exceptional, but we have observed a general trend of rising prices realised at auctions great and small, testifying to a steady increase of interest in paper money as a sound collectable. The strength of this market lies not in the major auction houses, however, but in the proliferation of small dealers, many of them operating by mail order or buying and selling on eBay. Paper money has the advantage over most other collectables (apart from stamps and postcards) of being readily transmissible by post in what has become a truly global market.

In producing this reference work we necessarily need to call on a number of experts in their field. As in previous editions we would particularly like to put on record the assistance we have received from our consultant editors Barry Boswell, Laurence Pope and Martin Mac Devitt. In addition thanks are also due to Michael Blackburne, Mark Brook, David Carew, Bruce Goulborn, Martin Purdy, Mark Ray, Noel Simpson and many others who have given freely of their help and advice.

9

# That was THE YEAR that was!

AN at-a-glance résumé of the main events and occurrences that affected banknotes and paper money during the past two years as reported in *Banknote News*, the note section of COIN NEWS.

## January 2005

Sadly Roy Spick, a Director of the International Bank Note Society, dies suddenly on January 7.

## February 2005

The European Central Bank increases its output of €500 notes, believed to be the preferred currency medium of the global drugs trade. Significantly, the number of forged €500 notes detected in 2004 rose to 1,136, compared with 435 in 2003.

As a result of rumours in the City of a takeover, shares in the banknote printers De La Rue rise to an all-time high of 400p by the end of the month.

## March 2005

Mavin of Singapore holds a major auction on March 19–20, including Monetary Authority of Singapore new issues with so-called "auspicious numbers" which are eagerly sought after by Chinese collectors.

Andrew Bailey, Chief Cashier of the Bank of England, signs 40 notes each denominated at £100 million. In the traditional design of the old "white fivers" but printed in red, these ultra-high value notes are used for the Bank's internal accounting purposes and thus augment the Bank's stock of 4,000 million pound notes.

Ian Gradon is appointed paper money consultant to the rapidly expanding auction division of London Coins.

## April 2005

At Noble's auction in Sydney on April 5–8 a set of Specimen notes of Australia's 1983 issue (one of only 12 such sets) sells for A$116,500. The sale realises a total of A$4.55 million.

The Maastricht Paper Money Show, organised by Jos Eijsermans, takes place at Valkenburg, The Netherlands on April 9–10. A notable feature is the display entitled "English Paper Money and its History, 1688-2004" given by Lawrence Pope. The show also coincides with the launch of the fourth edition of the *Banknote Yearbook*.

Spink dispose of the second part of the Karouni Collection at their sale on April 12. Top price is £47,300 paid for a Specimen £100 note of the Portsmouth branch of the Bank of England dated March 1912. A Bank of England manuscript note of 1804 realised £27,600.

A number of US $1,000 bills submitted to the Currency Grading and Authentication Bureau turn out to be counterfeits. As a result the Secret Service are notified and a number of arrests are made.

An exhibition entitled "Financial History of North eastern England, 1755–1937", organised by Brian Kemp, takes place at the Dales Centre, Stanhope, Co. Durham on April 16.

The death is announced of John Brangwyn Page at the age of 81. The Chief Cashier of the Bank of England from 1971 to 1981, he was the last of his line with full responsibility for the day-to-day running of the post.

Vincent Duggleby, author of the standard work on English paper money, is appointed a Member of the Most Excellent Order of the British Empire in recognition of his work as a radio presenter and financial journalist.

## May 2005

To mark the 60th anniversary of the end of World War II the Bank of England Museum stages an exhibition entitled "Business as Usual—the Bank of England and its Staff during WW2" and vividly illustrating how it coped during the dark days of the Blitz and notably the attempts by the Third Reich to destabilise sterling by the forgery of its notes. The exhibition continues till September 8.

## June 2005

US Treasurer Anna Escobedo Cabral signs her first notes as a special ceremony in Washington, DC.

Four counterfeiters are jailed for a total of 21 years at Manchester. The gang, operating from Ashton-under-Lyne, was caught as a result of a joint investigation by the US Secret Service and Scotland Yard. More than £2.5 million in forged £10 notes and $3.5 million in counterfeit US bills were seized.

The Bank of England is reported as seriously considering the adoption of polymer for £5 notes, as the average life of a fiver in the traditional rag paper is reduced by inflation to a few weeks.

De La Rue reports earnings up by 13 per cent on the previous year, largely due to the contract to print notes for the post-Saddam regime in Iraq as well as the supply of higher spec anti-counterfeit paper for many countries.

The coveted Book of the Year Award by the International Bank Note Society goes to Eng. Magdy Hanafy for his monumental work *The Egyptian Currency Note*.

## July 2005

The Bank of England and its Museum are open to the public as part of the City of London Festival on July 9.

The Royal Bank of Scotland issues a £5 note in honour of champion golfer Jack Nicklaus, only the third living person (after the Queen and the Queen Mother) to be thus honoured. The Nicklaus fiver is the ninth commemorative note from this bank in recent years and the second with a golfing theme, the previous £5 featuring the Royal and Ancient Golf Club of St Andrews and the legendary golfer Old Tom Morris.

At Noble's July auction in Sydney two Australian ten-shilling notes realise record sums. A 1913 Collins-Allen note with red serial number M000004 realised A$297,075 while a similar note with number M000005. fetches A$285,425. Both notes were presented to

Andrew Fisher, the Australian Prime Minister in May 1913. The letter from Fisher establishing their provenance is sold as a separate lot.

Gordon Brown, Chancellor of the Exchequer, demands a payment of £80 million from the Scottish and Northern Irish banks for the privilege of issuing their own notes, leading to speculation that they may relinquish this long-held tradition.

## August 2005

Claire Lobel gives an entertaining talk on the subject of English skit notes at the London Chapter of the IBNS.

## September 2005

Spink hold a sale of Scottish notes at the George Hotel, Edinburgh on September 12, when the Macmillan and McIntyre collections go under the hammer. A £1 note of the North of Scotland Banking Company of 31 July 1878 in extremely fine condition sells for £7,590, a new Scottish record.

At a London sale on September 30 Spink dispose of the third part of the Karouni Collection as well as a substantial selection of archive material.

The US Treasury announces the release of a colourised version of the $10 bill, in which the bust portrait of Alexander Hamilton is substantially redrawn.

## October 2005

The World Paper Money Fair hosted by the London branch of the International Bank Note Society, the 35th such annual event, takes place at the Trades Union Congress Centre over the weekend of October 1–2.

Paper money dealer Pam West gives a display of banknotes at the Royal Philatelic Society, the first time that paper money has been the subject of a talk at the world's premier stamp club.

After more than 20 years in business, Hugh Roper of Notability retires at the end of October, due to ill health.

## November 2005

Noble's auction number 80 in Sydney realises a staggering total of A$3.42 million, the undoubted highlight being the sale of "Australia's first banknote", issued on April 8, 1817, the day the Bank of New South Wales opened. Estimated at A$125,000, it was eventually knocked down after fierce bidding for A$283,095, a new record for a private banknote issue.

## December 2005

Ron Fife of Sheffield Coin Auctions and Marron Coins dies.

## January 2006

COIN NEWS launches a section on English banknotes in the monthly Price Guide.

Spink acquire the *Little Book of Roman Emperors* by Wolfgang Kopfel of Strasbourg, published in 1526, one of the world's earliest illustrated numismatic books, for the record sum of €102,935.

Writing in *Fabian Review*, historian Linda Colley suggests that the portraits on the Bank of England notes should reflect Britain's multi-racial character by featuring Olaudah Equiano, a former slave who became a prominent abolitionist in the late-18th century, or one of the Indian MPs of the 19th century.

## February 2006

The World Money Fair, previously held at Basle, moves to Berlin, taking place at the Estrel Hotel and Convention Centre on February 3–5.

The Irish International Coin and Banknote Show takes place at Ballsbridge, Dublin over the weekend of February 18–19.

## March 2006

The revamped colour version of the US $10 bill goes into circulation on March 2.

Thomson, Roddick and Medcalf of Carlisle auction the extensive numismatic, financial and banking history library formed by Alistair Gibb over a period of more than a quarter of a century.

At Noble's auction in Sydney, March 22–24 the star item was the first ever 10 shilling note of

the Australian Commonwealth, the celebrated M000001 presented by Prime Minister Andrew Fisher to Judith Denman, daughter of the Governor-General. The note had remained in the family's possession until 2000 when it was sold privately for A$1,000,000 (£406,000). It went on the block with an estimate of A$1,200,000 but failed to reach its reserve.

## April 2006

The Maastricht Paper Money Fair takes place at Valkenburg on April 1–2.

The Czech Civic Society of Gran Amazonia introduces "ara" notes to raise funds for the Indian-Czech Scientific Station at Rio Nichare, Venezuela. Which seeks to assist the indigenous peoples of Amazonia, a region divided among Venezuela, Brazil, Guyana and Peru. Versions of the notes retailing at €4 each have text in English, Dutch, French, Spanish or Portuguese.

The International Bank Note Society announced their Banknote of the Year issued in 2005 as the 1,000 kronur note of the Faroe Islands, depicting a purple sandpiper. This splendid example of intaglio printing incorporates a number of new security features such as Orion dots.

On April 19 the Reserve Bank of India announces the release of starred serials on replacement notes.

The 58th edition of the MRI Bankers' Guide to Foreign Currency is published.

The highlight of Spink's sale on April 27 was the 1705 Bank of England £100 note which realised £55,200 against a pre-sale estimate of £25,000 –£30,000.

Bogus high-denomination Euro notes (€300, €600 and €1,000) with pornographic images and a logo of twelve hearts instead of the EU stars are reported as circulating in Germany.

## May 2006

The Bank of England Museum re-opens after a five-month closure for extensive refurbishment.

## June 2006

Rare Fiji £20 notes are among the highlights of the auction by Colonial Coins and Medals at Brisbane on June 3.

Henry M. Paulson, Jr is nominated by President George W. Bush to become the 74th Secretary of the Treasury. His nomination is confirmed by the Senate on June 28 and is duly sworn in by Supreme Court Chief Justice John Roberts on July 10.

On June 21 Dix Noonan Webb offer the first part of the exceptional collection of Irish, Isle of Man and Channel Islands notes formed by Godfrey Burr over a period of 35 years.

At a sale held by Heritage Auction Galleries of Dallas, Texas a private collector pays $2,100,000 for a US $1,000 Treasury Note of 1891. A few minutes later the same bidder secures an 1863 $100 Gold Certificate for a similar record sum. The Treasury Note realised $1,425 when it first appeared at auction in 1944.

The Bahamas launches a new $10 note, the first to be issued with the new Counterfeit Resistant Integrated Security Product (CRISP).

## July 2006

Spink's auction of paper money rarities from Borneo, Malaya, Sarawak and the Straits Settlements takes place at the Oriental Hotel, Singapore on July 1.

The London Paper Money Fair takes place on July 2 at a new venue, the Victory Services Club, Seymour Street.

The Book of the Year award of the IBNS goes to Adnan Djaroueh for *The Encyclopedia of Syrian Paper Money.*

Russia releases a 5,000 rouble note on July 31.

## September 2006

The Banknote Society of Scotland, formerly the Scottish Chapter of the IBNS, holds its inaugural meeting at the West End Hotel, Edinburgh.

A unique consecutive pair of £10 Series D Bank of England notes of 1980, signed respectively by J. B. Page and D. H. F. Somerset, goes on sale on eBay and is eventually knocked down, after frenzied last-minute bidding, to Laurence Pope for a record £1,705.55.

At Spink's auction in London on September 29 one of the rarest Irish notes sells for £27,600, a new record price for an Irish note. The Bank of Ireland £50 note of 5 May 1827 is probably the only one of its kind in private hands.

## October 2006

The World Paper Money Fair organised by the London Chapter of the IBNS takes place at the Hotel Russell, Bloomsbury on October 1.

At Banking Memorabilia's sale on October 14, two cheques of Messrs Coutts & Co bear the signature of Prince Albert Victor, Duke of Clarence and Avondale, dated 1886 and 1890, believed to be the first time that cheques signed by members of the Royal Family have come up at auction.

The National Bank of Hungary released a 500 forint note on October 23 to mark the 50th anniversary of the Uprising of 1956. The obverse remains unchanged but the reverse shows a flag with the Communist red star cut out, against a view of the Parliament building.

## November 2006

The Bank of England reveals details of the new £20 note, portraying Adam Smith, the renowned 18th century philosopher and father of economics, scheduled for release in the spring of 2007.

The Ulster Bank introduces a £5 note on November 27 portraying football legend George Best. This is the first commemorative issue from the bank.

## December 2006

The European Numismatic Library based in Prague and also comprising the Czech Chapter of the IBNS holds an International Symposium on December 12.

The US Bureau of Engraving and Printing begins production of the Series 2006 notes with the signatures of Treasurer Anna Escobedo Cabral and Secretary Henry M. Poulson.

At the December sale of Heritage Auction Galleries in Dallas, Texas the only red seal $1,000 note in private hands, popularly known as the "Grand Watermelon", sells for $2,255,000, a new world record price. The only other example of this note is in the museum of the Federal Reserve Bank in San Francisco.

# The Best and worst
## of recent banknote designs

**D**URING the past two years two countries which had previously been plagued by inflation succeeded in reforming their monetary systems, with the result that entirely new series of notes had to be introduced.

Turkey was the worst affected, resulting in notes in denominations up to 20 million lirasi in circulation before the reform took effect on January 1, 2005. Six zeroes were lopped off to create the Yeni Turk Lirasi (YTL) or New Turkish Lira. This measure was accompanied by strict fiscal policies which drastically reduced the inflation rate to single figures as Turkey moved towards full membership of the European Union.

In line with a tradition that dates from the foundation of the republic in 1923, the front of all notes in this series (with the exception of the 20 YTL) bear portraits of Kemal Ataturk "Father of the Turks", although some variety is imparted in this set by the use of different images of the great man. The backs of the notes, however, provide an interesting and varied selection of landmarks, from ancient ruins to the great hydro-electric and irrigation Sanluirfa-Adiyaman Dam. Of particular interest is the motif on the 10 YTL, reproducing the map by Piri Reis (1513) charting the Americas, Greenland and Antarctica and now believed to have been based on Chinese voyages of the 1420s.

Romania's inflation was perhaps not so severe, but it did result in notes up to 1 million

lei. On July 1, 2005 the currency was reformed and in this instance four zeroes were removed, so that the new 1 leu note corresponds to the old 10,000 lei. For good measure a 500 lei denomination has been added to the series. Like Turkey, Romania was obliged to put its monetary house in order as a prerequisite of entry into the European Union. In this series different portraits of eminent personalities appeared on the right side of the obverse, including the playwrights George Enescu and Ion Caragiale, the painter Nicolae Grigorescu and national poet Mihai Eminescu. This approach gives considerable scope to the reverse motifs which included symbols and landmarks appropriate to each celebrity.

Both of these series were driven by political and economic incentives, whereas the series introduced by South Africa on February 1, 2005 merely reinforced the changes in that country since the collapse of Apartheid. If portraiture seems to be the current fashion, South Africa has played it safe with images of the "Big Five" animals, the rhino, elephant, lion, Cape buffalo and leopard which have graced the notes since 1992. What makes the latest series outstanding is the omission of Afrikaans as joint equal with

English, although it appears as one of the ten languages used for the bank titles (in lower-case lettering) which appear, two to a note, on the reverse sides. Although the stylised scenes on the reverse are rather muted, the small central vignettes of animal families on the obverse is a pleasing touch.

Only a relatively small number of countries have introduced entirely new series in the period under review. In many cases new notes merely fall into line with an already existing format. Typical of this conservative approach is Japan whose Nippon Ginko introduced three notes which fall into line with a 2000 yen note released in 2000 to commemorate a G8 Summit Conference but which has been retained as a permanent issue. The new notes follow a similar pattern with a bust portrait of a historic figure on the right of the obverse; in fact Yukichi Fukuzawa (10,000y) was portrayed on the 1000y of the previous series. The bacteriologist Hideyo Noguchi (1000y) is a newcomer as is Ichiyo Higuchi, a novelist who died in 1896 at the age of only 24 and is the first female to be featured on a Japanese note. There is nothing new in the style of these notes, but the reverse motifs blending traditional art forms with scenery (the obligatory view of Fujiyama) make for one of the most appealing sets of recent years.

Still in the Far East but adopting a different approach is Hong Kong which shares with Scotland the distinction of having three note-issuing banks in competition, although the fact that these issues are orchestrated by the Hong Kong Monetary Authority gives them some degree of uniformity. Each bank brought out three denominations predominantly in blue ($20), green ($50) and orange ($1000) and there is a similarity in the layout of the obverse in each case, although differing in inscriptions and actual content. The reverse motifs tend to follow similar themes. Thus the $20 notes show the Peak Tram and the Peak Terminus (HSBC) and the Peak Restaurant and shopping complex (Bank of China), although the Standard Chartered Bank has opted for a historical view of Hong Kong in 1850. The $50 notes respectively show the Big Buddha on Lantau Island, the Cultural Centre and Star

Ferry terminal in Tim Sha Tsui, and a view of Hong Kong in 1890, while the $1000 notes feature views of the Convention and Exhibition Centre (both HSBC and Bank of China) and a contemporary view of Hong Kong (SCB).

Neighbouring Macao only ever had a single monetary authority, the Portuguese National Overseas Bank, although in the past quarter of a century distinctive notes have tended to mirror the style of Hong Kong. Macao has recently introduced an entirely new series, consisting of 10, 20, 100, 500 and 1000 patacas. This is a very striking series distinguished by the array of fine modern buildings depicted on both sides, ranging from the colossal statue of the sea goddess A-Ma who gives her name to the territory (10p) to the impressive new international airport and the Cultural Centre. If banknotes may be regarded as a projection of how a country wishes to show itself to its people and the world at large then Macao certainly comes across as a bustling, forward-looking place.

That other erstwhile Portuguese colony, Mozambique has been battling with inflation in recent years, resulting in notes of 200,000 and 500,000 meticais whose obverse depicted the impressive façade of the Banco de Mocambique, with reverses that contrasted the traditional way of life (tribal dancers) and the modern world (a scene in an iron foundry). In July 2006, however, the currency was reformed and a new series duly appeared in which the new metical was equated to 10,000 old meticais. The standard obverse portrays Samora Machel, the leader of the long-running struggle for independence, while the reverses have the theme of wildlife: rhinoceros (20m), kudu (50m), giraffe (100m), lions (200m) and Cape buffalo (500m), but differing from their South African counterparts in the actual treatment of each motif.

Elsewhere, changes to the banknotes have been more piecemeal, generally resulting in changes to one or two denominations rather than a wholesale switch. Where an entire series has been revamped it is in minor details, usually resulting in improvements in the security features as the world's banks rise to the challenge posed by the sophisticated processes used by today's counterfeiters. The most obvious change is apparent in the notes of Samoa which has finally shed the adjective "Western', but the new notes are otherwise much the same as before.

Although the number of commemorative issues has tended to increase in recent years (as witness the prolific issues of the Scottish banks), in general the trend in the past two years has been a slowing down. An outstanding exception was the series of six notes released by Haiti to celebrate the bicentenary of independence and providing a veritable portrait gallery of the great and good among the patriots who threw off the shackles of slavery under French rule. The backs of each note show scenes and landmarks associated with each figure. Sadly, these patriots were often at war with each other and the story of Haiti's struggle for sovereignty is blackened by chicanery and skulduggery or bloody civil war between rival factions and warlords.

Nevertheless, the notes themselves, printed by Giesecke & Devrient, are extremely colourful. Incidentally, it's good to see this name re-emerging. Before World War II this was one of the world's leading security printers but ending up on the wrong side of the Iron Curtain it was transformed into the VEB Wertpapierdruckerei of the German Democratic Republic. With the collapse of Communism it was denationalised and now allowed to resume its original and much respected name.

A note for 10,000 leones is a reflection of how inflation has affected war-torn Sierra Leone whose contemporary history bears a

sad resemblance to that of Haiti two centuries ago. The back of this note is ironic for it features the centuries old giant cottonwood tree which stands in the very centre of Freetown where the old slave market once flourished. The front of the note, dominated by a peace dove and the national flag, proclaims the message "National Cohesion—Peace and Prosperity", a pious hope.

Most of the people portrayed on banknotes tend to come under the heading of worthy but dull, so it is refreshing to see the Ulster Bank and the Royal Bank of Scotland brightening things up with notes portraying stars of the sporting firmament. George Best, shown in both Northern Irish and Manchester United strip is sadly no longer with us, but champion golfer Jack Nicklaus is still very much in the land of the living. The number of sporting personalities featured on the world's paper money can be numbered on the fingers of one hand, but perhaps this is a trend that will grow in the future.

# A guide to
# Condition

T HE following introduction and Grading Guide is the result of work prepared under the guidance of the Grading Committee of the International Bank Note Society (IBNS) and is reproduced here with their kind permission. This grading guide has become the standard system used throughout the world.

## Introduction

Grading is the most controversial component of paper money collecting today. Small differences in grade can mean significant differences in value. The process of grading is so subjective and dependent on external influences such as lighting, that even a very experienced individual may well grade the same note differently on separate occasions.

To facilitate communication between sellers and buyers it is essential that grading terms and their meanings be as standardised and as widely used as possible. This standardisation should reflect common usage as much as practicable. One difficulty with grading is that even the actual grade themselves are not used everywhere by everyone. For example, in Europe the grade "About Uncirculated" (AU) is not in general use, yet in North America it is widespread. The European term "Good VF" may roughly correspond to what individuals in North America call "Extremely fine" (EF).

The grades and definitions as set forth below cannot reconcile all the various systems and grading terminology variants. Rather, the attempt is made here to try and diminish the controversy with some common sense grades and definitions that aim to give more precise meaning to the grading language of paper money.

## How to look at a banknote

In order to ascertain the grade of a note, it is essential to examine it out of a holder and under a good light. Move the note around so that the light bounces off at different angles. Try holding the note obliquely, so the note is even with your eye as you look up at the light.

Hard to see folds or slight creases will show up under such examination. Some individuals also lightly feel along the surface of the note to detect creasing.

## Cleaning, washing, pressing of banknotes

a. Cleaning, washing or pressing paper money is generally harmful and reduces both the grade and the value of the note. At the very least, a washed or pressed note may lose it original sheen and its surface may become lifeless and dull. The defects of a note had, such as folds and creases, may not necessarily be completely eliminated and their tell-tale marks can be detected under a good light. Carelessly washed notes may also have white streaks where the folds or creases where (or still are).

b. Processing of a note which started out as "Extremely Fine" will automatically reduce it at least one full grade.

## Unnatural defects

Glue, tape or pencil marks may sometime be successfully removed. While such removal will leave a cleaned surface, it will improve the overall appearance of the note without concealing any of its defects. Under such circumstances, the grade of that note may also be improved.

The words "pinholes", "staple holes", "trimmed". "writing on face", tape marks" etc should always be added to the description of a note. It is realised that certain countries routinely staple their notes together in groups before issue. In such cases, the description can include a comment such as "usual staple holes" or something similar. After all, not everyone knows that certain notes cannot be found otherwise.

The major point of this section is that one cannot lower the overall grade of a note with defects simply because of the defects. The price will reflect the lowered worth of a defective note, but the description must *always* include the specific defects.

**The term Uncirculated**

The word *Uncirculated* is used in this grading guide only as a qualitative measurement of the appearance of a note. It has nothing at all to do with whether or not an issuer has actually released the note to circulation. Thus, the term "About Uncirculated" is justified and acceptable because so many notes that have never seen hand to hand use have been mishandled so that they are available at best in AU condition.

Either a note is uncirculated in condition or it is not; there can be no degrees of uncirculated. Highlights or defects in colour, centering and the like may be included in a description but the fact that a note is or is not in uncirculated condition should not be a disputable point.

## GRADING GUIDE—Definitions of terms

**UNCIRCULATED**: A perfectly preserved note never mishandled by the issuing authority, a bank teller, the public or a collector. Paper is clean and firm without discoloration. Corners are sharp and square without any evidence of rounding (rounded corners are often a tell tale sign of a cleaned or "doctored" note). *Note: Some note issuers are most often available with slight evidence of very light counting folds which do not "break" the paper. Many collectors and dealers refer to such notes as AU–UNC.*

**ABOUT UNCIRCULATED**: A virtually perfect note, with some minor handling. May show very slight evidence of bank counting folds at a corner or one light fold through the centre, but not both. An "AU" note cannot be creased, a crease being a hard fold which has usually "broken" the surface of the note. Paper is clean and bright with original sheen. Corners are not rounded. *Note: Europeans will refer to an About Uncirculated or AU note as "EF–Unc" or as just "EF". The Extremely Fine note described below will often be referred to as "GVF" or "Good Very Fine".*

**EXTREMELY FINE**: A very attractive note with light handling. May have a maximum of three light folds or one strong crease. Paper is clean and firm without discoloration. Corners are sharp and square without evidence of rounding (rounded corners are often a tell tale sign of a cleaned or "doctored" note).

**VERY FINE**: An attractive note, but with more evidence of handling and wear. May have several folds both vertically and horizontally. Paper must have minimal dirt or possibly colour smudging. Paper itself is still relatively crisp and not floppy. There are no tears in the border area, although the edges do show slight wear. Corners also show wear but not full rounding.

**FINE**: A note that shows considerable circulation, with many folds, creases and wrinkling. Paper is not excessively dirty but may have some softness. Edges may show much handling with minor tears in the border area. Tears may not extend into the design. There will be no centre hole because of excessive folding. Colours are clear but not very bright. A staple hole or two would not be considered unusual wear in a Fine note. Overall appearance is still on the desirable side.

**VERY GOOD**: A well used note, abused but still intact. Corners may have much wear and rounding, tiny nicks, tears may extend in to the design, some discoloration may be present, staining may have occurred, and a small hole may sometimes be seen at centre excessive folding. Staple and pinholes are usually present and the note itself is quite limp but NO pieces of the note can be missing. A note in VG condition may still have an overall not unattractive appearance.

**GOOD**: A well worn and heavily used note. Normal damage from prolonged circulation will include strong multiple folds and creases, stains, pinholes and/or staple holes, dirt, discoloration, edge tears, centre hole, rounded corners and an overall unattractive appearance. No large pieces of the note may be missing. Graffiti is commonly seen on notes in G condition.

**FAIR**: A totally limp, dirty and very well used note. Larger pieces may be half torn off or missing besides the defects mentioned under the Good category. Tears will be large, obscured portions of the note will be bigger.

**POOR**: A "rag" with severe damage because of wear, staining, pieces missing, graffiti, larger holes. May have tape holding pieces of the note together. Trimming may have taken place to remove rough edges. A Poor note is desirable only as a "filler" or when such a note is the only one known of that particular issue.

# Mounting and housing notes

CERTAIN museum collections and official bank archives are housed in cabinets with sliding frames in which banknotes are mounted on cards between glass panes. While this is a very attractive way of displaying a collection it is also very expensive and takes up a great deal of room. Until relatively recently most notaphilists were content to house their collections in conventional loose-leaf stamp albums, the notes being held in place by transparent mounting corners and the relevant data, such as date of issue, bank and country, could be written up on the page above each note. The disadvantage of this system is that only one side of the banknote could be examined without taking it out of its mounting corners.

An alternative to this, small transparent hinges, like those used by stamp collectors, were used to affix the notes to the album page. By this method the note could easily be turned over so that the back could be examined. This was considered more satisfactory, although many collectors felt uneasy about using stamp hinges which could leave an unsightly mark on the backs of notes and this would detract from their value. This method of mounting is certainly not recommended today.

The solution to these problems, widely disseminated in the 1970s, was the special album with plastic sleeves into which the notes could be inserted. These albums were actually produced initially for housing collections of postcards, but were found to be about the right size for banknotes. Unfortunately it was soon discovered that those sleeves made of polyvinyl chloride (PVC) reacted chemically with notes, either badly discolouring them or even depositing a viscous film on them. Subsequently better types

of plastic such as Mylar film or polyethylene were developed, and these seem to have obviated the risk of contamination.

Today there are many different systems available to the note collector. There are cards (punched with holes to be inserted in ring-binders or peg-fitting albums) with clear rigid plastic fronts, as well as the more conventional "postcard" sleeves. The latter often come with black card inserts, so that notes can be inserted back to back, on either side of the card, but that then brings us back to the original album pages, with only one side of the note readily visible. There are also stout cards with a plastic face, slightly larger than postcard size, which can be stacked in a box or case, with the salient details of the note on narrow cards inserted at the top of the mount and then held upright as if in a filing cabinet. The main thing to remember is that, which ever system you adopt, you preserve your notes in a dust-free atmosphere, at an even temperature and humidity.

*A popular banknote **album** from Lindner.*

# Around the world

## Currency denominations of the world

Listed here are the names of all the currency units of the world found on banknotes or coins. Many of them have been around for a long time while others are no longer in use. Some of the denominations have been introduced only recently, whilst others are familiar household words, many have been superceded by the euro and other new names. A number of the names are shared by different countries and a few have even been used by different civilisations. We have included all that we know of, past and present.

**Abbasi, Abbassi**  Afghanistan, Georgia, Persia
**Afghani**  Afghanistan
**Agora (ot)**  Israel
**Ahmadi**  Mysore, Yemen
**Amani**  Afghanistan
**Anna**  Burma, India, Pakistan, Kenya, Muscat & Oman
**Argentino**  Argentina
**Ariary**  Malagasy Republic
**Ashrafi**  Afghanistan, Awadh, Bahawalpur, Egypt,  Hyderabad
**At**  Laos
**Atia**  Portuguese India
**Att**  Cambodia, Laos, Siam (Thailand)
**Aurar** (plural **Eyrir**)  Iceland
**Austral**  Argentina
**Avo**  Macau, Timor
**Baht**  Thailand
**Baiocco** (plural **Baiocchi**)  Papal States
**Baisa**  Oman
**Baiza**  Kuwait
**Baizah**  Muscat & Oman
**Balboa**  Panama
**Ban** (plural **Bani** or **Banu**)  Roumania
**Banica**  Croatia
**Belga**  Belgium
**Besa** (plural **Bese**)  Ethiopia, Somalia
**Bipkwele**  Equatorial Guinea
**Bir (r)**  Ethiopia
**Bogach**  Yemen
**Bolivar**  Venezuela
**Boliviano**  Bolivia
**Butut**  Gambia
**Cache**  French Indian Settlements
**Candareen**  China
**Carbovanetz**  Ukraine
**Cash**  China, Hong Kong, India, Mysore, Travancore, Turkestan, Vietnam
**Cauri**  Guinea
**Cent**  Australia, Bahamas, Barbados, Belize, Bermuda, Botswana, British East Caribbean Territories, British Honduras, British North Borneo, British Virgin Islands, Brunei, Canada, Cayman Island, Ceylon, China, Cochin China, Cocos (Keeling) Islands, Cook Islands, Curacao, Cyprus, Danish West Indies, East Africa, Ethiopia, Fiji, French Indochina, Gilbert and Ellice Islands, Guyana, Hawaii, Hong Kong, Indonesia, Jamaica, Kenya, Kiao Chau (Kiatschau), Kiribati, Laos, Liberia, Malaya, Malaysia, Malta, Mauritius, Netherlands, Netherlands Antilles, Netherlands Indies, New Zealand, Nova Scotia, Panama, Prince Edward Island, Sarawak, Seychelles, Sierra Leone, Singapore, Solomon Islands, South Africa, Sri Lanka, Straits Settlements, Suriname, Swaziland, Tanzania, Trinidad and Tobago, Tuvalu, Uganda, United States of America, Virgin Islands, Zanzibar, Zimbabwe
**Centas** (plural **Centa, Centu**)  Lithuania
**Centavo**  Angola, Argentina, Bolivia, Brazil, Cape Verde Islands, Chile, Colombia, Costa Rica, Cuba, Dominican Republic, Ecuador, El Salvador, Guatemala, Guinea-Bissau, Honduras, Mexico, Mozambique, Nicaragua, Paraguay, Peru, Philippines, Portugal, Portuguese Guinea, Portuguese India, Puerto Rico, St Thomas and Prince Islands, Timor, Venezuela
**Centecimo**  Bolivia
**Centesimo**  Bolivia, Chile, Dominican Republic, Ethiopia, Italian East Africa, Italy, Panama, Paraguay, San Marino, Somalia, Uruguay, Vatican
**Centime**  Algeria, Antwerp, Belgian Congo, Belgium, Cambodia, Cameroon, Cochin China, Comoro Islands, Djibouti, France, French Equatorial Africa, French Guiana, French Indochina, French Oceania, French Polynesia, French Somali Coast, French West Africa, Guadeloupe, Guinea, Haiti, Laos, Monaco, Morocco, New Caledonia, Reunion, Senegal, Switzerland, Togo, Tunisia, Vietnam, Westphalia, Yugoslavia, Zaire
**Centimo**  Costa Rica, Mozambique, Paraguay, Peru, Philippines, Puerto Rico, St Thomas and Prince Islands, Spain, Venezuela
**Centu**  Lithuania
**Chervonetz** (plural **Chervontzy**)  Russia
**Chetrum**  Bhutan
**Cheun**  South Korea

**Chiao** China, Formosa, Manchukuo
**Chi'en** China
**Chio** China
**Chon** Korea
**Chuckram** Travancore
**Colon** Costa Rica, El Salvador
**Condor** Chile, Colombia, Ecuador
**Cordoba** Nicaragua
**Corona** Austrian provinces of Italy, Naples
**Cruzadinho** Brazil, Portugal
**Cruzado** Brazil, Portugal
**Cruzeiro** Brazil
**Denar** Macedonia
**Deutschemark** Germany
**Dinar** Afghanistan, Algeria, Bahrain, Hejaz, Iraq, Kuwait, Morocco, Persia, Saudi Arabia, Serbia, Tunisia, Turkey, Yugoslavia
**Diner** Andorra
**Dinero** Peru, Spain
**Dirham** Jordan, Libya, Morocco, United Arab Emirates
**Dirhem** Dubai, Iraq, Morocco, Qatar
**Dobra** Sao Tome e Principe
**Dollar** Anguilla, Antigua and Barbuda, Australia, Bahamas, Belize, Bermuda, Canada, Cayman Islands, China, Cocos (Keeling) Islands, Cook Islands, East Caribbean Territories, Fiji, Great Britain, Grenada, Guyana, Hawaii, Hong Kong, Indonesia, Jamaica, Japan, Kiribati, Liberia, Malaysia, Mauritius, Montserrat, Newfoundland, New Zealand, Panama, St Kitts-Nevis, St Lucia, St Vincent, Scotland, Sierra Leone, Singapore, Solomin Islands, Straits Settlements, Trinidad and Tobago, Tuvalu, USA, Virgin Islands, Western Samoa, Zimbabwe
**Dong** Annam, Vietnam
**Drachma** Crete, Greece
**Dram** Armenia
**Ekuele** Equatorial Guinea
**Emalangeni** Swaziland
**Escudo** Angola, Argentina, Azores, Bolivia, Cape Verde Islands, Central American Republic, Chile, Colombia, Costa Rica, Ecuador, Guadeloupe, Guatemala, Guinea-Bissau, Madeira, Mexico, Mozambique, Peru, Portugal, Portuguese Guinea/India, St Thomas and Prince Islands, Spain, Timor
**Forint** Hungary
**Franc** Algeria, Belgian Congo, Belgium, Burundi, Cambodia, Cameroon, Central African Republic, Chad, Comoro Islands, Congo, Danish West Indies, Djibouti, Dominican Republic, Ecuador, France, French Colonies, Gabon, Guadeloupe, Guinea, Ivory Coast, Katanga, Luxembourg, Madagascar, Malagasy Republic, Mali, Martinique, Mauretania, Monaco, Morocco, New Caledonia, New Hebrides, Reunion, Ruanda-Urundi, Rwanda, St Pierre and Miquelon, Senegal, Switzerland, Togo, Tunisia, West African States
**Franchi** Switzerland
**Frang** Luxembourg
**Frank(en)** Belgium, Liechtenstein, Saar, Switzerland
**Franka Ara** Albania
**Gersh** Ethiopia
**Girsh** Hejaz, Nejd, Saudi Arabia, Sudan
**Golde** Sierra Leone
**Grivna** (plural **Grivny**) Ukraine
**Grosz** (plural **Grosze** or **Groszy**) Poland

**Grush** Albania
**Guarani** Paraguay
**Guerche** Egypt, Saudi Arabia
**Gulden** Austria, Curacao, German States, Netherlands, Netherlands Indies, Swiss Cantons
**Habibi** Afghanistan
**Hryvnia** Ukraine
**Hsien** China
**Hwan** Korea
**Imadi** Yemen
**Jeon** Korea
**Jiao** People's Republic of China
**Kapeikas** Latvia, Belarus
**Khoum** Mauritania
**Kina** Papua New Guinea
**Kip** Laos
**Korona** Bohemia and Moravia, Hungary, Slovakia
**Korun(a)** (plural **Koruny** or **Koruncic**) Czechoslo-vakia
**Krajczar** Hungary
**Kran** Iran, Persia
**Kreu(t)zer** Austria, Austrian States, Czechoslovakia, German States, Hungary, Liechtenstein, Poland, Roumania, Swiss Cantons
**Krona** (plural **Kronor** or **Kronur**) Iceland, Sweden
**Krona** (plural **Kroner** or **Kronen**) Austria, Denmark, German States, Greenland, Liechtenstein, Norway
**Kroon(i)** Estonia
**Kuna** (plural **Kune**) Croatia
**Kurus** Turkey
**Kuta** Congo-Kinshasa, Zaire
**Kwacha** Malawi, Zambia
**Kwanza** Angola
**Kyat** Burma, Myanmar
**Lari** Georgia
**Lati, Lats** Latvia
**Lei** Roumania
**Lek** (plural **Leke** or **Leku**) Albania
**Lempira** Honduras
**Leone** Sierra Leone
**Leu** (plural **Lei**) Roumania
**Lev(a)** Bulgaria
**Li** Manchukuo
**Licente** Lesotho
**Likuta** Zaire
**Lilangeni** Swaziland
**Lion d'Or** Austrian Netherlands
**Lira** (plural **Lire**) Eritrea, Italian East Africa, Italy, San Marino, Syria, Turkey, Vatican
**Lira** (plural **Lirot**) Israel
**Lisente** Lesotho
**Litas** (plural **Litai** or **Litu**) Lithuania
**Luhlanga** Swaziland
**Lweis** Angola
**Macuta** Angola
**Makuta** Zaire
**Maloti** Lesotho
**Manat Azerbaijan** Turkmenistan
**Mark** Germany, German States, German New Guinea, Norway, Poland, Sweden
**Marka** Estonia
**Markka** Finland
**Metical** Mozambique
**Milreis** Brazil
**Mon** Japan, Ryukyu Islands
**Mongo** Mongolia
**Mun** Korea

**Mung**   Mongolia
**Naira**   Nigeria
**Nafka**   Eritrea
**Ngultrum**   Bhutan
**Ngwee**   Zambia
**Omani**   Oman
**Ouguiya**   Mauritania
**Pa'anga**   Tonga
**Pahlavi**   Iran
**Pataca**   Macau
**Pengo**   Hungary
**Penni(a)**   Finland
**Perper(a)**   Montenegro
**Pesa**   German East Africa
**Peseta**   Andorra, Equatorial Guinea, Peru, Spain
**Pesewa**   Ghana
**Peso**   Argentina, Bolivia, Cambodia, Chile, Colombia, Costa Rica, Cuba, Dominican Republic, El Salvador, Guatemala, Guinea-Bissau, Honduras, Mexico, Netherlands Antilles, Nicaragua, Paraguay, Peru, Philippines, Puerto Rico, Uruguay, Venezuela
**Piastre**   Annam, Cambodia, Cochin China, Cyprus, Denmark, Egypt, French Indochina, Hejaz, Iraq, Khmer, Lebanon, Libya, Nejd, Saudi Arabia, Syria, Sudan, Tonkin, Tunisia, Turkey, Vietnam, Yemen
**Piso**   Philippines
**Pond**   Transvaal
**Pound**   Ascension, Australia, Biafra, Cyprus, Egypt, Falkland Islands, Ghana, Gibraltar, Great Britain, Guernsey, Iran, Ireland, Isle of Man, Israel, Jersey, Malta, Nigeria, Rhodesia, St Helena, South Arabia, South Africa, Sudan, Syria
**Pruta(ot)**   Israel
**Pul**   Afghanistan, China, Turkestan
**Pula**   Botswana
**Pya(t)**   Burma
**Qindar(ka)**   Albania
**Quetzal**   Guatemala
**Real(es)**   Argentina, Bolivia, Central American Republic, Chile, Colombia, Costa Rica, Dominican Republic, Ecuador, El Salvador, Venezuela
**Reichsmark**   Germany
**Reis**   Angola, Azores, Brazil, Madeira, Mozambique, Portugal, Portuguese India
**Renminbi**   People's Republic of China
**Rentenmark**   Germany
**Rial**   Iran, Morocco, Muscat and Oman, Oman, Persia, Yemen Arab Republic
**Riel**   Kampuchea
**Ringgit**   Malaysia
**Riyal**   Iran, Iraq, Saudi Arabia, United Arab Emirates, Yemen Arab Republic
**Rouble**   Russia, USSR
**Rubel**   German occupation of Russia
**Ruble**   Poland, Transnistria
**Rublis**   Latvia
**Rufiyaa**   Maldive Islands
**Rupee**   Afghanistan, Andaman Islands, Bhutan, Burma, China, Cocos Keeling Islands, India, Iran, Kenya, Mauritius, Nepal, Pakistan, Saudi Arabia, Seychelles, Sri Lanka, Tanzania, Tibet, United Arab Emirates, Yemen
**Rupia**   Portuguese India, Somalia
**Rupiah**   Indonesia
**Rupie**   German East Africa
**Ryal**   England, Hejaz, Iran, Muscat and Oman, Nejd, Oman, Persia, Quaiti State, Saudi Arabia, Yemen, Zanzibar
**Saidi**   Oman
**Satang**   Siam (Thailand)
**Scellino**   Somalia
**Schilling**   Austria, German States, Poland, Swiss Cantons
**Shahi**   Afghanistan, Iran, Turkestan
**Shamil**   Tatarstan
**Sheqal(im)**   Israel
**Shilin**   Somalia
**Shilingi**   Tanzania
**Shilling**   Australia, Biafra, British West Africa, Canada, Cyprus, East Africa, Fiji, Gambia, Ghana, Great Britain, Grenada, Guernsey, Ireland, Isle of Man, Jamaica, Jersey, Kenya, Malawi, Malta, New Guinea, New Zealand, Nigeria, Scotland, Somalia, South Africa, Trinidad and Tobago, Uganda, Zambia
**Sol(es)**   Argentina, Haiti, Peru,
**Soldo** (plural **Soldi**)   Italian States, Swiss Cantons, Papal States,
**Som**   Kyrgyr Republic
**Som**   Kyrgyzstan
**Somalo**   Somalia
**Somoni**   Tajikistan
**Srang**   Tibet
**Sucre**   Ecuador, Galapagos
**Sueldo**   Bolivia, Spain
**Sum**   Uzbekistan
**Syli**   Guinea
**Tael**   China, Laos
**Taka**   Bangladesh
**Tala**   Samoa, Tokelau
**Talaro**   Ethiopia
**Taler**   German States, Poland, Swiss Cantons
**Tambala**   Malawi
**Tamlung**   Siam
**Tanga**   Portuguese India
**Tangka**   Tibet
**Tanka**   Nepal
**Tenge**   Kazakhstan
**Thaler**   Austria, Austrian States, Courland, Czechoslovakia, German States, Hungary, Liechtenstein, Poland, Roumania, Switzerland
**Thebe**   Botswana
**Thetri**   Georgia
**Tical**   Cambodia, Thailand
**Tiyin**   Kazakhstan
**Toea**   Papua New Guinea
**Tola**   India, Nepal
**Tolar**   Slovenia
**Toman**   Iran, Persia, Azerbaijan
**Tughrik**   Mongolia
**Vatu**   Vanuatu
**Venezolano**   Venezuela
**Wan**   Korea
**Wark**   Ethiopia
**Warn**   Korean
**Wen**   China
**Whan**   Korea
**Won**   South Korea
**Xu**   Vietnam
**Yen**   Japan
**Yeni kurus**   Turkey
**Yeni Turk Lirasi**   Turkey
**Yuan**   China
**Zaire**   Zaire
**Zalat**   Yemen Arab Republic
**Zloty** (plural **Zlote** or **Zlotych**)   Poland

# Glossary of banknote terms

**Allied Military Currency**   Notes produced by the British and American governments for the use of military personnel in territories occupied during the World War II.

**Alteration**   A deliberate change in some feature of a note, usually of a fraudulent nature.

**Assignat**   Type of paper money used in France, 1789–96, representing confiscated Church land assigned to the holders.

**Asterisk Note**   Note issued in Canada and New Zealand since ther 1950s to replace a defective note and so-called on account of the asterisk in the serial number.

**Authorised Circulation**   The amount of money in notes which Scottish banks were permitted to have in circulation, under the Bank Act of 1845, based on a twelve-month average for the period prior to the Act coming into force. Any amount above this had to be backed by gold and silver.

**Auxiliary Payment Certificate**   Form of paper money intended for use by American military personnel in overseas countries. See also Baf, Behelfszahlungsmittel and Scrip.

**Babel Note**   Nickname derived from the biblical Tower of Babel, given to the paper currency of the Russian Socialist Federated Republic (1919) because it bore the slogan "workers of the world unite" in seven languages.

**Back**   The side of a note generally regarded as of lesser importance than the front, and otherwise known as the reverse or verso. In early notes the back was often left blank, but in more recent times it has been used for a florid representation of the national arms or vignettes of scenery and landmarks.

**Baf**   Acronym from British Armed Forces, the popular name for the vouchers which could only be exchanged for goods in service canteens from 1945 onwards.

**Banknote**   Form of paper money issued by banks and usually promising to pay the bearer on demand in coin of the realm.

**Banknote**   Strictly speaking, this is a piece of paper money issued by a bank, although the term is often loosely applied to any form of paper in circulation as currency.

**Bearer Cheque**   A piece of paper which looks like a cheque but actually payable for the stated sum to any person holding it (the bearer) without requiring endorsement. Some of the emergency money used in Italy in the late 1970s consisted of such cheques.

**Behelfszahlungsmittel**   German term for auxiliary payment certificates used in occupied Europe from 1939 to 1945.

**Bill of Credit**   An American term denoting the paper money of the Colonial and early Continental period, from which comes the common expression 'bill' meaning a paper note.

**Bill of Exchange**   The law defines this as "an unconditional order in writing, addressed by one person to another, signed by the person giving it, requiring the person to whom it is addressed to pay on demand or at a fixed or determinable future time, a sum certain in money to or to the order of a specified person or to bearers". It is addressed to a person or company, rather than a bank. The earliest examples are entirely handwritten although examples from the 19th century onwards often had the stock formula printed, with the details inserted by hand.

**Billet de Confiance**   French for "tickets of trust", signifying small-denomination notes of the French Revolution issued to meet a shortage of coin due to hoarding.

**Block Number**   Tiny numerals often found in the corners of notes, denoting the block or plate from which the notes were printed.

**Bogus**   A note which is entirely false, in that it purports to be the money of a non-existent bank or country.

**Bon Pour**   French for "good for", inscribed on tokens, coupons and vouchers which circulated as cash during periods of shortage of coinage.

**Bond**   A certificate of intention to pay the holder a specified sum, with or without interest, on a specified date.

**Bradbury**   Popular name for the UK Treasury notes introduced in August 1914 when specie payments were suspended on the outbreak of World War I, from the Treasury official, Sir John Bradbury, who signed them.

**Braille**   A system of reading by means of patterns of raised dots, invented by Louis Braille. In recent years such dots have been embossed on many banknotes to help identification by the blind and partially sighted, as well as provide an additional security feature.

**Branch Banknote**   A note which includes in its inscription a reference to the particular branch of a bank which issued it. In the USA such notes even had quite distinctive designs, but in England the name of the town or city sufficed to distinguish such notes from those of the head office in London.

**British Armed Forces Special Voucher**   Note issued from 1945 onwards for use in NAAFI canteens operated all over the world on behalf of the British armed services. Denominated in sterling, they could not be used outside the camp area and thus prevented black market operations between servicemen and the local population.

**Broken Banknote**   Note issued by a bank which has failed, but often applied more generally to banknotes which have been demonetised.

**Burele**   French term indicating a network of intersecting curved lines used as a security underprint.

**Cancelled**   A note withdrawn from circulation and rendered worthless by means of an overprint or perforated inscription, generally the word CANCELLED or its equivalent in other languages, e.g. Annule (French), Annulado (Spanish) or Ausser Kurs (German). Such notes sometimes come on to the market at a fraction of their original face value.

**Carton**   A form of soft card, much thicker than conventional paper, which has been used occasionally for emergency money, notably the small notes in Mexico, 1914–17.

**Cartouche**   Oval or circular frame enclosing a portrait or armorial device, setting it apart from the rest of the design.

**Changeling**   A note or cheque whose colour is altered from the norm as a result of exposure to humidity, sunlight or chemical action.

**Chartered Bank**   A bank operating under charter from the government, as opposed to a private or commercial bank.

**Cheque**   (American Check)   A written order directing a bank to pay money.

**Cheque Form**   A printed form issued by banks for the convenience of customers. Collectors use this term to denote an unused cheque (preferably with the counterfoil still intact).

**Chop**   From the Hindi word chap, it means a stamp or seal used in India, China and other countries of Asia to make an official mark. The earliest paper money, for example, bore the chop of the Khan of Cathay, applied in vermilion, and this tradition continues to this day in the paper money of China and Japan.

**Clearing Bank**   A bank which is a member of a Clearing House.

**Clearing House**   A banking institution where notes and cheques are exchanged between banks.

**Clearing House Certificate**   A form of emergency money backed by coin or bullion deposited with the clearing house through which banks exchanged notes and cheques. Specifically the term is applied to American issues of 1907-8 and the early 1930s, during periods of economic crises and runs on banks.

**Coin Note**   A note issued by the US Treasury in 1890–1, so-called because it was redeemable in coin. A special reserve of silver dollars was established to cope with the redemption of these notes.

**College Currency**   Imitation money used in simulated transactions by business schools and colleges, mainly in the USA.

**Colonial Currency**   Paper money issued by the thirteen American colonies in the period from 1690 to 1776 or even later in some cases, before the emergence of the United States.

**Colour Shifting Ink**   Ink which appears to change colour as the note is tilted at a different angle.

**Commemorative**   A note issued for the specific purpose of marking a current event or the anniversary of a historic event or personality. Apart from notes with distinctive designs, such notes may consist of an additional or overprinted inscription, or even cyphers and serial numbers arranged in the form of anniversary dates or initials.

**Company Note**   A note issued by a commercial undertaking rather than a bank and redeemable in goods from the company store rather than actual cash. Such notes were common in Britain before they were rendered illegal by the Truck Acts of the 1840s.

**Compound Interest Note**   Note issued during the American Civil War, so-called on account of the six per cent interest which was compounded every six months.

**Concentration Camp Money**   Various forms of notes and vouchers produced immediately before and during the World War II in a number of Nazi concentration camps. These notes were intended to reward slave workers for their labour and were exchangeable for a limited range of goods, but more usually for such luxuries as the loan of library books or admission to camp concerts. Notes of this type are known to have been used in Oranienburg, Ravensbruck, Dachau, Sachsenhausen, Buchenwald, Mauthausen, Auschwitz, Westerburg, Gross-Rosen and Mittelbau-Dora as well as in the ghettoes of

Warsaw, Lodz (Litzmanstadt), Bielsk-Podlavsky and Theresienstadt. Notes denominated in US currency were also used in Deggendorf, Feldafing and Scheinfeld, former Nazi concentration camps which were used as displaced persons' camps, mainly for survivors of the Holocaust, prior to their immigration to Palestine in 1945–46. The British authorities also provided canteen money for Jews interned at camps in Cyprus in 1946–48, after being turned back from Palestine as illegal immigrants.

**Continental Currency**   Paper money authorised by the Continental Congress between 1775 and 1779 in the early stages of the American War of Independence.

**Counterfeit**   The forgery or imitation of a note intended for circulation to deceive the public and defraud the state or the issuing bank.

**Counterfoil**   The left-hand portion of a note or cheque, retained by the issuer as a record of the issue. It was usually divided from the main portion by some highly elaborate vertical design which, in the case of cheques especially, tended to become more pictorial in the 19th and early 20th centuries. From the 1840s the counterfoil was separated from the main part by some form of perforation, but earlier examples were cut apart by scissors, often in a serpentine or irregular line so that the two portions could be matched later on if required.

**Coupon**   Term from French couper, to cut, denoting a piece of paper which may be exchanged for goods or services, hence a detachable ticket or voucher entitling the holder to something. In the notaphilic context it denotes a detachable portion of a share certificate entitling the holder to a dividend, and has also been used to signify small notes used as emergency money.

**Crossed Cheque**   A cheque which bears parallel diagonal lines across the middle, either printed or handwritten, giving instructions to the paying bank to limit negotiability to the payee.

**Crossing Stamp**   A brass or rubber stamp applied by hand across the face of a cheque by the negotiating bank.

**Currency**   Notes intended to pass current in general circulation as money.

**Current**   Note still in circulation.

**Cut Note**   A note which has been officially cut into halves or quarters and re-issued, each part thereby serving as a note of appropriate value. As a rule, each portion bears an overprint signifying its new value.

**Cypher**   Term for the combination of letters which serve as a prefix in the serial number. In recent years such cyphers have often been deliberately contrived to serve a quasi-commemorative purpose, eg RLS (Robert Louis Stevenson), AGB (Alexander Graham Bell), SP (Scottish

Parliament) and G/AD Glasgow, City of Architecture and Design) on Scottish notes of the 1990s.

**Darlehnskassen**   German for 'state loan note', a form of paper money issued during the World War I in an abortive bid to fill the shortage of coinage in circulation. These low-denomination notes failed to meet demand and were superseded by local issues of Notgeld in 1916.

**Date**   In many cases the year, or even a full date, merely denotes the point in time at which a note was authorised or introduced, and may antedate the actual time or even the year of release. In other cases, however, the date signifies the actual time of issue.

**Demand Notes**   Name generally given to the first series of paper money authorised by the US federal government by Act of Congress in 1861 at the beginning of the American Civil War, and so-called because the United States promised to pay the bearer on demand. The formula, of course, is widely used on the notes of many other countries and is by no means confined to the USA.

**Demonetisation**   The withdrawal of notes from circulation and declaring them to be worthless.

**Denomination**   The face value of a note, expressed in words of figures or often a combination of both.

**Depression Scrip**   American term for temporary makeshifts issued in various parts of the USA during the Depression of the early 1930s.

**Device**   Heraldic term for the pattern or emblem on banknotes.

**Devil's Head**   Collectors' term for certain notes of Canada and the Seychelles in which an image of the Devil was fancifully detected in the hair of Queen Elizabeth.

**Die**   Hardened piece of metal, usually steel but sometimes copper, bearing a positive image of the device to be transferred to the printing plate.

**Die Proof**   An impression, usually pulled on soft carton or India paper, of an intaglio engraving of a banknote, usually taken during the progress of engraving in order to check the detail. Proofs of this nature usually consist of the portrait or some detail of the design, such as the border, rather than the complete motif.

**Dividend Warrant**   A cheque issued in payment of a dividend to a shareholder, often attached to a document setting out the details of the dividend.

**Dix Note**   Collectors' term for $10 notes of the Citizens' Bank of Louisiana in New Orleans, from the French word DIX (ten) inscribed on their backs. The widespread notion that this gave rise to the term 'Dixie' denoting the Southern States of the USA is utterly false. Apart from the fact that many Canadian notes are similarly inscribed, it should be stated that the term 'Dixie', first popularised by the patriotic song of 1859 by Daniel D. Emmett, comes from the Mason-Dixon Line which separated the states of the free North and slave-owning South, Charles Mason and Jeremiah Dixon being the surveyors who mapped the southern boundary of Pennsylvania in the late 18th century.

**Double Note**   A note in which the front and back bear no relation to each other. This apparently first arose during the American Civil War when unfinished notes of a broken bank were pressed into service, with a new device on the blank side, by other banks as a result of a chronic shortage of paper.

**Draft**   An alternative name for a cheque, sometimes used in the context of a bank draft.

**Drawer**   The person drawing or issuing a cheque and whose signature appears on it.

**Dual Currency**   Notes inscribed with values in two different currency systems. This situation sometimes arises during a period of transition from one currency to another, usually as a result of monetary reforms.

**Educational Notes**   Name given to the US silver certificates of 1896 on account of the didactic nature of their designs.

**Embossing**   A printing process which entails the use of male and female dies or matrices to raise a portion of the design above the normal surface. It is commonly found on old cheques and bills of exchange which bear an embossed device denoting the payment of stamp duty, but in many banknotes of recent vintage it is used as a security device and an aid to blind and partially sighted persons to identify the face value correctly.

**Emergency Money**   Any form of money used in times of economic and political upheaval, when traditional kinds of currency are not available. In paper money this takes the form of all kinds of coupons, vouchers and scrip employed in military campaigns or in towns under siege, the Notgeld issued by many towns in Austria and Germany (1916–23), encased money, fractional currency, guerrilla notes, invasion, liberation and occupation money from the two world wars and minor campaigns. Among more recent examples may be cited the use of cheques in Italy (1976–77) and the issue of talons or coupons in many of the countries of the former Soviet Union pending the introduction of their own distinctive currencies.

**Encased Money**   Postage and revenue stamps enclosed in small metal and mica-faced discs, circulated as small change in times of emergency. The device was invented by John Gault, a Boston sewing-machine salesman, during the American Civil War (1862). The face of the stamp was visible through the transparent window, while the back of the disc was embossed with firms' advertisements. This practice was revived during and after the World War I when there was again a shortage of small coins. Encased stamps have also been recorded from Austria, France, Germany, Monaco and Norway. See also Stamp Money.

**Endorsement**   The signature of the payee on the back of a cheque.

**Endorsement Guarantee**   A statement indemnifying the paying bank in the case of an incorrect endorsement on a cheque, usually indicated by means of a rubber handstamp.

**Engine Turning**   An intricate pattern of spiral and curved lines created by the Rose Engine, patented by Jacob Perkins between 1811 and 1819 as part of the process of steel engraving or siderography which established the fortunes of the security printing firm variously known as Perkins, Fairman & Heath, Perkins, Bacon & Heath or Perkins, Bacon. The French term guilloche is sometimes used.

**Engraving**   The art of cutting lines or grooves into a die for recess-printing (intaglio) or cutting away parts of the surface leaving the portion to be printed standing out (letterpress). See these terms for further details.

**Error**   Mistakes in paper money may be caused at the design or engraving stage, or as a result of a fault in the production processes. In the first category come misspellings in text or inscriptions, but more usually mistakes or inaccuracies in details of the design. In the second category the back of a note may be printed upside down in relation to the front, or a part of the design may be doubly printed or misplaced. Faulty registration of the printing plates may result in one colour being out of alignment. Other errors include serial numbers partially or wholly omitted or printed upside down. The commonest error consists of miscut notes.

**Essay**   (From the French essai, a trial piece). In paper money this refers to any design, from the original artwork to a preliminary printing, for the purpose of examination by parliamentary or financial bodies, prior to the authorisation of an actual issue of notes, the counterpart of patterns in coinage or medals.

**Face**   The surface of a banknote, more usually referred to as the front, the recto or obverse.

**Face Value**   The value inscribed in words and/or figures at which the note passes current.

**Facsimile**   An imitation, usually authorised officially, of a note, perhaps created long after the original has been withdrawn from circulation. Such notes, usually marked in some way to indicate their true nature, were sometimes produced for exhibition purposes or to complete gaps in the bank's official collection, often utilising the original plates or dies.

**Fantasy**  A note purporting to be the currency of a country which does not exist. Recent examples include the notes of the Hutt River Province which declared its independence of Western Australia.

**Federal Reserve Bank Note**  Type of note issued by the Federal Reserve Bank of the USA between 1915 and 1933 and thus inscribed.

**Federal Reserve Note**  A note issued by the Federal Reserve of the USA from 1914 to the present day and thus inscribed. These notes are backed by the federal government and not by individual banks.

**Fei-ch'ien**  Chinese for "flying money", denoting the earliest form of paper money in the world and dating from the 7th–9th centuries.

**Fiat Money**  Notes issued by a government but not redeemable in coin or bullion.

**Fiduciary Issue**  Notes issued purely on trust, without the backing of gold or other securities.

**Flying Money**  See Fei-ch'ien.

**Forced Issue**  Paper money imposed on a populace without any backing and usually issued by the authority of an occupying power in time of war.

**Forgery**  An unauthorised copy or imitation of a note, made with the intention of deceiving collectors. Forgeries intended to pass current for real notes are more properly termed counterfeits.

**Foxing**  Unsightly spots, ranging from yellow to brown or dark red, caused by iron impurities in old paper. It is, in fact, a form of fungus which can spread across the paper or attack other paper with which it comes in contact. It can often be checked, if not always entirely eliminated, by treating the affected part with a very weak solution of a bleaching agent such as Chloramine-T. It is exacerbated by lack of air circulation and for that reason it is important that notes should be examined periodically and allowed to breathe.

**Fractional Currency**  Emergency issue of small-denomination notes by the USA in 1863-65, following a shortage of coins caused by the Civil War. This issue was superseded by the Postage Currency notes, but bore the inscription "Receivable for all US stamps", alluding to the most popular medium of small change at that time. Denominations ranged from 3c to 50c.

**Frame**  That part of the design forming the border, prevalent in note design until the 1960s when a much lighter, open style of design came into fashion. In many older notes the frame was elaborately engraved and ornamented to defeat counterfeiters.

**Front**  The main side of a note, otherwise the obverse or recto, on which appears the name of the bank and/or country, together with signatures of bank officials, the date and place of issue and usually some form of promise to pay the bearer in coin of the realm.

**Fund Raising Note**  A note produced by an exiled organisation to raise money for the campaign to gain independence. Good examples are the notes issued mainly in the USA by Irish and Hungarian nationalists in the 19th century.

**Funeral Money**  Imitations of banknotes, used in China and Latin America in funeral ceremonies. See also Hell notes.

**Gold Bank Note**  A note issued in the 1870s by nine banks in California and one in Boston, so-called because they promised to pay the bearer in gold coin.

**Gold Certificate**  A series of nine issues in the USA between 1863 and 1922, redeemable in gold coin.

**Gold Note**  Term generally applied to any note specifically redeemable in gold.

**Goodfor**  Popular name for emergency money made of paper or card, from the inscription "Good for" or its equivalent in other languages (e.g. French bon pour or Dutch goed voor) followed by a monetary value. Notes of this type have been recorded from Europe, Africa and America during times of economic crises or shortage of coinage.

**Granite Paper**  Type of security paper which has tiny coloured threads enmeshed in it.

**Greenback**  Popular name for the paper money issued under the authority of the US government, from the predominant colour of the verso.

**Guerrilla Money**  Money issued in areas under the control of guerrillas and partisans during wartime range from the veld ponds of the Boer War (1899–1902) to the notes issued by the Garibaldi Brigade in Italy and the anti-fascist notes of Tito's partisans in Yugoslavia. The most prolific issues were those produced in Luzon, Mindanao and Negros Occidental by the Filipino resistance (1942–45).

**Guilloche**  French term signifying the intricate pattern of curved lines produced by the rose engine and used as a security feature in the production of banknotes, cheques, stocks and share certificates. See also engine turning.

**Gutschein**  German word for voucher or coupon, denoting the paper money used aboard ships of the Imperial Navy during the World War I. The last issue was made at Scapa Flow, Orkney, during the internment of the High Seas Fleet (1918–19). The term is also widely used in Germany nowadays for any giveaway, exchangeable for goods or services as part of a sales promotion.

**Halved Note**   A note which has been cut in half as a precaution during transmission by post. On the safe arrival of the first half being notified, the other half is then sent by post. This practice was widespread in the early 19th century when highway robbery was prevalent. The two halves were subsequently re-united, often using specially printed strips of gummed paper.

**Handsigned Notes**   which have been individually signed by hand, rather than by means of an engraved facsimile signature.

**Hansatsu**   Japanese term denoting notes of purely local validity, usually printed by woodblocks on soft, thick handmade paper, hence the derisive trerm "blotter money".

**Hell Notes**   Imitation paper money used in Chinese funeral ceremonies and buried with the dead to pay for services in the next world.

**Holed**   Term denoting notes which have either been pierced with pins or staples to attach them to each other or to documents, thereby detracting from their collectable condition, or notes which have been deliberately punched with small holes as a security precaution. The latter device is sometimes applied to specimen notes or printers' samples to prevent them getting into general circulation. See also perforated.

**Hologram**   A security device consisting of an image which changes colour or design depending on how it is tilted towards the light. It was first applied to credit cards in the early 1980s and to banknotes in 1988 (Australia), but has become much more widespread in very recent years.

**Imitation Money**   Also known as play money or toy money, it consists of notes produced for games of chance (like Monopoly), children's toy shops and post offices, as tourist souvenirs or for political satire (e.g. the shrinking pound or dollar). See also funeral money, hell notes and skit notes.

**Imprint**   Inscription on a note giving the name of the printer, usually found in the lower margin.

**Indented**   Description of an irregular edge on the left-hand side of a note, matching a corresponding pattern in the counterfoil, used in the 19th century as a precaution against forgery.

**Inflation Money**   Notes produced in Germany (1921–23), Austria (1923), Poland (1923), Hungary (1945–46), Greece (1946), China (1946–48) and many countries of Latin America and the former communist bloc since the 1980s and, most recently, by Angola and Turkey. Hungary holds the record for the highest value of any note ever issued—one thousand million adopengos equivalent to no less than 20,000,000,000,000,00 0,000,000,000,000 pengos.

**Inscription**   Any kind of text printed on the back or front of a note.

**Intaglio**   In the production of paper money, intaglio engraving is still commonly practised. In this process the engraver cuts the design into a steel die and the printing ink lies in the grooves. The paper is forced into the grooves under great pressure where it takes up the ink and results in the ridges which are characeristic of this process.

**Interest Bearing Note**   A note whose promise to pay the bearer includes a reference to interest payable at the time of redemption.

**Invasion Money**   Notes prepared in advance of a military invasion, either solely for the use of the invading forces, or also extended forcibly to the civil population and thus employed as means of controlling the local economy. *See also* liberation and occupation money.

**Jugate**   (From Latin Jugum, a yoke). Heraldic term denoting the overlapping profiles of two or more persons portrayed on banknotes. A good recent example is provided by the notes of Thailand celebrating the Golden Wedding of the King and Queen, released in April 2000.

**Kreditivsedlar**   (Swedish for "credit notes"). The name given to the first issue of paper money made in the western world. Paper money of this type was the invention of Johan Palmstruch at Riga in 1652 but nine years elapsed before it was implemented by the Stockholm Bank. The notes were issued up to 1666 and were mainly redeemable in copper platmynt though latterly in silver coin.

**Labour Note**   A form of paper money devised by the industrialist and philanthropist Robert Owen and used to pay his employees at the textile mills in New Lanark, Scotland in the 1830s. The value was expressed in hours worked rather than any monetary terms. The concept spread briefly to England and America, but was generally frowned on as an abuse of the workers' rights to spend their money freely, rather than at the company store.

**Latent Image**   A security device on a banknote which takes the form of an image that only becomes apparent when the surface of the note is tilted in a particular direction, and thus was a precursor of the hologram as a safeguard against forgery.

**Leather Money**   Pieces of leather embossed with an official device have been used as money on several occasions, during the sieges of Faenza and Leiden and in the Isle of Man in the 15th and 16th centuries. Several towns in Austria and Germany produced lether tokens during and after the World War I.

**Legal Tender**   Notes which are declared by law to be current money and which tradesmen and shopkeepers are obliged to accept in payment for goods or services. (*See* Banknotes and the Law).

**Legend**   The inscription on a banknote.

**Letterpress**   A printing process in which the ink is applied to the raised portions of a die or plate and then transferred to paper . It takes its name from the fact that this method was originally used in the printing of books and newspapers consisting mainly of lettering although from the outset it also included illustrations from woodblocks. This process is much cheaper and less secure than intaglio, and was used for many early banknotes. *See also* typeset.

**Liberation Money**   Paper money prepared for use in parts of Europe and Asia, formerly under Axis occupation. Liberation notes were used in France, Belgium and the Netherlands in 1944-45, while various Japanese and Chinese notes were overprinted for use in Hong Kong when it was liberated in 1945. Indian notes overprinted for use in Burma were issued in 1945-46 when that country was freed from Japanese occupation.

**Lithography**   A printing process patented by Alois Senefelder in 1795 and since widely used in the production of banknotes and cheques, mainly as an underprint, often in special fugitive inks. The name comes from the Greek lithos, a stone and graphein, to write, and alludes to the polished limestone slabs originally employed, although nowadays zinc or even paper plates are used instead. The image is laid down on the stone in greasy ink or by means of transfers. The printing ink adheres to the grease but is repelled by the blank areas of the plate.

**Low Number**   A note with a very low serial number, either one or two digits preceded by a string of noughts, is regarded by collectors as very desirable, indicating very early issue. Pandering to this, however, many banks now set aside the low-numbered notes for inclusion in presentation folders sold to collectors.

**Mandat**   Name given to a form of paper money issued in the period of the French Revolution. Like the assignat, which it replaced, the value of the mandat was theoretically backed by land confiscated from the Church and the aristocracy.

**Margin**   That portion of a note lying between the outer border of the design and the edge of the paper. Notes with regular margins on all four sides often command a premium, whereas notes with irregular margins are often discounted. Margins may be clean-cut (by guillotine), rough or even deckle-edged if produced from individual pieces of handmade paper instead of being printed in sheets.

**Master Die**   The original piece of steel or copper engraved by hand. It is then hardened chemically and an image taken by means of a transfer roller which, after hardening, transfers the image in reverse to the printing plate. Alterations to the master die, by means of punches or subsequent engraving, create secondary dies (often for the production of different denominations using the same basic design).

**Metal Thread**   A security device in the form of a thin strip of metal embedded in the paper pulp during manufacture.

**Microprint**   Printing in very tiny lettering, usually endlessly repeated, as a security precaution. It is often used in doubly fugitive ink on those parts of cheques where handwriting appears, to prevent attempts to alter or falsify details by washing, bleaching or chemical means.

**Military Currency**   Notes issued under military authority, mainly for the use of troops on active service.

**Military Payment Certificate**   A note produced by the US military authorities for the use of service personnel in PX (post exchange) canteens to prevent black market trading with local civilians.

**Ming Note**   A large-sized Chinese note issued during the Ming Dynasty (1368-1644), using paper made from mulberry bark. Now highly desirable as the earliest form of paper money available to the collector market.

**Miscut**   A note with very irregular margins, or even showing a portion of an adjoining note in the sheet, caused by misalignment of the blades cutting up the sheets of notes prior to issue. In some cases an additional piece of paper remains attached as a result of part of the wide sheet margin being accidentally folded over. Such errors in production are of curiosity interest rather than high monetary value, although they often command a premium.

**Model**   A mock-up of a banknote, produced at a preliminary stage of production, often incorporated the pasted-up portions of previously issued notes or a composite of different elements which may eventually form the complete design,

**Moiré**   French for "watering", denoting a security underprint of close wavy lines having the effect of watered silk.

**Money Order**   Certificate for a specific amount of money, which may be transmitted by post and encashed at a money order office or post office. This system was pioneered by Britain and the USA in the early 19th century and is now virtually worldwide. The term is now confined to certificates above a certain value, the terms postal order and postal note being used for similar certificates covering small amounts.

**Moses Crowns**   Popular name for the notes issued under the authority of the Jewish Council of Elders in Theresienstadt concentration camp during World War II, and so-called on account of the principal motif showing Moses holding up the Ten Commandments. *See also* concentration camp money.

**Mule**   A note whose back and front are printed from plates which were not originally intended to be paired together.

**Multilingual** A note bearing inscriptions in many different languages. Apart from the so-called Babel notes of revolutionary Russia, good examples may be found in the issues of the Habsburg Empire, with values in up to eight languages and two scripts, or Indian notes with inscriptions in English and many different indigenous scripts. The Euro notes of the European Community bear the initials of the European Central Bank in the different languages and scripts of the member countries.

**Multiple Denomination** A note with values expressed in two or more different currencies, generally to facilitate exchange. *See also* dual currency.

**National Bank Note** American term applied specifically to the notes issued by banks, chartered by the federal government between 1863 and 1935, and backed by US Treasury bonds.

**Negotiable** Term applied to a banknote or cheque which can be readily converted into coin.

**Notaphily** Hybrid word from Latin nota (note) and Greek philos (love), coined in 1969 to denote the branch of numismatics devoted to the collection and study of paper money. *See also* syngraphics.

**Note** A piece of paper money. In former times the term was also loosely applied to cheques or IOUs.

**Notgeld** German word meaning "emergency money", applied to the various forms of currency, including notes, which circulated during the World War I when coinage disappeared from circulation, but rapidly overtaken by infinitely more prolific issues of paper money produced by shops, chambers of commerce, businesses and local authorities. Collectors distinguish between kleine Notgeld (small emergency money) in denominations from 10 to 50 pfennigs during and immediately after the war, and the large Notgeld whose denominations were in thousands, and later millions, of marks. Some 3,000 types appeared in 1922 and over 60,000 in 1923 alone. These quaint and colourful mementoes of the German hyperinflation ceased to circulate in 1924 when the currency was reformed.

**Obsolete** Term denoting a note which is no longer issued and has been withdrawn from circulation. Notes which are no longer issued but which may still be current during a brief overlapping period are more properly described as obsolescent.

**Obverse** The front of a note, equivalent to the "heads" side of a coin or medal, although the term recto is more appropriate for a piece of paper.

**Occupation Money** Any form of money, but usually notes or vouchers, issued in wartime by enemy forces in the territory which they invade and occupy.

**Order Cheque** A cheque payable to a specified person or to his or her order.

**Out of Date Cheque** A cheque which is considered by the paying bank to have been in circulation for "an unreasonable period of time". This is usually regarded as at least six months, although there is apparently no statutory limit.

**Overprint** Any form of printing added to a note or cheque after it was originally produced. Such a practice may be employed to alter the name of the issuing bank or authority or, in times of inflation and monetary reform, to convert the denomination to the reformed system. An overprint may also signify a change of government or regime, or even the name of the country.

**Paid Cheque** A cheque which has been honoured by a bank and the amount debited to the drawer's account.

**Paid Stamp** The handstamp applied to a cheque by the paying bank after debiting the sum to the drawer's account.

**Paper Money** Any form of currency based on paper.

**Partisan Note** A note produced by Tito's partisans operating in Serbia, Croatia and other parts of Yugoslavia after it was dismembered by the Axis during World War II, and used in those parts of the country which were effectively under their control.

**Payee** The person to whom a cheque is made payable.

**Perforation** A series of small holes punched out of paper. The earliest form, dating from the 1840s, was used to facilitate the separation of the cheque or banknote from its counterfoil, but later the punches were often arranged in the form of letters or numerals and could thus be applied to cheques to indicate the date on which they were presented for payment. In banknotes, perforation has sometimes been employed to mark them as Specimens intended for archival or publicity purposes and not valid for circulation. *See also* Cancelled.

**Pilgrim Receipt** A form of paper money overprinted for the use of people going on a religious pilgrimage. Notes of Pakistan, for example, are specially overprinted for use by pilgrims from that country making the haj to the Moslem holy places of Mecca and Medina in Saudi Arabia.

**Pinhole** A blemish on a banknote caused by it having been pinned or stapled to a document or another note. It should be noted, however, that certain notes only exist with this feature as they were put into circulation in batches stapled together for the sake of convenience.

**Plain Back** A note which has no printing of any kind on the reverse. *See also* Uniface.

**Plate Number** A small number incorporated in the design of some notes to indicate the plate from which it was printed.

**Play Money** Imitations of banknotes produced for use in such games of chance as Monopoly or as part of children's toy outfits for shops and post offices. Of passing interest to notaphilists only in so far as the designs are often vaguely derived from actual notes.

**Playing Card Money** A form of emergency money created in French Canada from 1685 onwards during shortages of coin supplied from France. Governor Duplessis hit upon using playing cards, with his signature and the denomination added in handwriting.

**Polymer** A chemical compound containing repeating structural units and formed by chemical combination of many small molecules. In notaphily the term is applied to various plastic materials used in the manufacture of banknotes since the 1970s.

**Postage Currency** Small notes in denominations of 5, 10, 25 and 50 cents, issued by the US federal government in 1862–63, were thus inscribed and had reproductions of postage stamps engraved on them—five 5c stamps on the 25c and five 10c stamps on the 50c notes. The earliest issue even had perforations in the manner of stamps, but this unnecessary device was soon dispensed with. *See also* stamp money.

**Postal Notes or Orders** Low-value notes intended for transmission by post and encashable at post offices. Introduced by Britain in 1883, they were an extension of the earlier money order system and are now issued by virtually every country.

**Post-dated** A cheque bearing a date subsequent to that on which it is presented for payment. As banks are not obliged to honour such cheques they are invariably handed back to the payee or returned to the drawer for re-presentation on or after the due date.

**Prisoner of War Money** Under the terns of the Geneva Convention the belligerents on both sides during the world wars provided special issues of notes for use within prisoner of war camps. Similar provisions were also made for the camps in which civilian enemy aliens were interned.

**Promissory Note** A written promise to pay, either on demand or at some future time, a sum of money to a specified individual or to the bearer.

**Proof** A preliminary test printing of the back or front of a note, taken from the master die or the printing plate before actual production, in order to ensure that every detail is correct.

**Propaganda Note** A piece of paper money containing political slogans or a didactic element. During the World War II forgeries of German

and Japanese notes were produced by the Allies and additionally inscribed or overprinted with slogans such as "Co-Prosperity Sphere—What is it worth?" (a reference to the Japanese occupied areas of Southeast Asia). Forged dollars with Anti-American propaganda were airdropped over Sicily by the Germans in 1943 and counterfeit pounds with Arabic propaganda over Egypt in 1942-43. Various anti-communist organisations liberated propaganda forgeries of paper money by balloon over Eastern Europe during the Cold War period.

**Provincial Note** A note issued by a provincial bank or under the authority of a provincial government (as in Canada). Provincial banks in England were only permitted to issue notes so long as they did not have an office in London. The last of the English provincial banks was Fox, Fowler of Wellington Somerset, whose notes ceased in 1921 when the bank became part of the Lloyd's group.

**Psywar Note** A note produced as part of a campaign of psychological warfare. Effectively this means some kind of imitation paper money dropped as a leaflet by aircraft over enemy-held territory with the intention of demoralising the enemy and boosting the morale of the people enduring occupation.

**Punched** A note or cheque which bears the mark of a ticket punch to denote that it has been cancelled.

**Rag Paper** Paper made of linen rags, sometimes with an admixture of cotton or other textile substances, to produce a very tough, hard-wearing material for the production of banknotes.

**Raised Note** A note which has been revalued by means of an official overprint.

**Reckoning Note** A form of paper money issued to German troops on the eve of an invasion and exchangeable for local currency, usually at a considerable disadvantage to the economy of the occupied country.

**Recto** The proper term for the face or front of a note.

**Refunding Certificate** The official name for a $10 note issued by the US government in 1879 and made more acceptable to the general public on account of the 4 per cent interest per annum for an unspecified period. However, these notes were called in in 1907 by which time they were worth $21.30.

**Reichskreditkassen** German for State Credit Treasury, inscribed on certain notes intended for circulation in occupied territories of Europe during the World War II.

**Re-issue** A note issued again after an extended lapse of time.

**Remainder** A note from a bank or issuing

authority which has never been circulated, due to inflation, political changes or bank failure. Such notes, sometimes in partial or unfinished state (e.g. missing serial numbers or signatures) are generally unloaded on to the numismatic market at a nominal sum and provide a good source of inexpensive material for the beginner.

**Repaired**   A note which has suffered damage, usually tears or splitting, and bearing the evidence of having been restored. Unless they are very rare, such specimens are usually heavily discounted.

**Replacement Note**   A note issued to replace a defective note of the same serial number but generally identified as such by the inclusion of an asterisk or star alongside the number.

**Reprint**   A note produced from the original plates but long after production has been generally discontinued. Such notes often differ subtly from the originals, either in the type of paper used or, more often, in the shade of inks employed.

**Revalidation**   The process of bringing back into use notes which had previously been withdrawn from circulation and declared invalid. This has sometimes happened as a result of changes in political regime, such as in Austria where the notes of the early postwar period were similar to those immediately before the Nazi takeover in 1938, identifiable only by their dates.

**Revalue**   An overprint which alters the face value of a note, usually as a result of currency reform.

**Reverse**   The back of a note, more properly termed the verso.

**Saddle Blanket**   Nickname for the very large notes of the United States in the 19th century.

**Safe Conduct Pass**   A form of propaganda note airdropped behind enemy lines promising safe conduct to military personnel who decide to surrender.

**Safety Paper**   A form of security paper which dramatically changes colour (usually deep blue) when exposed to water. It was formerly widely used in the production of cheques, in order to deter people from trying to alter signatures or other handwritten portions by washing off the ink.

**Scrip**   Paper money of restricted validity or circulation, such as Bafs and other military notes used in service canteens and post exchanges.

**Scripophily**   Term coined in the 1970s to denote the study and collection of stocks, bond and share certificates.

**Seal**   A device, usually circular, which simulates the seal of a bank, a treasury or the state, formerly applied to documents in red sealing wax or embossed in metal foil, but now more generally applied by lithography or letterpress to the banknote design to enhance its official character. See also chop.

**Sealskin Money**   Notes of 1818-30 issued by the Russian Company trading in Alaska, using a form of parchment derived from the skins of seals.

**Secret Mark**   Any device concealed within the mass of engraving with the intention of tripping up the would-be counterfeiter. Such hidden marks, generally overlooked by forgers when fabricating notes, are known to the Secret Service (USA) and bank inspectors and are regarded as a test of genuineness.

**Security Features**   Since 1820 various devices have been incorporated in the design and production of banknotes in order to obviate forgery. These include guilloche engraving, watermarks, metal threads, granite paper, latent images, images visible only under ultra-violet light, microprinting, colour shifting ink, embossing, lithographic underprinting and holograms.

**Segmented Security Thread**   Security device in the form of a line of dashes running across the back of a note, either as a metallic thread or a minute holographic image.

**Serial**   The sequence of figures in numerical order which identifies each individual note. As a rule, numbers are combined with prefix and/or suffix letters which considerably extend the range of serials. As well as very low serial numbers, indicating early issue, collectors also take note of different styles or colours of figures and the presence of symbols (asterisks or stars) denoting replacement notes.

**Series**   A set of different denominations more or less issued within a clearly definable period if not always simultaneously, which possess common features in inscription, style or design. In some cases the word SERIES actually appears on the notes, followed by the date of its introduction.

**Share Certificate**   A piece of paper, often highly ornate or intricately printed, which certifies that the holder possesses a certain specified number of shares in a company.

**Shinplasters**   Derisory term originally applied to the Continental currency notes issued during the American War of Independence, the fractional currency of the Civil War period and also the low-denomination notes of Canada between 1870 and 1935, but often applied indiscriminately to any other low-denomination, small-format notes.

**Shoshi**   Adhesive stamps affixed to Japanese banknotes in the immediate postwar period in order to revalidate them.

**Siderography**   A printing process patented between 1811 and 1819 by Jacob Perkins and applied to the manufacture of printing plates for banknotes from 1820 onwards. From the Greek sideros, iron and graphein, to write.

**Siege Note** A note produced by the defenders during the siege of a town, when supplies of normal currency are cut off. Notable examples include the notes issued at Venice during the Austrian siege of 1848 and by Mafeking in 1900 during the Boer War.

**Sight Note** A type of promissory note, so-called on account of the formula "At . . . [number of days] after Sight, pay this to . . . Or Order, the Sum of . . ." Although in some cases the word "Sight" itself was inserted in manuscript, the period specified being usually 30 days.

**Silk Thread** A security device patented in the 1830s by John Dickinson of Croxley Green and incorporated into some banknotes of the mid-19th century as a precursor of the metallic thread used nowadays.

**Silver Certificate** Type of paper money introduced by the United States in 1878, redeemable by the Treasury in silver coin.

**Signature** From the earliest times, bills, promissory notes, cheques and banknotes relied heavily on the signature of an individual or bank official. Handsigned notes survived in some instances until the late 19th century but from the 1820s onwards the vast majority of signatures have been engraved facsimiles. They are of importance to collectors as constituting a major variety in any series of notes, each change of signature constituting a collectable variant. One, two or even three signatures of different bank officials are the norm, although notes of the Austro-Hungarian Bank had three Austrian and three Hungarian signatures, on the front and back respectively.

**Skit Note** A piece of paper masquerading as a banknote. It differs from a counterfeit in that its design parodies that of a genuine note, often for political, satirical or advertising reasons. Others were produced as April Fools' Day jokes or a form of Valentine (e.g. The Banks of Hearts or Lovers). In recent years they have been produced as advertising gimmicks or as coupons permitting a discount off the list price of goods. Also known as "Flash" notes.

**Small Size Note** Collectors' term for the series of notes, in a reduced size from the preceding issues, which came into use in the USA in 1929 and are still in use.

**Special Cheque** A cheque drawn on a form specially printed for the drawer and not of the standard design. Such cheques usually give far greater prominence to the names of the drawers (usually a company or institution) and may even be embellished with pictures of factories, premises or products. For this reason they are of immense interest to local historians.

**Specie** Money in coin. Many issues of paper owe their existence to the suspension of specie payment in time of war or monetary crisis.

**Specimen** Term generally used to denote a single item but more specifially applying to a note intended for circulation between banks or for press publicity and distinguished from the generally issued version by zero serial numbers, punch holes or a security overprint, usually the word SPECIMEN or its equivalent in other languages.

**Stage Money** Notes specially printed for use in dramatic productions, on stage, screen or television, sometimes in vague imitation of real notes but often completely different to avoid any charge of counterfeiting.

**Stamp Duty** A government tax on transactions involving money, and therefore applied in Britain to cheques between the beginning of the 19th century and 1962. The earliest duty was denoted by a colourless embossed stamp, followed in 1853-81 by various adhesive revenue stamps, then the small uprignt oval embossed stamps in red (1d) or blue (2d) and finally by the small circular crowned medallion stamps printed in black. Similar systems applied in many other countries. In the USA, for example, the duty could be denoted by a variety of adhesive stamps or by a device printed in orange-yellow across the middle of the cheque.

**Stamped** Banknotes to which have been affixed adhesive stamps, either to denote the payment of a tax or to authenticate them. The latter practice has sometimes been used in lieu of an overprint to alter the validity of notes.

**Stamp Money** Both postage and revenue stamps have circulated as money during shortages of coins, from the American Civil War onwards. Encased postage stamps were used in the USA (1861–62) before they were superseded by Postage Currency notes, but the same expedient was adopted by many other countries immediately after the World War I. Stamps afficed to special cards have circulated as money in Rhodesia (now Zimbabwe) in 1900, the French colonies and Turkey during the World War I, in Spain during the Civil War (1936–39) and the Philippines during the Japanese occupation (1942–45). Stamps printed on thick card, with an inscription on the reverse signifying their parity with silver coins, were issued in Russia (1917–18) and also in Armenia, the Crimea and the Ukraine (1918–20). During World War II Ceylon (which is now Sri Lanka) and several Indian states issued small money cards with contemporary stamps printed on them.

**Star Note** A replacement note issued in the USA, so-called on account of the five-pointed star before or after the serial number.

**State Bank Note** A note issued by a bank chartered by one of the states in the USA, as opposed to the issues of the Treasury, Federal Reserve or other agencies of the federal government.

**State Note** A note issued in the early 19th century by one of the states in the USA.

**Stopped Cheque** A cheque on which payment has been countermanded by the drawer before it is presented at the paying bank.

**Stub** Another term for the counterfoil, retained as a record of a bank transaction.

**Subject** Term indicating an individual note which is part of a sheet. Thus a 20-subject sheet would contain 20 impressions of the note.

**Surface Printing** An alternative name for letterpress, the printing process mainly employed in the production of banknotes before 1820.

**Sutlers' Notes** A form of scrip issued by US army canteen-keepers for use on military posts and redeemable in merchandise. They were mainly issued during the late 19th century.

**Syngraphics** Term coined in the 1970s, from the Greek syn (together) and graphein (to write) to denote the study and collection of cheques.

**Travellers' Cheques** (American, Travelers' Checks) Notes in various denominations issued by Thomas Cook, American Express and many banks which can be converted into cash by tourists and businessmen when travelling abroad. They are validated by the traveller who signs each note in the presence of the issuing agent and then signs them again at the point of encashment. They are issued in sterling, US dollars or some other widely recognised currency but can then be converted into the equivalent in local money. Since the advent of credit cards and bank cards, however, the use of travellers' cheques has dropped very dramatically.

**Treasury Note** Paper money worth 10 shillings or one pound, issued by the British treasury on the outbreak of the World War I when specie payments were suspended, and continuing till 1928 when the Bank of England took over responsibility for note-issuing. They were popularly known as Bradburys, from the signature of the Treasury official, Sir John Bradbury, engraved on them.

**Type** A major design.

**Typeset** A note in which the design is entirely composed of lettering, ornament being confined to printer's rule and the use of conventional symbols, usually to create a border.

**Uncirculated** A note which is in the most perfect condition, as received at the bank from the printer and never passed from hand to hand.

**Uncut** A sheet or part of a sheet in which two or more notes are still unsevered.

**Underprint** The background to the principal motif and inscriptions of a banknote, generally printed by a different process (e.g. lithography instead of intaglio) and in contrasting, lighter colours incorporating security features such as microprinting and latent images.

**Uniface** A note which has printing on one side only.

**Upham** A Philadelphia printer whose patriotism during the Civil War led him to produce facsimiles of Confederate notes. The reproduction was excellent and the imitations could only be readily distinguished by Upham's imprint and advertisement in the bottom margin. Unfortunately most of his notes had the advert trimmed off and swiftly found their way to the Confederacy where they were promptly circulated as genuine. As a result, Upham facsimiles with the imprint still intact are now relatively scarce, and certainly rarer than the notes they imitated.

**Validating Stamp** A handstruck mark applied to notes either at the time of issue to render them valid or subsequently applied to extend their usage.

**Varible Optical Ink** Ink which appears to change colour or density depending on the angle at which the note is viewed.

**Variety** Variation in, or modification of type, effigy or inscription.

**Verso** The proper term for the reverse or back of a note.

**Victory Note** A banknote of the Philippines overprinted VICTORY from October 20, 1944 onwards to celebrate the liberation of the islands after almost three years of Japanese rule.

**Vignette** Strictly speaking the pictorial element of a note, shading off into the surrounding unprinted paper rather than having a clearly defined border or frame, but nowadays applied generally to the picture portion of a banknote, as opposed to the portrait, armorial or numeral elements.

**Voucher** A piece of paper exchangeable for goods or services of a specified value and therefore regarded as a form of paper money.

**War Lord Note** A note issued by one of the many tuchuns or war lords who operated in various parts of China in the period between the fall of the Manchu Dynasty and the communist takeover in 1949. Seldom, if ever, backed by gold or collateral other than the barrel of the gun, these notes were often well designed and printed (employing the leading security printers of Europe and America to lend them respectability), but rendered worthless as the fortunes of civil war ebbed and flowed. They have left a rich legacy of relatively cheap but colourful material for the collector market.

**Watermark** A security device, generally visible when the note is held up to the light, and ranging from an overall geometric or curvilinear pattern to state emblems and even portraits, the lastnamed often set within a circular or oval cartouche. The watermark derives its name from the fact that it is created at the wet pulp stage in the manufacture of the paper, in which the pressure from brass wires or "bits" of the required pattern causes a slight thinning in the paper. In some cases notes have been printed on paper bearing the papermaker's name or trademark, only a portion of which is visible on any one note.

**White Note** Collector's term for the early notes of the Bank of England which were printed in black ink on white paper, using a relatively large format. This tradition, dating from 1695, continued as late as 1957 when the "white fiver" was superseded by a £5 note of more conventional design. These white notes were deceptively simple, which may have encouraged the Germans, under Operation Bernhard, to forge them during the World War II, using skilled counterfeiters in prisons and concentration camps for the purpose. But in fact the secret of these notes lay in the quality of paper used, with

its extremely intricate watermark pattern, and it was the failure to secure paper of the right quality which defeated the forgers in the long run.

**Wildcat Notes** Notes issued in the USA and Canada in the early 19th century by unscrupulous persons who purported to act on behalf of non-existent banks. Poor communications and lax banking laws enabled them to get away with these frauds for a short time before their notes were unmasked as false and worthless. Nevertheless they are not without considerable interest on account of their colourful designs and their role in the rather freewheeling commerce of the period.

**Withdrawn Note** A note which has been taken out of circulation. Sometimes, though by no means always, such notes are overprinted, perforated or punched in some way to indicate that they have no legal tender status or any actual worth.

# The anatomy of a banknote

**B**ELOW we illustrate typical banknotes in order to show the various elements which combine to make up the design. Modern banknotes generally involve two or more different printing processes, applied to specially prepared paper which may incorporate one or more security features. The notes reproduced here have been chosen to represent the various details which the collector is likely to encounter in notes in general, as well as demonstrate how the design is built up as a result of very considerable thought—even though most members of the public may never give it a second glance.

## Bank of England £20

### Front (Obverse)

1. Denomination, comprising the pound sign £ (from Latin Libra = pound) and numerals, both horizontally lined and in contrasting colours.
2. Numerals of value (upper right) cross-hatched.
3. Bank of England in Old English upper and lower case lettering.
4. Paraphs or flourishes for decorative effect.
5. Promise: I PROMISE TO PAY THE BEARER ON DEMAND THE SUM OF TWENTY Pounds in three different fonts.
6. Signature of Merlyn Lowther who personally makes the promise in her capacity as Chief Cashier.
7. Cypher or serial, consisting of a two-letter prefix followed by eight digits. The left-hand cypher is made up of numerals of varying sizes and colours, whereas that on the right is of uniform size and colour.
8. Three-quarter facing portrait of Her Majesty Queen Elizabeth.
9. Hologram, crowned and scrolled, containing the seated figure of Britannia, based on the original motif, with the numerals 20 in an overall background pattern. Tilt the note in another direction and the image appears as 20 on an engine-turned background. In both positions, microscopic numerals also appear across the foot.
10. Place of issue: "London, For the Govr. and Compa. of the BANK of ENGLAND" in antique copperplate script.
11. Watermark, showing a bareheaded portrait of Queen Elizabeth.
12. The Royal monogram E II R on a solid rectangular ground.
13. Copyright symbol followed by THE GOVERNOR AND COMPANY OF THE BANK OF ENGLAND, 1999.
14. Musical notes, symbolising the subject on the back of the note.
15. Continuous band inscribed £20 in microprint.
16. Value in words TWENTY POUNDS in microprint on a lithographed underprint.
17. Underprint consisting of a subtly changing pattern of ornament and wavy lines.
18. Anaglyphic pattern, creating the illusion of a three-dimensional motif.
19. Band containing word TWENTY and numerals 20 alternately.
**Plus** a solid vertical metal strip showing through when viewed from the front.

## Back (Reverse)

1. Vertical metal strip showing as short dashes.
2. BANK OF ENGLAND in double-lined capitals.
3. Value £20 in different styles in the upper corners.
4. Portrait of the composer, Sir Edward Elgar (1857-1934).
5. View of the West Face of Worcester Catherdal.
6. St Cecilia, patron saint of music.
7. Angel blowing a trumpet.
8. Latin motto.
9. Underprint of musical notes and symbols, repeated in various colours.
10. Copyright symbol and text around the watermark portrait.
The bulk of the detail on the reverse is lithographed, but the inscriptions are intaglio, like most of the features on the front.

A selection of spectacular error notes from the Bruce Goulborn collection

# To err is human;
## to collect, divine

**T**HE mistakes made by others have always fascinated us, whether we are collectors or merely onlookers, and never is that fascination greater than when such mistakes are made by institutions renowned for their probity and quality. The Bank of England is a byword for strength, standing and accuracy and given the vast numbers of banknotes printed every day, errors in the production process are few and far between. However, notwithstanding the strictest of quality controls, real howlers do escape the eagle eyes of the checkers leading astonished collectors to exclaim, "How on earth did the Bank miss this one?". Many minor errors are actually much rarer than major ones, simply because the public are much less likely to spot them. But it is the really spectacular errors which attract the most attention, fuelling demand from all those keen on adding an extra dimension to their collections.

Paper money errors are inextricably linked with the production process and classification of them to some extent reflects differences in the printing method used by the issuer. Production of a banknote generally involves four distinct phases of treatment: (1) Paper, (2) Printing, (3) Numbering and (4) Cutting. However, at any stage during production the paper may be damaged, so for the purpose of error classification, folding and creasing must be added as a fifth category. Within each of these stages there are sub-categories and the classification for the purposes of this catalogue is therefore as follows:

1. PAPER
    (a) Watermark (i) misplaced, (ii) exposed on surface, (iii) inverted.
    (b) Security features (i) completely exposed, (ii) partly exposed, (iii) joined, (iv) missing.
    (c) Join (i) white cotton tape, (ii) red adhesive paper, (iii) yellow adhesive paper.

2. PRINTING
    (a) Uniface.
    (b) Missing colour (i) underprint, (ii) main colour, (iii) dry print.
    (c) Extra colour (i) streaks, (ii) solid lines, (iii) blobs and blots, (iv) excess of one or more colours, (v) wrong colour.
    (d) Offset (i) front on back, (ii) back on front, (iii) misaligned.
    (e) Part design missing (i) at edge of note, (ii) in body of note.
    (f) Print flaws (i) lines, (ii) spots, (iii) other.
    (g) Missing signature.

3. NUMBERING
    (a) No number. Sometimes a missing number is entered in pencil or ink.
    (b) Only one number of two. Sometimes all or part of the number appears on the reverse.
    (c) Shift. A major shift of a serial number to either the right or the left.
    (d) Missing digits (i) single, (ii) multiple.
    (e) Numeral misplaced (i) misaligned, (ii) parts of two numerals visible.
    (f) Different numbers (i) different prefix, (ii) one different serial numeral, (iii) two or more different serial numerals.
    (g) Identical numbers on two or more notes.
    (h) Slip and stick. Two or more identically numbered notes where the upper number differs from the lower one.

(j) Double number. A second different number is printed over the first one. (i) one serial number affected, (ii) both serial numbers affected.

(k) Dry print of number.

## 4. CUTTING
(a) Design misplaced (i) vertically, (ii) horizontally.
(b) Rough edges.

## 5. FOLDING
(a) Folds during the production process (i) extra paper, (ii) extra paper with marginal markings or colour bars, (iii) extra paper with part of adjoining note, (iv) without extra paper.
(b) Creases within the sheet (i) single narrow, (ii) single wide or multiple.

Errors prior to 1960 are rare and so, for this edition, they have only been listed from the start of Series C, when the introduction of reel-fed presses led to the occurrence of almost every kind of error. The listings, commencing with the 10/- Portrait Issue Series C, follow on immediately after the last note of each denomination. They use an "E" reference standing for "Error" combined with a numbering system based on the classification outlined above. So, for example, a 10/- error with no numbers is listed as E3a and a £1 error missing the underprint is listed as E2b(i). Since many errors vary in degree a distinction, where relevant, is also made between a major example and a minor example, the former being indicated by two asterisks and the latter by one. By far the widest variety of errors occur with the £1 Series C note and the listings for this denomination form the benchmark for all the other notes. No attempt has been made to list any errors for Series E New Historical, because these are still being issued and more time is needed before these can be accurately evaluated.

It should be noted that the checkers at the printing works indicate rejected notes by marking them with a solid orange phosphor band. This can be applied to an entire sheet, in which case the phosphor band will extend for the whole width of the note, or to individual notes, in which case the phosphor band will usually be slightly shorter. Phosphor bands on an error note add interest for collectors and may warrant a small premium. Very occasionally perfect notes are released with phosphor bands and these are very collectable. Errors on replacement and column sort notes are keenly collected and where these were actually used as such (as opposed to their general release as ordinary issued notes at the end of the Page era) dealers are likely to charge a premium.

Prices have been given for the three grades of Very Fine (VF), Extremely Fine (EF) and Uncirculated (Unc). Although condition is important for error notes, it is generally not so important as for perfect notes and the pricing between the grades reflects this. Three very important points, however, must be considered here: first, where a fold is the cause of an error, it should never be taken into account when grading it; secondly, erasure of pencilled or inked numbers on a note where these have been omitted is undesirable and reduces the grade; and thirdly, the prices given for uncirculated notes do not include notes which have been pressed, frequently to remove those folds which originally gave rise to the error. The grade of such notes should be reduced by at least one full grade.

It must be appreciated that error notes vary enormously in both type and extent and any attempt to price them cannot be an exact science. In particular, it should be noted that usually no attempt has been made to distinguish any of the error notes by signature, because with a few exceptions, this is not generally a factor in determining the value. Where it is definitely known to be, the signature of the Chief Cashier has been mentioned in the description. Occasionally where an error is found in many degrees of severity a price is given as "from" a stated value. If a variety is not listed, it may be appropriate to check it under a different denomination in the same series, because this will give some idea as to its relative scarcity. Notwithstanding these limitations, it is hoped that by listing a representative sample of errors for each denomination, collectors will be provided with some guidelines to assist them in that frequently tricky decision on what to pay for an error note.

A further selection of spectacular error notes from the Bruce Goulborn collection

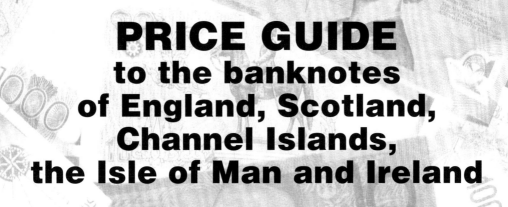

# PRICE GUIDE
## to the banknotes
## of England, Scotland,
## Channel Islands,
## the Isle of Man and Ireland

The price one should pay for a banknote can vary depending on a whole variety of criteria. In this price guide the figures given are intended as a *guide only* to prices that one should expect to pay for notes in the condition noted at the top of each column—the grading is as explained in the grading table on page 25. Notes in lower grades would obviously cost far less and notes in exceptional condition can command higher prices than those given.  The notes listed are ordinary circulating examples. To comply with current legislation illustrations of all modern notes have been endorsed with the word SPECIMEN—this, of course, does not appear on the notes themselves. Proofs, specimen printings and other varieties are beyond the scope of this publication—for further information the reader is referred to the relevant specialist book as listed in the Bibliography in the Directory section at the end of this book.

# EARLY BANK OF ENGLAND NOTES

By the close of the 17th century London was becoming one of the most important trading and commercial centres of the world. Its rich merchants and goldsmiths, many of whom are remembered to this day in the names of the banks such as Martins, Lloyds, Barclays and Glyn Mills, had been issuing promissory notes and receipts for valuables for many years and these pieces of paper were accepted as if they were actually money. By 1680 there were about fifty of these merchants whose promissory notes were readily acceptable. With the rapid development of England as a trading nation it became necessary to establish some sort of national bank. In 1694, the Bank of England was founded by William Paterson, a Scotsman whose proposals were readily endorsed by Charles Montagu, the Chancellor of the Exchequer at the time. In the year of its foundation the Bank issued only a few notes, for £20 and £50, and these were entirely hand-written like the merchants' notes.

The first printed notes were released on June 5, 1695 but had a very short life, being hurriedly withdrawn when a cunning forger obtained a quantity of paper from the same supplier as the Bank and then produced excellent counterfeits. The Bank got around this problem by using a different type of paper, with a marbled pattern. As a further precaution against fraud, these marbled notes were cut in half and only one half given to the customer. When the note came back to the bank it could be checked against the other half to prove that it was genuine. None of these marbled notes has survived, but the practice of cutting notes in half continued for some time. Later notes may be found with curved cuts between the two halves as well as a printed design.

A watermark was adopted as a security feature in 1697 and specially watermarked paper has been used for all Bank of England notes since then. The notes from 1696 to 1725 had the amounts written in by hand and could be issued for any odd amount from £10 upwards. Regular denominations were re-introduced in 1725 and were issued in values from £20 to £1000. In 1759 notes for £10 and £15 were added, and six years later a £25 was introduced. The Bank of England did not issue notes of lower value, and it was left to the many private banks to fill the gap. The first £5 notes appeared in 1793, a year when many private banks crashed as a result of the outbreak of war with Revolutionary France.

During a shortage of gold coin during the Napoleonic Wars, notes of £1 and £2 were added to the series and these continued until 1829, but thereafter the Bank reverted to notes from £5 to £1000 only. All of these 19th century notes are of the greatest rarity. They are generally grouped according to the signature of the Chief Cashier which appears on them. At various times from 1826 onwards branches of the Bank of England were opened in a number of provincial cities, resulting in notes specifically inscribed. Our listing of Bank of England notes is confined to the notes issued in London which are available in collectable condition. It has been decided to omit the higher values, including the £500 and £1000 (which ceased in 1943), which are of considerable rarity. Included are the notes issued by the Treasury following the outbreak of World War I. The Bank of England, at that time was only empowered to issue notes of £5 and over and due to the predicted restrictions on gold, Treasury notes were issued in denominations of ten shillings and one pound with the intention of replacing the sovereign and half sovereign.

# BANK OF ENGLAND
## Pre 1925

All of the black and white notes (commonly known as "White" notes) issued before 1913 are rare and only the £1 Hase is offered with any regularity by dealers and then only occasionally. All of the "White" notes were issued from London and most were also issued from branch offices in Birmingham, Bristol, Hull, Leeds, Liverpool, Manchester, Newcastle, Plymouth and Portsmouth. These branch notes are usually scarcer than the London issues and most are beyond the scope of this yearbook. Occasionally, however, a branch issue is either commoner than the corresponding London note or available in sufficient quantities to warrant a listing.

*These notes were all printed in black on white paper in sheets of two notes (except for the smaller £1 and £2 values which were printed in sheets of four) which were then cut up to give one straight edge and three uncut (deckled) edges.*

Later issues of the famous "White" notes are found under "Bank of England issues from 1928".

## ONE POUND

BE1

| (1803-07) | | *F* | *VF* |
|---|---|---|---|
| **BE1** | *Chief Cashier: A. Newland* | | |
| | Hand written date and serial numbers ............................. | £3500 | £6000 |

BE2a

|  |  | F | VF |
|---|---|---|---|

**(1807-21)**
**BE2a** *Chief Cashier: H. Hase*
Printed date and serial numbers .......................................... £1400 £2750
**(1825-26)**
**BE2b** *Chief Cashier: H. Hase*
Printed date and serial numbers, emergency issue .......... £1500 £2850

## TWO POUNDS

BE3

**(1807-21)**
**BE3** *Chief Cashier: H. Hase*
Printed date and serial numbers .......................................... £4000 £7500

**BE4–BE9** [*Held in reserve*]

## FIVE POUNDS

| | | F | VF | EF |
|---|---|---|---|---|
| **(1902-18)** | | | | |
| **BE10** | *Signature: J. G. Nairne* | | | |
| | London ............................................ | £275 | £400 | £650 |

*BE11*

| | | | | |
|---|---|---|---|---|
| **(1918-25)** | | | | |
| **BE11** | *Signature: E. M. Harvey* | | | |
| | London ............................................ | £160 | £250 | £450 |

## TEN POUNDS

*BE12*

| | | | | |
|---|---|---|---|---|
| **(1902-18)** | | | | |
| **BE12** | *Signature: J. G. Nairne* | | | |
| | London ............................................ | £400 | £650 | £1100 |

| | | F | VF | EF |
|---|---|---|---|---|
| **(1918-25)** | | | | |
| **BE13** | *Signature: E. M. Harvey* | | | |
| | London ................................................... | £250 | £400 | £675 |

## TWENTY POUNDS

| | | F | VF | EF |
|---|---|---|---|---|
| **(1902-18)** | | | | |
| **BE14** | *Signature: J. G. Nairne* | | | |
| | Manchester.......................................................... | £1250 | £2000 | £3500 |

BE15

| | | F | VF | EF |
|---|---|---|---|---|
| **(1918-25)** | | | | |
| **BE15** | *Signature: E. M. Harvey* | | | |
| | London ................................................... | £650 | £1000 | £2200 |

## FIFTY POUNDS

*BE16*

| (1902-18) | | F | VF | EF |
|---|---|---|---|---|
| **BE16** | Signature: J. G. Nairne | | | |
| | Manchester ........................................................................ | £1000 | £1850 | £3250 |

| (1918-25) | | | | |
|---|---|---|---|---|
| **BE17** | Signature: E. M. Harvey | | | |
| | London ............................................................................... | £675 | £1100 | £2300 |

## ONE HUNDRED POUNDS

*BE18*

| (1902-18) | | F | VF | EF |
|---|---|---|---|---|
| **BE18** | Signature: J. G. Nairne | | | |
| | Manchester............................................................................ | £900 | £1600 | £2850 |

| (1918-25) | | | | |
|---|---|---|---|---|
| **BE19** | Signature: E. M. Harvey | | | |
| | London ............................................................................... | £700 | £1300 | £2400 |

# TREASURY NOTES

Notes of one shilling (1/-), two shillings and sixpence (2/6) and five shillings (5/-) signed by John Bradbury and Norman Fenwick Warren Fisher, were produced between December 1917 and November 1919 but were never issued. However, a few notes survived destruction and, along with some examples of proof status, somehow escaped. They very occasionally come onto the market and command very high prices.

## TEN SHILLINGS
### FIRST (EMERGENCY) BRADBURY ISSUE (August 1914)
*Red. 127 x 63mm. Blank reverse*
*Signature: John Bradbury*

*TR1a*

|  |  | VF | EF | UNC |
|---|---|---|---|---|
| **TR1a** | Prefix A.N<u>o</u> (*with **dash***) followed by letter over number followed by 6 serial numbers | £385 | £625 | £1000 |

*TR1b*

| **TR1b** | Prefix S and T. Letter over number followed by *No.* (*with **dot***) followed by 6 serial numbers | £575 | £1000 | £1650 |
|---|---|---|---|---|
| **TR1c** | Prefix B and C. Letter over number followed by *No.* (*with **dot***) followed by 5 serial numbers | £675 | £1200 | £2200 |

# SECOND BRADBURY ISSUE (January 1915)
*Red. 136 x 76mm. Blank reverse.De La Rue printing*
*Signature: John Bradbury*

*TR2a*

| | | VF | EF | UNC |
|---|---|---|---|---|
| **TR2a** | Prefix A-M. Letter over number followed by 5 serial numbers | £250 | £450 | £750 |
| **TR2b** | Prefix A1-M1. Letter and figure 1 over number followed by 5 serial numbers | £260 | £485 | £800 |
| **TR2c** | Prefix A2-C2. Letter and figure 2 over number followed by 5 serial numbers | £275 | £500 | £900 |

*Red. 136 x 76mm. Blank reverse.Waterlow printing*
*Signature: John Bradbury*

*TR3a*

| | | VF | EF | UNC |
|---|---|---|---|---|
| **TR3a** | Prefix N-Z. Letter over number followed by 6 serial numbers | £300 | £550 | £900 |
| **TR3b** | Prefix O1-Z1. Letter and figure 1 over number followed by 6 serial numbers | £300 | £550 | £900 |

## SECOND BRADBURY ISSUE DARDANELLES OVERPRINT
## (May 1915)
*Overprint in Turkish "60 silver piastres" on TR3a above for the use of the British Expeditionary Forces in Turkey in 1915*

TR4

|  |  | F | VF | EF |
|---|---|---|---|---|
| **TR4** | Prefix Y and Z. Letter over number followed by 6 serial numbers ....................................................... | £550 | £850 | £1600 |

## THIRD BRADBURY ISSUE
## (October 1918)
*Green, brown and purple. 138 x 78mm.*
*Signature: John Bradbury*

|  | VF | EF | UNC |
|---|---|---|---|

TR5a

|  |  | | | |
|---|---|---|---|---|
| **TR5a** | Prefix A. Letter over number followed by *No.* (*with **dot***) and serial numbers in black ..................................................... | £375 | £650 | £1000 |

*TR5b*

|  |  | VF | EF | UNC |
|---|---|---|---|---|
| **TR5b** | Prefix A. Letter over number followed by N*o* (*with* **dash**) and serial numbers in black ........................................................ | £375 | £650 | £1000 |

## (December 1918)

| **TR6a** | Prefix B and C. Letter over number followed by *No.* (*with* **dot**) and serial numbers in red ........................................................ | £1000 | — | — |

*TR6b*

| **TR6b** | Prefix B and C. Letter over number followed by *No* (*with* **dash**) and serial numbers in red ........................................................ | £285 | £500 | £900 |

## FIRST FISHER ISSUE
## (September 1919)
*Green, brown and purple. 138 x 78mm.*
*Signature: N. F. Warren Fisher*

| **TR7a** | Prefix D-H. Letter over number followed by *No.* (*with* **dot**) and serial numbers in red ........................................................ | £165 | £350 | £550 |

*TR7b*

|  |  | F | VF | EF |
|---|---|---|---|---|
| **TR7b** | Prefix D-H. Letter over number followed by *No(with **dash**)* and serial numbers in red ...................................................... | £150 | £325 | £500 |

# SECOND FISHER ISSUE
## (November 1922)
*Green, brown and purple. 138 x 78mm.*
*Signature: N. F. Warren Fisher*

*TR8*

|  |  | VF | EF | UNC |
|---|---|---|---|---|
| **TR8** | Prefix J-S. Letter over number followed by serial numbers | £130 | £250 | £425 |

## THIRD FISHER ISSUE ("NORTHERN" ADDED TO TITLE)
## (July 1927)
*Green, brown and purple. 138 x 78mm.*
*Signature: N. F. Warren Fisher*

TR9

| | VF | EF | UNC |
|---|---|---|---|
| **TR9** Prefix S-U, W. Letter over number followed by serial numbers | £130 | £250 | £425 |

# ONE POUND

## FIRST (EMERGENCY) BRADBURY ISSUE (August 1914)
*Black. 127 x 63mm. Blank reverse*
*Signature: John Bradbury*

TR10a

| | F | VF | EF |
|---|---|---|---|
| **TR10a** Prefix A., B. and C. (*with dot*) followed by 6 serial numbers | £700 | £1200 | £2350 |
| **TR10b** Prefix A, B and C (*without dot*) followed by 6 serial numbers | £1000 | £1800 | £3500 |
| **TR10c** Prefix G (possibly others) Letter over number followed by No. (*with dot*) and 4 serial numbers | £850 | £1350 | £2800 |

| | VF | EF | UNC |
|---|---|---|---|
| **TR10d** Prefix B-W (not inclusive). Letter over number followed by No. (*with dot*) and 5 serial numbers | £600 | £1100 | £1750 |

*TR10e*

| | | F | VF | EF |
|---|---|---|---|---|
| **TR10e** | Prefix A-**X**. Letter over number followed by *No.*(*with **dot***) and 6 serial numbers .................................................... | £550 | £900 | £1500 |
| **TR10f** | Prefix B (possibly others). Letter over number followed by *No.* (*with **dot***)and 7 serial numbers ............................................ | £750 | £1200 | £2500 |
| **TR11a** | Prefix L (possibly others). Letter over number followed by *No* (*with **dash***) and 4 serial numbers.......................................... | £850 | £1400 | £3000 |
| **TR11b** | Prefix E, J, K and L (possibly others). Letter over number followed by *No* (*with **dash***) and 5 serial numbers............... | £475 | £800 | £1500 |
| **TR12a** | Prefix B and D. Letter over number followed by *No* (*with **dash***) and 6 serial numbers in smaller type ............... | £475 | £800 | £1500 |
| **TR12b** | Prefix B (possibly others). Letter over number followed by *No.* (*with **dot***) and 7 serial numbers in smaller type.................. | £800 | £1350 | £2500 |

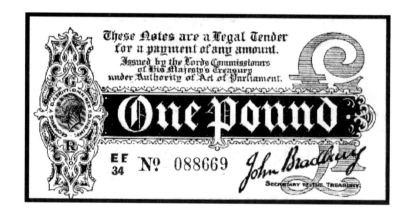

*TR13*

| | | F | VF | EF |
|---|---|---|---|---|
| **TR13a** | Prefix AA-LL. Double letter over number followed by *No.* (*with **dot*** ) and 6 serial numbers .......................................... | £400 | £750 | £1400 |
| **TR13b** | Prefix LL. Double letter over number followed by *No.* (*with **dot***) and 4 serial numbers ............................................... | — | Rare | — |

# SECOND BRADBURY ISSUE (October 1914)

*Black. 149 x 85mm. Blank reverse*
*Signature: John Bradbury*

*TR14a*

*TR14b*

|  |  | VF | EF | UNC |
|---|---|---|---|---|
| **TR14a** | Prefix A-Z. Letter over number followed by 5 serial numbers................................................................................ | £275 | £500 | £800 |
| **TR14b** | Prefix A1-L1. Letter and figure 1 over number followed by. 5 serial numbers ................................................................... | £275 | £500 | £800 |

## SECOND BRADBURY ISSUE DARDANELLES OVERPRINT
## (May 1915)

*Overprint in Turkish "120 silver piastres" on TR14a above for the use of the British Expeditionary Forces in Turkey in 1915*

TR15

| | | VG | F | VF |
|---|---|---|---|---|
| **TR15** | Prefix F, J, M, Y. Letter over number followed by 5 serial numbers ........................................................ | £2000 | £3250 | £5500 |

## THIRD BRADBURY ISSUE
## (January 1917)

*Green, brown and purple.151 x 84mm.*
*Signature: John Bradbury*

| | | VF | EF | UNC |
|---|---|---|---|---|
| **TR16a** | Prefix A. Letter over number followed by serial numbers | £130 | £275 | £450 |

TR16b

| | | | | |
|---|---|---|---|---|
| **TR16b** | Prefix C-H. Letter over number followed by serial numbers | £100 | £190 | £325 |
| **TR16c** | Prefix Z. Letter over number followed by serial numbers. | £140 | £285 | £475 |
| **TR16d** | Prefix A and B. Variety with small anchor beneath Big Ben on reverse ................................................................ | £1200 | £2400 | — |

## FIRST FISHER ISSUE
### (September 1919)
*Green, brown and purple. 151 x 84mm.*
*Signature: N. F. Warren Fisher*

**TR17a**   Prefix K. Letter over number followed by serial numbers        £80      £165      £280

*TR17b*

**TR17b**   Prefix L-Y. Letter over number followed by serial numbers      £65      £130      £220
**TR17c**   Prefix Z. Letter over number followed by serial numbers.       £85      £175      £295

# SECOND FISHER ISSUE
## (February 1923)
*Green, brown and purple. 151 x 84mm.*
*Signature: N. F. Warren Fisher*

| | | VF | EF | UNC |
|---|---|---|---|---|
| **TR18a** | Prefix A1. Letter and figure 1 over number followed by *No.* and serial numbers.......................................................... | £70 | £150 | £250 |
| **TR18b** | Prefix B1-R1. Letter and figure 1 over number followed by *No.* and serial numbers.......................................................... | £65 | £130 | £220 |

*TR18c*

| | | VF | EF | UNC |
|---|---|---|---|---|
| **TR18c** | Prefix Z1. Letter and figure 1 over number followed by *No.* and serial numbers.......................................................... | £75 | £160 | £275 |

*TR18d*

| | | VF | EF | UNC |
|---|---|---|---|---|
| **TR18d** | Prefix H1-R1. As *TR18b* but with square dot below ........... | £185 | £350 | — |
| **TR18e** | Prefix Z1. As *TR18c* but with square dot below ................. | £225 | £425 | — |

# THIRD FISHER ISSUE
# ("NORTHERN" ADDED TO TITLE)
# (July 1927)
*Green, brown and purple. 151 x 84mm.*
*Signature: N. F. Warren Fisher*

| | | VF | EF | UNC |
|---|---|---|---|---|
| **TR19a** | Prefix S1. Letter and figure 1 over number followed by *No.* and serial numbers...................................................... | £85 | £180 | £300 |

*TR19b*

| | | | | |
|---|---|---|---|---|
| **TR19b** | Prefix T1-X1. Letter and figure 1 over number followed by *No.* and serial numbers...................................................... | £70 | £160 | £275 |
| **TR19c** | Prefix Z1. Letter and figure 1 over number followed by *No.* and serial numbers...................................................... | £95 | £190 | £325 |
| **TR19d** | Prefix S1-X1. As *TR19b* but with square dot below............. | £185 | £350 | — |

*TR19e*

| | | | | |
|---|---|---|---|---|
| **TR19e** | Prefix Z1. As *TR19c* but with square dot below .................. | £225 | £425 | — |

# BANK OF ENGLAND
## From 1928

## TEN SHILLINGS
### SERIES "A" BRITANNIA ISSUE

### (November 1928)
*Red-brown. 138 x 78mm*
*Signature: C. P. Mahon*

*Prefix sequence: Letter/Number/Number*

*BE20a*

|        |                                            | *VF* | *EF* | *UNC* |
|--------|--------------------------------------------|------|------|-------|
| **BE20a** | Prefix A01 followed by serial number ...... | £550 | £1000 | £1350 |
| **BE20b** | Prefix Z01 ................................ | £285 | £500 | £750 |
| **BE20c** | Prefix Z- -................................ | £90 | £200 | £350 |
| **BE20d** | Prefix Y- -, X- -, W- - .................... | £80 | £185 | £300 |
| **BE20e** | Prefix V- - *(traced to V13)* ............. | £550 | £1000 | |

## (July 1930)

*Red-brown. 138 x 78mm*
*Signature: B. G. Catterns*

*Prefix sequence: Letter/Number/Number*

*BE21a*

| | | VF | EF | UNC |
|---|---|---|---|---|
| **BE21a** | Prefix V- - followed by serial number (*traced from V14*) ..... | 80 | £175 | £285 |
| **BE21b** | Prefix U- - to L- - …………..………………………………….. | £45 | £80 | £150 |
| **BE21c** | Prefix K- - (*traced to K99*) …………………………………….. | £70 | £160 | £265 |

## October 1934)

*Red-brown. 138 x 78mm*
*Signature: K .O. Peppiatt*

*Prefix sequence: Letter/Number/Number*

*BE22b*

| | | VF | EF | UNC |
|---|---|---|---|---|
| **BE22a** | Prefix J01 followed by serial number .................................... | £350 | £750 | — |
| **BE22b** | Prefix J- - .................................................................. | £55 | £120 | £195 |
| **BE22c** | Prefix H- - to B- - ...................................................... | £30 | £70 | £110 |
| **BE22d** | Prefix A- - (*traced to A99*)............................................. | £55 | £120 | £195 |

BE23b

Prefix sequence: Number/Number/Letter

|  |  | VF | EF | UNC |
|---|---|---|---|---|
| **BE23a** | Prefix 01Z followed by serial number ................................. | £275 | £600 | — |
| **BE23b** | Prefix - -Z ........................................................................... | £60 | £125 | £220 |
| **BE23c** | Prefix - -Y to - -R ............................................................... | £30 | £70 | £110 |
| **BE23d** | Prefix - -O (*traced to 42O*) ............................................... | £45 | £100 | £170 |

## (October 1940)

*Mauve (shades). 138 x 78mm. With metal security thread*
*Signature: K .O. Peppiatt*

Prefix sequence: Letter/Number/Number/Letter

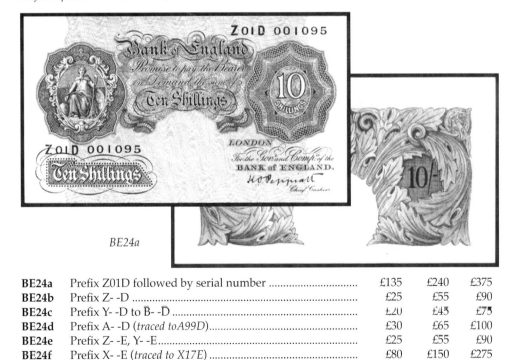

BE24a

| **BE24a** | Prefix Z01D followed by serial number ............................. | £135 | £240 | £375 |
|---|---|---|---|---|
| **BE24b** | Prefix Z- -D ......................................................................... | £25 | £55 | £90 |
| **BE24c** | Prefix Y- -D to B- -D ........................................................... | £20 | £45 | £75 |
| **BE24d** | Prefix A- -D (*traced to A99D*)............................................. | £30 | £65 | £100 |
| **BE24e** | Prefix Z- -E, Y- -E .............................................................. | £25 | £55 | £90 |
| **BE24f** | Prefix X- -E (*traced to X17E*) ........................................... | £80 | £150 | £275 |
| **BE24g** | Prefix X21E......................................................................... | £200 | £400 | — |
| **BE24h** | Prefix T- -D Replacement note ........................................... | £200 | £400 | — |

## (June 1948)

*Red-brown. 138 x 78mm. Without metal security thread*
*Signature: K .O. Peppiatt*

*Prefix sequence: Number/Number/Letter*

BE25a

|  |  | VF | EF | UNC |
|---|---|---|---|---|
| **BE25a** | Prefix - -O (*traced from 42O-70O*) followed by serial number | £60 | £135 | £200 |
| **BE25b** | Prefix - -L (*traced from 05L-71L*) ............................................ | £55 | £125 | £190 |

## (October 1948)

*Red-brown. 138 x 78mm. With metal security thread*
*Signature: K .O. Peppiatt*

*Prefix sequence: Number/Number/Letter*

BE26a

| **BE26a** | Prefix - -L followed by serial number (*traced from 71L*) ...... | £100 | £250 | £400 |
|---|---|---|---|---|
| **BE26b** | Prefix - -K, - -J, - -H ................................................. | £25 | £55 | £80 |
| **BE26c** | Prefix - -E (*traced to 91E*) ......................................... | £30 | £70 | £100 |

BE27c

|  |  | VF | EF | UNC |
|---|---|---|---|---|
| **BE27a** | Prefix 01A Replacement note | £700 | £1250 | £2000 |
| **BE27b** | Prefix 02A Replacement note | £400 | £750 | £1350 |
| **BE27c** | Prefix 03A Replacement note | £475 | £900 | £1500 |

## (March 1950)

*Red-brown. 138 x 78mm. With metal security thread*
*Signature: P. S. Beale*

*Prefix sequence: Number/Number/Letter*

BE28b

| **BE28a** | Prefix 92E followed by serial number | £250 | £450 | £800 |
|---|---|---|---|---|
| **BE28b** | Prefix –E | £65 | £110 | £250 |
| **BE28c** | Prefix - -D, - -C | £15 | £35 | £65 |
| **BE28d** | Prefix - -B (*traced to 99B*) | £18 | £40 | £75 |
| **BE29a** | Prefix 04A Replacement note | £400 | £750 | — |

*BE29b*

|  |  | VF | EF | UNC |
|---|---|---|---|---|
| **BE29b** | Prefix - -A Replacement note (*traced to 35A*) ...................... | £75 | £135 | £300 |

*Prefix sequence: Letter/Number/Number/Letter*

*BE30b*

| **BE30a** | Prefix Z01Z followed by number ......................................... | £200 | £350 | £600 |
|---|---|---|---|---|
| **BE30b** | Prefix Z- -Z ............................................................................ | £15 | £30 | £55 |
| **BE30c** | Prefix Y- -Z to E- -Z .............................................................. | £12 | £25 | £50 |
| **BE30d** | Prefix D- -Z (*traced to D85Z*) ............................................... | £18 | £35 | £70 |

## (November 1955)
*Red-brown. 138 x 78mm.*
*Signature: L. K. O'Brien*

*Prefix sequence: Letter/Number/Number/Letter*

| **BE31a** | Prefix D86Z followed by serial number.............................. | £90 | £165 | £325 |
|---|---|---|---|---|
| **BE31b** | Prefix D- -Z............................................................................ | £40 | £70 | £130 |
| **BE31c** | Prefix C- -Z, B- -Z.................................................................. | £8 | £18 | £40 |
| **BE31d** | Prefix A- -Z............................................................................ | £12 | £25 | £50 |
| **BE31e** | Prefix Z- -Y............................................................................ | £14 | £30 | £55 |
| **BE31f** | Prefix Y- -Y to B- - Y ............................................................ | £7 | £16 | £32 |
| **BE31g** | Prefix A- -Y............................................................................ | £12 | £25 | £50 |
| **BE31h** | Prefix Z - -X............................................................................ | £12 | £25 | £50 |
| **BE31i** | Prefix Y- -X............................................................................ | £20 | £45 | £80 |

*BE31e*

|  | | VF | EF | UNC |
|---|---|---|---|---|
| **BE31j** | Prefix Y25X *(last prefix of Britannia Series "A"10/-)*............... | £60 | £120 | £225 |

*Prefix sequence: Number/Number/Letter*

*BE32*

| **BE32** | Prefix - -A Replacement note *(traced from 35A-69A)*..........£ | 45 | £90 | £190 |

# SERIES "C" PORTRAIT ISSUE

## (October 1961)

*Red-brown. 140 x 66.7mm.*
*Signature: L. K. O'Brien*

*Prefix sequence: Letter/Number/Number*

*BE33a*

| | | VF | EF | UNC |
|---|---|---|---|---|
| **BE33a** | Prefix A01 followed by serial number ............................... | £50 | £90 | £180 |
| **BE33b** | Prefix A- -. ............................................................... | £3 | £7 | £14 |
| **BE33c** | Prefix B- - to J- - ..................................................... | FV | £3 | £7 |
| **BE33d** | Prefix K- - (*traced to K64*) ....................................... | £6 | £14 | £25 |
| **BE34a** | Prefix M01 Replacement note ............................................. | £70 | £130 | £275 |

*BE34b*

| | | | | |
|---|---|---|---|---|
| **BE34b** | Prefix M- - (*traced to M18*) ......................................... | £25 | £50 | £100 |

# (April 1963)
*Signature: J. Q. Hollom*

*Prefix sequence: Letter/Number/Number*

*BE35a*

|  |  | VF | EF | UNC |
|---|---|---|---|---|
| **BE35a** | Prefix K65 followed by serial number ................................. | £90 | £160 | £320 |
| **BE35b** | Prefix K- -. ................................................................................ | £9 | £18 | £35 |
| **BE35c** | Prefix L- - to Y- -. ................................................................... | FV | £3 | £6 |
| **BE35d** | Prefix Z- - ................................................................................. | £6 | £12 | £20 |
| **BE35e** | Prefix Z99 ................................................................................. | £55 | £100 | £180 |

*BE36b*

| **BE36a** | Prefix M19 Replacement note ................................................. | £80 | £150 | £325 |
|---|---|---|---|---|
| **BE36b** | Prefix M- - Replacement note................................................. | £12 | £25 | £55 |
| **BE36c** | Prefix M55 Replacement note ................................................. | £70 | £125 | £260 |

|  | VF | EF | UNC |
|---|---|---|---|

*Prefix sequence: Number/Number/Letter*

**BE37a**  Prefix 01A followed by serial number ................................. £75 £140 £260

*BE37b*

| **BE37b** | Prefix - -A ........................................................... | £3 | £6 | £12 |
| **BE37c** | Prefix - -B to - -N .............................................. | FV | £3 | £6 |
| **BE37d** | Prefix - -R (*traced to 26R* ). ........................... | £8 | £15 | £35 |

## (February 1967)
*Signature: J. S. Fforde*

*Prefix sequence: Number/Number/Letter*

**BE38a**  Prefix 26R followed by serial number ................................. £140 £250 —

*BE38b*

| **BE38b** | Prefix - -R.......................................................... | £6 | £12 | £20 |
| **BE38c** | Prefix - -S to - -Y . ........................................... | FV | £3 | £6 |
| **BE38d** | Prefix - -Z ........................................................... | £4 | £7 | £12 |
| **BE38e** | Prefix 99Z ........................................................... | £120 | £200 | — |

|  | *VF* | *EF* | *UNC* |
|---|---|---|---|

*Prefix sequence: Letter/Number/Number/Letter*

| | | *VF* | *EF* | *UNC* |
|---|---|---|---|---|
| **BE39a** | Prefix A01N followed by serial number. ............................. | £50 | £90 | £160 |
| **BE39b** | Prefix A- - N. .................................................................. | £5 | £10 | £18 |
| **BE39c** | Prefix B- -N, C- -N.......................................................... | FV | £3 | £6 |
| **BE39d** | Prefix D- -N ................................................................... | £3 | £6 | £10 |

*BE39e*

| | | *VF* | *EF* | *UNC* |
|---|---|---|---|---|
| **BE39e** | Prefix D38N (*last prefix of Portrait Series "C"10/-*). ............... | £18 | £35 | £70 |
| **BE40a** | Prefix M56 Replacement note ............................................... | £50 | £90 | £160 |
| **BE40b** | Prefix M- - ...................................................................... | £4 | £8 | £12 |

*BE40c*

| | | | | |
|---|---|---|---|---|
| **BE40c** | Prefix M80 (Last re*placement prefix of Portrait Series "C"10/-*) | £6 | £12 | £25 |

# SERIES "C" PORTRAIT 10/- ERRORS

**N.B.** *All Series "C" 10/- errors are very scarce*

|  |  | VF | EF | UNC |
|---|---|---|---|---|
| **E2b(i)** | Missing colour—no underprint............................................. | £100 | £175 | £250 |
| **E2b(iii)\*** | Missing colour—dry print (minor) on front or back ..........from £35 | | £60 | £80 |

*E2b(iii)\*\**

| | | | | |
|---|---|---|---|---|
| **E2b(iii)\*\*** Missing colour—dry print (major) on front or back.......... | £100 | £175 | £250 |

*E2d(i)\**

| | | | | |
|---|---|---|---|---|
| **E2d(i)\*** | Offset—front on back (minor)................................................from £35 | | £60 | £80 |
| **E2d(i)\*\*** | Offset—front on back (major) ........................................ | £125 | £225 | £300 |
| **E2d(ii)** | Offset (partial and misaligned)........................................ | £50 | £90 | £150 |
| **E3a** | No number........................................................................ | £125 | £225 | £300 |
| **E3b** | Only one number .......................................................... | £90 | £140 | £225 |
| **E3d(i)** | Missing digits—single ................................................. | £18 | £35 | £50 |
| **E3d(ii)** | Missing digits—multiple .......................................from £30 | | £65 | £90 |

|  |  | VF | EF | UNC |
|---|---|---|---|---|

E3g

| E3g | Identical numbers on a pair of notes | £350 | £500 | £700 |
|---|---|---|---|---|
| E5a(i)* | Folds with extra paper (minor) ………………………… from £50 | £80 | £125 | |
| E5a(i)** | Folds with extra paper (major) | £125 | £200 | £275 |
| E5a(iii) | Extra paper with part of adjoining note | £140 | £240 | £325 |

# ONE POUND
# SERIES "A" BRITANNIA ISSUE
## (November 1928)
*Green. 150.7 x 84.4mm*
*Signature: C. P. Mahon*

*Prefix sequence: Letter/Number/Number*

E41a

| BE41a | Prefix A01 followed by serial number | £550 | £1000 | £1350 |
|---|---|---|---|---|
| BE41b | Prefix A- - | £70 | £135 | £225 |
| BE41c | Prefix B- - to G- - | £55 | £100 | £185 |
| BE41d | Prefix H- - (*traced to H32*) | £85 | £175 | £325 |

*BE42*

| | | VF | EF | UNC |
|---|---|---|---|---|
| **BE42** | Presentation set of Ten Shillings and One Pound notes with matching A01 serial numbers in special Bank of England parchment envelope dated 22 November 1928. Only 125 sets were issued numbered A01 000001 to A01 000125.............. | --- | £4500 | £7000 |

## (July 1930)
*Green. 150.7 x 84.4mm*
*Signature: B. G. Catterns*

*Prefix sequence: Letter/Number/Number*

*BE43a*

| | | | | |
|---|---|---|---|---|
| **BE43a** | Prefix H- - followed by serial number (*traced from H33*) .... | £50 | £100 | £165 |
| **BE43b** | Prefix J- - to Y- - .................................................................... | £25 | £50 | £90 |
| **BE43c** | Prefix Z- - (*traced to Z99*) ........................................................ | £30 | £60 | £100 |

|  | VF | EF | UNC |
|---|---|---|---|

*Prefix sequence Number/Number/Letter*

**BE44a**   Prefix 01A ................................................................... £250   £400   —

*BE44b*

**BE44b**   Prefix - -A ................................................................... £80   £160   £240

## (October 1934)
*Green. 150.7 x 84.4mm*
*Signature: K .O. Peppiatt*

*Prefix sequence: Number/Number/Letter*

**BE45a**   Prefix 01B followed by serial number ................................. £350   £750   —
**BE45b**   Prefix - -B ................................................................... £30   £65   £110
**BE45c**   Prefix - -C to - -Y ....................................................... £18   £40   £65

*BE45d*

**BE45d**   Prefix - -Z (*traced to 99Z*) ......................................... £25   £55   £85

|  | | | VF | EF | UNC |
|---|---|---|---|---|---|

*Prefix sequence Letter/Number/Number/Letter*

| | | VF | EF | UNC |
|---|---|---|---|---|
| **BE46a** | Prefix A01A followed by serial number … ........................ | £750 | — | — |
| **BE46b** | Prefix A -A …............................................................. | £25 | £55 | £90 |
| **BE46c** | Prefix B- -A to K- -A ................................................ | £14 | £35 | £55 |

*BE46d*

| | | VF | EF | UNC |
|---|---|---|---|---|
| **BE46d** | Prefix L- -A …............................................................. | £20 | £45 | £70 |
| **BE46e** | Prefix L39A …............................................................. | £100 | £200 | £350 |

## (March 1940)

*Blue (various shades). 150.7 x 84.4mm. With metal security thread*
*Signature: K .O. Peppiatt*

*Prefix sequence: Letter/Number/Number/Letter*

*BE47a*

| | | VF | EF | UNC |
|---|---|---|---|---|
| **BE47a** | Prefix A01D followed by serial number ............................ | £75 | £175 | £300 |
| **BE47b** | Prefix A- -D ................................................................ | £15 | £35 | £60 |

|  |  | VF | EF | UNC |
|---|---|---|---|---|
| **BE47c** | Prefix A- -E, A- -H ............................................................ | £15 | £35 | £60 |
| **BE47d** | Prefix B- -D to Y- -D ......................................................... | £6 | £14 | £25 |
| **BE47e** | Prefix Z- -D ...................................................................... | £12 | £35 | £50 |
| **BE47f** | Prefix Z87D ....................................................................... | — | — | — |
| **BE47g** | Prefix B- -E to U- -E......................................................... | £6 | £14 | £25 |
| **BE47h** | Prefix W- -E ...................................................................... | £12 | £35 | £60 |
| **BE47i** | Prefix W48E ...................................................................... | £90 | £200 | £350 |
| **BE47j** | Prefix B- -H to W- -H......................................................... | £6 | £14 | £25 |
| **BE47k** | Prefix X- -H ...................................................................... | £12 | £35 | £60 |
| **BE47l** | Prefix X96H....................................................................... | £175 | £325 | — |
| **BE47Aa** | Prefix S01D, S01E, S01H Replacement note ........................ | £125 | £250 | £450 |
| **BE47Ab** | Prefix S- -D, S- -E, S- -H Replacement note ........................ | £90 | £175 | £300 |

# THE STATES OF GUERNSEY OVERPRINTS
## (September 18th 1941)

*Green. 150.7 x 84.4mm. Without metal security thread*
*Signatures: C. P. Mahon, B. G. Catterns and K .O. Peppiatt*
*Overprinted "Withdrawn from circulation September 18th, 1941." With stop after 1941 on front but not on back*

*Prefix sequence: Various*

| **BE48a** | Signature Mahon. Prefix A- - to H- - *(48 known)* ................. | £675 | £1200 | — |
|---|---|---|---|---|
| **BE48b** | Signature Catterns. Prefix H- - to Z- - *(69 known)* .............. | £500 | £900 | — |
| **BE48c** | Signature Catterns. Prefix - -A *(5 known)*............................ | £3000 | £5500 | — |
| **BE48d** | Signature Peppiatt. Prefix - -B to - -Z *(330 known)*.............. | £350 | £550 | — |

*BE48e*

| **BE48e** Signature Peppiatt. Prefix A- -A to L- -A *(1,885 known)*........... | £200 | £350 | £500 |
|---|---|---|---|

## (September 18th 1941)

*Blue (various shades). 150.7 x 84.4mm. With metal security thread*
*Signature: K .O. Peppiatt*
*Overprinted "Withdrawn from circulation September 18th, 1941."With stop after 1941 on front but not on back*

*Prefix sequence: Letter/Number/Number/Letter*

BE49a

|  |  | VF | EF | UNC |
|---|---|---|---|---|
| **BE49a** | Prefix A- -D (*35 known*) ............................................................ | £850 | £1400 | — |
| **BE49b** | Prefix C- -D (*85 known*) ............................................................ | £450 | £700 | £1000 |

## (November 10th 1941)

*Green. 150.7 x 84.4mm. Without metal security thread*
*Signature: K .O. Peppiatt*
*Overprinted "Withdrawn from circulation November 10th, 1941."*

*Prefix sequence: Letter/Number/Number/Letter*

BE50a

| **BE50a** | Prefix E03A. With stop after 1941 front and back (*75 known*) | £375 | £675 | £950 |
|---|---|---|---|---|
| **BE50b** | Prefix E15A. With stop after 1941 back only (*403 known*) .. | £250 | £475 | £700 |

|  | VF | EF | UNC |
|---|---|---|---|

## (June 1948)

*Green. 150.7 x 84.4mm. Without metal security thread*
*Signature: K .O. Peppiatt*

*Prefix sequence: Letter/Number/Number/Letter*

| | | VF | EF | UNC |
|---|---|---|---|---|
| **BE51a** | PrefixR01A followed by serial number.................................. | £70 | £140 | £275 |
| **BE51b** | PrefixR- -A ........................................................................... | £18 | £40 | £60 |

BE51c

**BE51c** Prefix S- -A (*traced to S48A*) ......................................................... £20 £45 £70

## (September 1948)

*Green. 150.7 x 84.4mm. Withmetal security thread*
*Signature: K .O. Peppiatt*

*Prefix sequence: Letter/Number/Number/Letter*

BE52a

| | | VF | EF | UNC |
|---|---|---|---|---|
| **BE52a** | Prefix S- -A (*traced from S39A*) followed by serial number. | £20 | £45 | £75 |
| **BE52b** | Prefix T- -A to Y- -A........................................................... | £10 | £15 | £25 |
| **BE52c** | Prefix Z- -A (*traced to Z99A*) ......................................... | £20 | £35 | £50 |
| **BE52d** | Prefix A- -B (*traced from A01B*)...................................... | £20 | £35 | £50 |
| **BE52e** | Prefix B- -B to E- -B ......................................................... | £8 | £15 | £25 |
| **BE52f** | Prefix H- -B (*traced to H36B*) . ...................................... | £20 | £40 | £55 |

|        |                                                    | VF   | EF   | UNC  |
|--------|----------------------------------------------------|------|------|------|
| **BE53a** | Prefix S01SReplacement note ........................... | £250 | £375 | £550 |

*BE53b*

| **BE53b** | Prefix S- -S Replacement note .............................. | £125 | £225 | £350 |
|-----------|------------------------------------------------------------|------|------|------|
| **BE53c** | Prefix S09S Replacement note ............................... | £150 | £275 | £450 |

## (March 1950)
*Green. 150.7 x 84.4mm.*
*Signature: P .S. Beale*

*Prefix sequence: Letter/Number/Number/Letter*

| **BE54a** | Prefix H37B followed by serial number........................ | £150 | £275 | £450 |
|-----------|--------------------------------------------------------------|------|------|------|

*BE54b*

| **BE54b** | Prefix H- -B.................................................. | £12 | £25 | £40 |
|-----------|----------------------------------------------------------------|-----|-----|-----|
| **BE54c** | Prefix J- -B to Y- -B ......................................... | £5 | £9 | £16 |
| **BE54d** | Prefix Z- -B (*traced to Z99B*) ............................... | £7 | £12 | £25 |
| **BE54e** | Prefix A- -C (*traced from A01C*) ............................. | £7 | £12 | £25 |
| **BE54f** | Prefix B- -C to Y- -C ......................................... | £5 | £9 | £16 |
| **BE54g** | Prefix Z- -C (*traced to Z99C*)................................ | £7 | £12 | £25 |
| **BE54h** | Prefix A- -J (*traced from A01J*) ............................. | £7 | £12 | £25 |
| **BE54i** | Prefix B- -J to K- -J ......................................... | £5 | £9 | £16 |
| **BE54j** | Prefix L- -J................................................... | £12 | £25 | £40 |
| **BE54j** | Prefix L63J ................................................... | £70 | £125 | £240 |

|  |  | *VF* | *EF* | *UNC* |
|---|---|---|---|---|
| **BE55a** | Prefix S10S Replacement note ................................................. | £100 | £190 | £350 |

*BE55b*

| **BE55b** | Prefix S- -S Replacement note ................................................. | £18 | £35 | £65 |
|---|---|---|---|---|
| **BE55c** | Prefix S70S Replacement note ............................................. | £150 | £275 | £450 |

## (November 1955)

*Green. 150.7 x 84.4mm.*
*Signature: L .K. O'Brien*

*Prefix sequence: Letter/Number/Number/Letter*

| **BE56a** | Prefix L64J followed by serial number.................................. | £85 | £160 | £280 |
|---|---|---|---|---|
| **BE56b** | Prefix L- -J............................................................................ | £8 | £15 | £30 |
| **BE56c** | Prefix M- -J to Y- -J ........................................................... | £3 | £7 | £15 |
| **BE56d** | Prefix Z- -J *(traced to Z99J)* ............................................. | £6 | £12 | £25 |
| **BE56e** | Prefix A- -K *(traced from A01K)* ....................................... | £8 | £15 | £30 |
| **BE56f** | Prefix B- -K to Y- -K ........................................................... | £3 | £7 | £15 |
| **BE56g** | Prefix Z- -K *(traced to Z99K)* ............................................ | £6 | £12 | £25 |
| **BE56h** | Prefix A- -L *(traced from A01L)*........................................ | £8 | £15 | £30 |
| **BE56i** | Prefix B- -L to J- -L ............................................................ | £3 | £7 | £15 |
| **BE56j** | Prefix K- -L ........................................................................ | £22 | £40 | £70 |

*BE56k*

| **BE56k** | Prefix K13L *(last prefix of Britannia Series "A" £1)* ................ | £135 | £260 | £425 |
|---|---|---|---|---|

|  |  | VF | EF | UNC |
|---|---|---|---|---|
| **BE57a** | Prefix S71S Replacement note ............................................. | £85 | £150 | £325 |
| **BE57b** | Prefix S- -S Replacement note (*traced to S99S*) .................... | £18 | £35 | £65 |
| **BE58a** | Prefix S01T Replacement note............................................... | £85 | £150 | £325 |

*BE58b*

| **BE58b** | Prefix S- -T Replacement note (*traced to S23T*) ................... | £20 | £40 | £75 |
|---|---|---|---|---|

# SERIES "C" PORTRAIT ISSUE
## (March 1960)
*Green. 151 x 71.8mm.*
*Signature: L .K. O'Brien*

*Prefix sequence: Letter/Number/Number*

*BE59a*

| **BE59a** | Prefix A01 followed by serial number ................................. | £70 | £130 | £275 |
|---|---|---|---|---|
| **BE59b** | Prefix A- - ........................................................................ | £5 | £10 | £18 |
| **BE59c** | Prefix B- - to Y- -.. ........................................................... | £2 | £4 | £7 |

|  |  | VF | EF | UNC |
|---|---|---|---|---|
| **BE59d** | Prefix Z- - (*traced to Z99*). ............................................ | £5 | £10 | £18 |

BE60a

|  |  | VF | EF | UNC |
|---|---|---|---|---|
| **BE60a** | Prefix M01 Replacement note ............................... | £90 | £160 | £300 |
| **BE60b** | Prefix M- - Replacement note (*traced to M68*) ................... | £10 | £18 | £35 |

*Prefix sequence: Number/Number/Letter*

| **BE61a** Prefix 01A followed by serial number.............................. | £110 | £200 | £350 |
|---|---|---|---|
| **BE61b** Prefix - -A.................................................................. | £5 | £10 | £18 |
| **BE61c** Prefix - -B to - - Y........................................................ | £2 | £4 | £7 |
| **BE61d** Prefix - -Z (traced to 99Z) ......................................... | £5 | £10 | £18 |
| **BE61e** Prefix 99Z . .............................................................. | £110 | £200 | £350 |

*Experimental printing on a research machine*
*Prefix sequence: Letter/Number/Number/Letter*

BE62a

| **BE62a** | Prefix A01N (*small long tail 'R' on reverse for research*) ......... | £195 | £375 | £600 |
|---|---|---|---|---|
| **BE62b** | Prefix A05N (*small short tail 'R' on reverse*)............................. | £225 | £425 | £700 |
| **BE62c** | Prefix A06N (*small short tail 'R' on reverse*)........................... | £250 | £450 | £750 |

*Prefix sequence: Letter/Number/Number/Letter*

| **BE63a** | Prefix B01N ................................................................... | £60 | £110 | £220 |
|---|---|---|---|---|
| **BE63b** | Prefix B- -N ................................................................... | £8 | £15 | £30 |
| **BE63c** | Prefix B76N ................................................................... | £90 | £175 | £350 |

| | VF | EF | UNC |
|---|---|---|---|

## (February 1963)

*Green. 151 x 71.8mm.*
*Signature: J .Q. Hollom*

*Prefix sequence: Letter/Number/Number/Letter*

| | | VF | EF | UNC |
|---|---|---|---|---|
| **BE64a** | Prefix B77N followed by serial number................................ | £80 | £150 | £325 |

*BE64b*

| | | VF | EF | UNC |
|---|---|---|---|---|
| **BE64b** | Prefix B- -N ................................................................. | £20 | £45 | £85 |
| **BE64c** | Prefix C- -N to L- -N, A- -R to L- -R, A- -S to L- -S, A- -T to L- -T, A- -U to L- -U, A- -W to L- -W, A- -X to K- -X, A- -Y | £2 | £4 | £6 |
| **BE64d** | Prefix B- -Y (*last series traced to B10Y*) .................................. | £22 | £50 | £100 |

*Prefix sequence: Letter/Number/Number*

| | | VF | EF | UNC |
|---|---|---|---|---|
| **BE65a** | Prefix M68 Replacement note ............................................... | £40 | £90 | £200 |
| **BE65b** | Prefix M- - Replacement note ............................................... | £12 | £25 | £45 |
| **BE65c** | Prefix M99 Replacement note ............................................... | £70 | £150 | --- |

*Prefix sequence: Number/Number/Letter*

| | | VF | EF | UNC |
|---|---|---|---|---|
| **BE66a** | Prefix 01M Replacement note ............................................... | £60 | £125 | £275 |

*BE66b*

| | | VF | EF | UNC |
|---|---|---|---|---|
| **BE66b** | Prefix - -M Replacement note (traced to 99M).................... | £9 | £18 | £35 |

|  | VF | EF | UNC |
|---|---|---|---|

*Prefix sequence: Letter/Number/Number/Letter*

**BE67a** Prefix M01R Replacement note .................................................... £65 £140 £300

*BE67b*

**BE67b**   Prefix M- -R Replacement note (*traced to M08R*) ................. £28 £60 £100

*With small 'G' on reverse (indicating that note printed on a Goebel machine)*
*Prefix sequence: Letter/Number/Number/Letter*

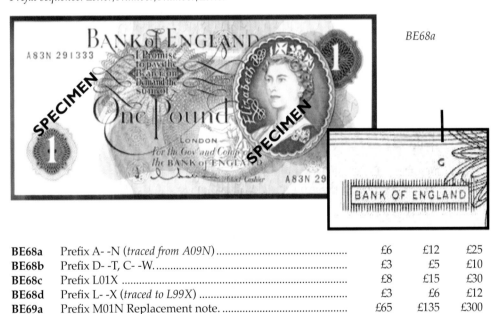

*BE68a*

| | | VF | EF | UNC |
|---|---|---|---|---|
| **BE68a** | Prefix A- -N (*traced from A09N*) ............................................... | £6 | £12 | £25 |
| **BE68b** | Prefix D- -T, C- -W. ........................................................ | £3 | £5 | £10 |
| **BE68c** | Prefix L01X ................................................................ | £8 | £15 | £30 |
| **BE68d** | Prefix L- -X (*traced to L99X*) ............................................ | £3 | £6 | £12 |
| **BE69a** | Prefix M01N Replacement note. ........................................... | £65 | £135 | £300 |

VF     EF     UNC

BE69b

**BE69b**    Prefix M- -N Replacement note (*traced to M28N*) ...............     £14     £30     £60

## (February 1967)
*Green. 151 x 71.8mm.*
*Signature: J .S. Fforde*

*Prefix sequence: Letter/Number/Number/Letter*

BE70a

| | | | | |
|---|---|---|---|---|
| **BE70a** | Prefix B11Y followed by serial number ................................ | £110 | £200 | £450 |
| **BE70b** | Prefix B- -Y ................................................................................ | £15 | £30 | £55 |
| **BE70c** | Prefix C- -Y to L- -Y, A- -Z to J- -Z.......................................... | £2 | £5 | £10 |
| **BE70d** | Prefix L- -Z (*traced to L99Z*)...................................................... | £7 | £15 | £35 |

BE71

**BE71**    Prefix M- -R Replacement note (*traced from M09R to M49R*)     £12     £28     £60

|  |  | VF | EF | UNC |
|---|---|---|---|---|
| **BE72a** | Prefix N01A............................................................ | --- | --- | --- |
| **BE72b** | Prefix N- -A............................................................. | £25 | £55 | £100 |
| **BE72c** | Prefix N- -B to N- -L, R- -A to R- -K, S- -L, T- -A to T- -L, |  |  |  |
|  | U- -A to U- -H, W- -A to W- -D, X- -B................................. | FV | £3 | £6 |
| **BE72d** | Prefix S87L, S88L, S89L, S90L *(Overlaps with Page BE78a,b below)* £15 | £35 | £70 |

*BE72e*

|  |  | VF | EF | UNC |
|---|---|---|---|---|
| **BE72e** | Prefix X- -C *(traced to X42C)*...................................... | £14 | £30 | £50 |
| **BE73a** | Prefix R01M Replacement note...................................... | £85 | £200 | £500 |
| **BE73b** | Prefix R- -M Replacement note *(traced to R54M)* ................ | £7 | £15 | £25 |
| **BE73c** | Prefix S01M Replacement note  ..................................... | £85 | £200 | £500 |
| **BE73d** | Prefix S- -M Replacement note *(traced to S78M)* ................ | *£7* | £15 | £25 |
| **BE73e** | Prefix T01M Replacement note ...................................... | £135 | £275 | £550 |
| **BE73c** | Prefix T- -M Replacement note *(traced to T04M)*.................. | £75 | £175 | £375 |

*BE73d*

| **BE73d** | Prefix U01M Replacement note *(traced in U01M only)*........ | £135 | £275 | £550 |
|---|---|---|---|---|

*With small 'G' on reverse (indicating that note printed on a Goebel machine.)*

|  |  | VF | EF | UNC |
|---|---|---|---|---|
| **BE74a** | Prefix E01Y.. ......................................................... | £70 | £150 | £275 |
| **BE74b** | Prefix E- -Y *(traced to E99Y)*...................................... | £3 | £6 | £10 |
| **BE74c** | Prefix K01Z.. ......................................................... | £70 | £150 | £275 |
| **BE74d** | Prefix K- -Z *(traced to K99Z)*...................................... | £3 | £6 | £10 |

BE75a

| | | VF | EF | UNC |
|---|---|---|---|---|
| **BE75a** | Prefix M29N Replacement note ............................................ | £60 | £125 | £275 |
| **BE75b** | Prefix M- -N Replacement note........................................... | £18 | £40 | £70 |
| **BE75c** | Prefix M42N Replacement note. ......................................... | £70 | £135 | £300 |
| | | | | |
| **BE76a** | Prefix R01B............................................................... | £120 | £250 | — |
| **BE76b** | Prefix R—B *(traced to R99B)* ......................................... | £3 | £7 | £14 |
| **BE76c** | Prefix R01L............................................................... | £45 | £90 | £150 |
| **BE76d** | Prefix R- -L *(traced to R99L)*.......................................... | £3 | £7 | £14 |
| **BE76e** | Prefix U01E .............................................................. | £55 | £100 | £175 |
| **BE76f** | Prefix U- -E *(traced to U45E)*......................................... | £4 | £8 | £15 |
| | | | | |
| **BE77a** | Prefix N01M Replacement note .......................................... | £185 | £350 | £600 |
| **BE77b** | Prefix N- -M Replacement note........................................... | £35 | £65 | £130 |
| **BE77c** | Prefix N14M Replacement note .......................................... | £45 | £100 | £200 |

BE77d

| | | | | |
|---|---|---|---|---|
| **BE77d** | Prefix T29M Replacement note ........................................... | £45 | £95 | £185 |
| **BE77e** | Prefix T- -M Replacement note ........................................... | £55 | £120 | £225 |
| **BE77f** | Prefix T32M Replacement note ........................................... | £120 | £250 | £400 |

## (1970 – date unknown)

*Green. 151 x 71.8mm.*
*Signature: J .B. Page*

*Prefix sequence: Letter/Number/Number/Letter*

| | | | | |
|---|---|---|---|---|
| **BE78a** | Prefix S87L followed by serial number................................. | £450 | £750 | £1250 |
| **BE78b** | Prefix S89L and S90L only ...................................... | £350 | £500 | £950 |

|  | | VF | EF | UNC |
|---|---|---|---|---|
| **BE78c** | Prefix T- -B to T- -L, U- -A to U- -H, W- -A to W- -H (*traced to W99H*) .................................................................................. | FV | £3 | £5 |
| **BE78d** | Prefix X- -A to X- -L, Y- -A to Y- -L, Z- -A to Z- -K ............... | FV | £3 | £5 |
| **BE78e** | Prefix Z- -L (*traced to Z84L*) ...................................................... | £4 | £10 | £20 |
| **BE79a** | Prefix R- -M Replacement note (*traced from R44M to R99M*) | £8 | £20 | £50 |
| **BE79b** | Prefix S- -M Replacement note (*traced from S32M to S99M*) | £6 | £12 | £28 |
| **BE79c** | Prefix W01M Replacement note ........................................... | £40 | £70 | £175 |
| **BE79d** | Prefix W- -M Replacement note (*traced to W84M*) ............... | £4 | £10 | £25 |
| **BE79e** | Prefix X01M Replacement note............................................ | £65 | £120 | £225 |
| **BE79f** | Prefix X- -M Replacement note (*traced to X60M*) ................. | £4 | £10 | £25 |

*BE80*

| **BE80** | Pair of consecutively numbered notes with signatures of J. S. Fforde and J. B. Page (*traced in prefixes S- -L, T- -D, T- -H, T- -K, T- -L, U- -C, U- -D, W- -A, W- -B, W- -C, X- -B, X- -C, R- -M and S- -M*).£150 | | £275 | £475 |
|---|---|---|---|---|

*Prefix sequence: Letter/Letter/Number/Number*

| **BE81a** | Prefix AN01 followed by serial number .............................. | £65 | £110 | £240 |
|---|---|---|---|---|
| **BE81b** | Prefix AN- - . ....................................................................... | £3 | £6 | £10 |
| **BE81c** | Prefix AR- - to AZ- -, BN- - to BZ- -, CN- - to CZ- -, DN- - to DZ- -, EN- - to EZ- -, HN- - to HY- - ...................................... | FV | £3 | £5 |
| **BE81d** | Prefix HZ- - . ....................................................................... | £3 | £6 | £10 |
| **BE81e** | Prefix HZ63 (*last prefix of Portrait Series 'C' £1*) ................... | — | — | — |

*BE82a*

| **BE82a** | Prefix MR01 Replacement note............................................. | £70 | £125 | £260 |
|---|---|---|---|---|

|  | | *VF* | *EF* | *UNC* |
|---|---|---|---|---|
| **BE82b** | Prefix MR- - Replacement note (*traced to MR48*) ................. | £7 | £16 | £40 |
| **BE82c** | Prefix MS01 Replacement note. ............................................. | £35 | £60 | £125 |
| **BE82d** | Prefix MS- - Replacement note (*traced to MS84*) ................. | £3 | £7 | £14 |
| **BE82e** | Prefix MT01 Replacement note. ............................................. | £35 | £60 | £125 |
| **BE82f** | Prefix MT- - Replacement note (*traced to MT23*)................. | £3 | £7 | £14 |
| **BE82g** | Prefix MU01 Replacement note. ............................................ | £15 | £28 | £50 |
| **BE82h** | Prefix MU- - Replacement note (*traced to MU19*). ............. | £3 | £7 | £14 |
| **BE82i** | Prefix MW01 Replacement note. ........................................... | £30 | £55 | £115 |
| **BE82j** | Prefix MW- - Replacement note. ........................................... | £3 | £7 | £14 |

*BE82k*

| **BE82k** | Prefix MW19 Replacement note ............................................ | £45 | £80 | £150 |
|---|---|---|---|---|

# SERIES "C" PORTRAIT £1 ERRORS

| **E1a(ii)** | Inverted watermark................................................................. | £100 | £150 | £200 |
|---|---|---|---|---|
| **E1b(i)** | Securitythread—completely exposed ................................... | £25 | £35 | £50 |
| **E1b(iii)** | Securitythread—joined .......................................................... | £7 | £12 | £20 |
| **E1b(iv)** | Security thread—missing ....................................................... | £75 | £100 | £150 |

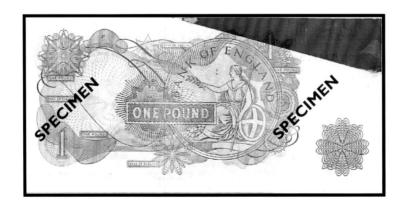

*E1c(ii)*

| **E1c(i)** | Paper join using coarse white cotton tape............................ | £75 | £120 | £180 |
|---|---|---|---|---|

| | | VF | EF | UNC |
|---|---|---|---|---|
| **E1c(ii)** | Paper join using red adhesive paper........................................ | £100 | £150 | £220 |

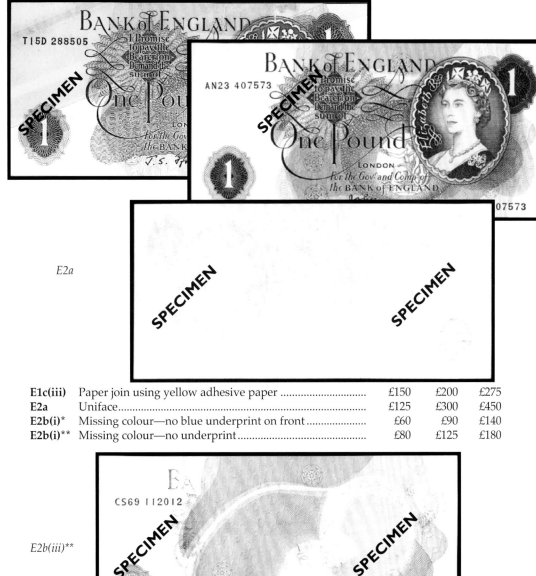

*E2a*

*E2b(iii)\*\**

| | | VF | EF | UNC |
|---|---|---|---|---|
| **E1c(iii)** | Paper join using yellow adhesive paper ............................... | £150 | £200 | £275 |
| **E2a** | Uniface..................................................................................... | £125 | £300 | £450 |
| **E2b(i)\*** | Missing colour—no blue underprint on front ..................... | £60 | £90 | £140 |
| **E2b(i)\*\*** | Missing colour—no underprint .............................................. | £80 | £125 | £180 |
| **E2b(ii)** | Missing colour—no main green on front ............................. | £125 | £250 | £375 |
| **E2b(iii)\*\*** | Missing colour—dry print (major) main green on back .... | £100 | £200 | £275 |
| **E2c(i)** | Extra colour—streak................................................................ | £10 | £18 | £30 |
| **E2c(ii)** | Extra colour—solid line ......................................................... | £12 | £25 | £40 |
| **E2c(iii)\*** | Extra colour—blobs & blots (minor).................................... | £12 | £25 | £35 |

VF    EF    UNC

E2c(iii)**

| | | VF | EF | UNC |
|---|---|---|---|---|
| E2c(iii)** | Extra colour—blobs & blots (major) | £30 | £60 | £100 |
| E2d(i)* | Offset—front on back (minor) | from £40 | £75 | £110 |
| E2d(i)** | Offset—front on back (major) | £100 | £200 | £275 |
| E2e(i) | Part design missing at edge | £40 | £60 | £80 |
| E2e(ii) | Part design missing in body of note | £60 | £90 | £120 |
| E2f | Print flaws | from £10 | £25 | £40 |
| E3a | No number sometimes with number entered in pencil or ink | £75 | £125 | £175 |
| E3b | Only one number of two | £50 | £80 | £125 |
| E3d(i) | Missing digits—single | £5 | £12 | £25 |
| E3d(ii) | Missing digits—multiple | from £12 | £25 | £45 |

E3e(i)    E3e(ii)    E3e(i)

| | | VF | EF | UNC |
|---|---|---|---|---|
| E3e(i) | Numeral misplaced—misaligned (major) | £8 | £15 | £40 |
| E3e(ii) | Numeral misplaced—parts of two numerals visible | £10 | £20 | £55 |
| E3f(i) | Different numbers—different prefix | £75 | £125 | £200 |
| E3f(ii) | Different numbers—one different serial numeral | £15 | £30 | £50 |
| E3f(iii) | Different numbers—two or more different serial numerals | £25 | £50 | £75 |
| E3g | Identical number on two notes | £150 | £250 | £450 |
| E3h | Slip & stick pair | £65 | £100 | £180 |

| | | VF | EF | UNC |
|---|---|---|---|---|
| E4a(i) | Design misplaced—vertically | £40 | £80 | £125 |
| E4a(ii) | Design misplaced—horizontally | £10 | £25 | £50 |
| E5a(i) | Folds with extra paper | £35 | £75 | £140 |
| E5a(ii) | Folds with extra paper with marginal markings | £50 | £100 | £180 |

|          |                                                            | VF   | EF    | UNC   |
|----------|------------------------------------------------------------|------|-------|-------|
| **E5a(iii)** | Folds with extra paper with part of adjoining note........... | £60  | £120  | £200  |
| **E5a(iv)**  | Folds without extra paper ........................................ | £75  | £150  | £275  |

*E5b(i)*

|          |                                                            | VF   | EF    | UNC   |
|----------|------------------------------------------------------------|------|-------|-------|
| **E5b(i)**  | Crease within the sheet—single............................. | £20  | £40   | £70   |
| **E5b(ii)** | Crease within the sheet—multiple........................ | £35  | £80   | £175  |

# SERIES "D" PICTORIAL ISSUE
## (February 1978)
*Green and multicoloured. 134.5 x66.7mm.*
*Reverse depicting Isaac Newton*
*Signature: J .B. Page*

*Prefix sequence: Letter/Number/Number*

*BE83a*

|          |                                                            | VF   | EF    | UNC   |
|----------|------------------------------------------------------------|------|-------|-------|
| **BE83a** | Prefix A01 followed by serial number................................. | £3   | £7    | £15   |
| **BE83b** | Prefix A- - ........................................................... | FV   | £4    | £7    |
| **BE83c** | Prefix B- - to Y- - ................................................. | FV   | £3    | £5    |
| **BE83d** | Prefix Z- - ........................................................... | £3   | £7    | £15   |
| **BE83e** | Prefix Z80 ........................................................... | £70  | £135  | £275  |

| | VF | EF | UNC |
|---|---|---|---|

*BE84*

| **BE84** | Prefix M01 Replacement note ............................................... | £80 | £150 | £300 |
|---|---|---|---|---|

*Prefix sequence: Number/Number/Letter*

| **BE85a** | Prefix 01A followed by serial number ................................. | £15 | £30 | £55 |
|---|---|---|---|---|
| **BE85b** | Prefix - -A ............................................................................. | £2 | £4 | £7 |
| **BE85c** | Prefix - -B to - -X .................................................................. | FV | £3 | £5 |
| **BE85d** | Prefix - -Y *(traced to 80Y)* ................................................. | £3 | £7 | £15 |
| **BE85e** | Prefix 81A ............................................................................ | £185 | £350 | — |
| **BE85f** | Prefix 81B, C, D, E, H, K, N, R, S, T, U, W, X, Y .................. | £90 | £185 | £350 |

*BE85g*

| **BE85g** | Prefix 81Z ............................................................................ | £135 | £275 | £480 |
|---|---|---|---|---|

*Prefix sequence: Letter/Number/Number/Letter*

| **BE86a** | Prefix A01N followed by serial number. ............................. | £15 | £35 | £60 |
|---|---|---|---|---|
| **BE86b** | Prefix A- -N ......................................................................... | £3 | £7 | £15 |
| **BE86c** | Prefix B- -N to D- -N ........................................................... | FV | £3 | £5 |
| **BE86d** | Prefix E- -N *(traced to E84N)* ........................................... | £4 | £9 | £20 |

|  | VF | EF | UNC |
|---|---|---|---|

## (March 1981)

*Green and multicoloured with enhanced background colours. 134.5 x66.7mm.*
*Printed by web- offset with small "W" at lower left on reverse*
*Signature: D. H. F. Somerset*

*Prefix sequence: Letter/Letter/Number/Number*

*"W" on reverse*

BE87a

| | | VF | EF | UNC |
|---|---|---|---|---|
| **BE87a** | Prefix AN01 followed by serial number. ............................. | £12 | £28 | £50 |
| **BE87b** | Prefix AN- -. ............................................................... | £2 | £4 | £8 |
| **BE87c** | Prefix AR- - to DY- -. ................................................. | FV | £3 | £5 |
| **BE87d** | Prefix DY21 (*last prefix of Pictorial Series "D" £1*).. .............. | £8 | £20 | £45 |
| **BE88** | Prefix MN- - Experimental note (traced from MN04 to MN18) ...................................................................... | £1750 | £3000 | — |

## SERIES "D" PICTORIAL £1 ERRORS

E2b(i)**

| | | VF | EF | UNC |
|---|---|---|---|---|
| **E2b(i)*** | Missing colour—underprint, "bite out of orange" on back | £30 | £55 | £90 |
| **E2b(i)**** | Missing colour—almost all underprint, missing on back.. | £45 | £100 | £180 |

*VF*   *EF*   *UNC*

E2b(ii)**

| | | VF | EF | UNC |
|---|---|---|---|---|
| **E2b(ii)\*\*** | Missing colour—main green, front, Page signature ........... | £125 | £200 | £300 |
| | *N.B. the same error for Somerset is thought to be fraudulent.* | | | |
| **E2b(iii)** | Missing colour—dry print (major, green and orange on back) £250 | | — | — |
| **E2c(ii)\*** | Extra colour—solid line, front (minor) ................................ | £10 | £15 | £22 |
| **E2d(i)\*** | Offset—front on back (minor).............................................from £50 | | £80 | £125 |
| **E2d(i)\*\*** | Offset—front on back (major) ....................................... £140 | | £240 | £350 |
| **E2e(ii)\*** | Part design missing in body of note—underprint by caduceus£200 | | — | — |
| **E2e(i)\*\*** | Part design missing at edge, back (major) ..................................... £90 | | £150 | £225 |
| **E2f(i)** | Print flaw—front, line in tiara and another in garter sash.......... £10 | | £18 | £25 |

*Examples of E2f(ii)*

| | | VF | EF | UNC |
|---|---|---|---|---|
| **E2f(ii)** | Print flaw—front, white spot at right edge or back, spot on Newton's arm or spot on Newton's shoulder .............................. £12 | | £20 | £30 |
| **E2g\*** | Incorrect colour registration—front main green (over 1.5mm) £60 | | £100 | £150 |
| **E2g\*\*** | Incorrect colour registration—front main green (over 5mm) £100 | | £150 | £200 |
| **E3a** | No number, sometimes with number entered in pencil or ink £100 | | £150 | £225 |

E3c

| | | VF | EF | UNC |
|---|---|---|---|---|
| **E3c** | Shift of number—much too far to right or left .................... | £50 | £100 | £160 |
| **E3d(i)** | Missing digit.......................................................................... | £40 | £75 | £100 |
| **E3e(i)** | Numeral misplaced—misaligned, major ............................. | £25 | £40 | £75 |
| **E3e(ii)** | Numeral misplaced – parts of two numerals visible.......... | £35 | £55 | £90 |
| **E3j** | Dry print of number............................................................. | £50 | £80 | £110 |

| | | VF | EF | UNC |
|---|---|---|---|---|
| E4a(ii) | Design misplaced horizontally with blue and white line at right | £30 | £50 | £80 |
| E4b | Rough edges (major) | £10 | £25 | £40 |
| E5a(ii) | Fold with extra paper with marginal markings | £60 | £110 | £200 |
| E5a(iv) | Fold without extra paper | £40 | £75 | £130 |
| E5b(i) | Crease within the sheet (single) | £30 | £70 | £125 |
| E5b(ii) | Crease within the sheet (multiple) | £40 | £100 | £200 |

# FIVE POUNDS

**BLACK AND WHITE SERIES (continued)**

*BE89*

| | | F | VF | EF |
|---|---|---|---|---|
| **(1925-29)** | | | | |
| **BE89** | *Signature: C. P. Mahon* | | | |
| | London | £200 | £350 | £575 |
| **(1929-34)** | | | | |
| **BE90** | *Signature: B. G. Catterns* | | | |
| | London | £140 | £265 | £450 |

BE91

### (1934-44)

**BE91**    *Signature: K. O. Peppiatt*

London ................................................................................. £135    £240    £385

*NB. There are deceptive German World War II forgeries of the White £5 note, almost all of these being forgeries of BE90 and BE91.*

### (1944-45—issued 1945)

*Thicker paper. With metal security thread*
*Signature: K. O. Peppiatt*
*Prefix sequence: Letter/Number/Number*

BE92a

| | | VF | EF | UNC |
|---|---|---|---|---|
| **BE92a** | Prefix E- - followed by serial number ................................. | £90 | £150 | £225 |
| **BE92b** | Prefix H- - to K- -............................................................... | £85 | £140 | £200 |
| **BE92c** | Prefix L- - (*traced to L02*)........................................................ | £175 | £300 | £475 |

VF     EF     UNC

## (1947 issued 1948)

*Thinner paper. With metal security thread*
*Signature: K. O. Peppiatt*
*Prefix sequence: Letter/Number/Number*

BE93b

| | | VF | EF | UNC |
|---|---|---|---|---|
| **BE93a** | Prefix L- - followed by serial number (*traced from L03*)...... | £80 | £130 | £195 |
| **BE93b** | Prefix M- - (*traced to M71*) ....................................................... | £80 | £130 | £195 |

## (1949-52)

*Thinner paper. With metal security thread*
*Signature: P. S. Beale*
*Prefix sequence: Letter/Number/Number*

| | | VF | EF | UNC |
|---|---|---|---|---|
| **BE94a** | Prefix M- - followed by serial number (*traced from M72*) ... | £85 | £135 | £225 |
| **BE94b** | Prefix N- - to X- -........................................................................ | £70 | £120 | £195 |

BE94c

| | | VF | EF | UNC |
|---|---|---|---|---|
| **BE94c** | Prefix Y- - (*traced to Y70*)............................................................ | £90 | £140 | £240 |

|  | VF | EF | UNC |
|---|---|---|---|

**(1955-56)**
*Thinner paper. With metal security thread*
*Signature: L. K. O'Brien*
*Prefix sequence: Letter/Number/Number*

| | | VF | EF | UNC |
|---|---|---|---|---|
| **BE95a** | Prefix Y- - followed by serial number (*traced from Y71*)....... | £85 | £135 | £225 |
| **BE95b** | Prefix Z- - (*traced to Z99*) ......................................... | £70 | £125 | £200 |

*Prefix sequence: Letter/Number/Number/Letter*

BE96a

| | | VF | EF | UNC |
|---|---|---|---|---|
| **BE96a** | Prefix A- -A followed by serial number................................ | £85 | £135 | £225 |
| **BE96b** | Prefix B- -A and C- -A.................................................... | £70 | £120 | £195 |
| **BE96c** | Prefix D- -A (*traced to D99A*)....................................... | £90 | £140 | £240 |

# SERIES "B" HELMETED BRITANNIA ISSUE
## (February 1957)

*Blue on multicoloured underprint. Shaded £5 symbols on reverse. 159 x 89mm*
*Signature: L. K. O'Brien*

*Prefix sequence: Letter/Number/Number*

*shaded £5 symbol*

*unshaded £5 symbol*

*BE97a*

|  |  | *VF* | *EF* | *UNC* |
|---|---|---|---|---|
| **BE97a** | Prefix A01 followed by serial number .................................. | £125 | £240 | £425 |
| **BE97b** | Prefix A- - ....................................................................... | £18 | £40 | £85 |
| **BE97c** | Prefix B- - to D- - ........................................................... | £15 | £32 | £70 |
| **BE97d** | Prefix E- - ....................................................................... | £20 | £45 | £100 |
| **BE97e** | Prefix E37 ........................................................................ | £130 | £250 | £450 |

## (July 1961)

*Blue on multicoloured underprint. Unshaded £5 symbols on reverse. 159 x 89mm*
*Signature: L. K. O'Brien*

*Prefix sequence: Letter/Number/Number*

|  |  | | | |
|---|---|---|---|---|
| **BE98a** | Prefix H01 followed by serial number .................................. | £275 | £500 | £900 |
| **BE98b** | Prefix H- - ....................................................................... | £18 | £40 | £85 |
| **BE98c** | Prefix J- - ......................................................................... | £15 | £32 | £70 |

|  | VF | EF | UNC |
|---|---|---|---|

BE98d

| | | VF | EF | UNC |
|---|---|---|---|---|
| **BE98d** | Prefix K- - ................................................. | £20 | £45 | £100 |
| **BE98e** | Prefix K45 (*last prefix of Helmeted Britannia Series "B" £5*)... | £225 | £400 | £650 |

# SERIES "C" PORTRAIT ISSUE
## (February 1963)

*Blue 140 x 85mm.*
*Signature: J .Q. Hollom*

*Prefix sequence: Letter/Number/Number*

BE99a

| **BE99a** | Prefix A01 followed by serial number ................................ | £55 | £100 | £185 |
|---|---|---|---|---|

|  |  | VF | EF | UNC |
|---|---|---|---|---|
| **BE99b** | Prefix A- - … .......................................................... | £12 | £25 | £45 |
| **BE99c** | Prefix B- - to N- - ................................................... | £10 | £22 | £40 |
| **BE99d** | Prefix R- -(*traced to R19*) ...................................... | £15 | £35 | £75 |
| **BE100a** | Prefix M01 Replacement note.. ............................... | £185 | £350 | — |

*BE100b*

| **BE100b** | Prefix M- - Replacement note (*traced to M12*) ...................... | £100 | £220 | £350 |
|---|---|---|---|---|

## (January 1967)
*Blue 140 x 85mm.*
*Signature: J .S. Fforde*

*Prefix sequence: Letter/Number/Number*

*BE101a*

| **BE101a** | Prefix R20 followed by serial number.................................. | £50 | £95 | £200 |
|---|---|---|---|---|
| **BE101b** | Prefix R- -................................................................ | £15 | £28 | £55 |
| **BE101c** | Prefix S- - to Y- - ...................................................... | £12 | £20 | £35 |
| **BE101d** | Prefix Z- - ............................................................... | £14 | £25 | £45 |
| **BE101e** | Prefix Z99 ............................................................... | £90 | £175 | £325 |
| **BE102** | Prefix M- - Replacement note (*traced from M08 to M28*) ..... | £50 | £110 | £225 |

| | VF | EF | UNC |
|---|---|---|---|

*Prefix sequence: Number/Number/Letter*

| | | VF | EF | UNC |
|---|---|---|---|---|
| **BE103a** | Prefix 01A followed by serial number ................................. | £90 | £150 | — |
| **BE103b** | Prefix - -A .......................................................................... | £14 | £25 | £45 |
| **BE103c** | Prefix - -B to - -K (*overlaps with Page BE105b, c, d below*) ..... | £12 | £20 | £35 |
| **BE103d** | Prefix - -L(*traced to 40L*)........................................................ | £75 | £135 | £250 |
| **BE104a** | Prefix 01M Replacement note ................................................ | £130 | £250 | — |

BE104b

| | | VF | EF | UNC |
|---|---|---|---|---|
| **BE104b** | Prefix - -M Replacement note (*traced to 15M*) ..................... | £55 | £100 | £200 |

*Signature: J .B. Page*
*Prefix sequence: Number/Number/Letter*

| | | VF | EF | UNC |
|---|---|---|---|---|
| **BE105a** | Prefix 03C followed by serial number ................................. | £150 | £275 | £500 |
| **BE105b** | Prefix - -C (*overlaps with Fforde BE103c above*) ..................... | £22 | £40 | £75 |
| **BE105c** | Prefix - -D and - -E (*overlaps with Fforde BE103c above*) ....... | £12 | £22 | £40 |

BE105d

| | | VF | EF | UNC |
|---|---|---|---|---|
| **BE105d** | Prefix - -H (*overlaps with Fforde BE 103c above*).................... | £70 | £135 | £250 |

| | | VF | EF | UNC |
|---|---|---|---|---|
| **BE105e** | Prefix 36H (*last reported prefix of Portrait Series "C" £5*)........ | £250 | £400 | — |
| **BE106** | Prefix - -M Replacement note (*traced from 04M to 18M*) ..... | £65 | £130 | £250 |

BE107

| | | | | |
|---|---|---|---|---|
| **BE107** | Pair of consecutively numbered notes with signatures of J. S. Fforde and J. B. Page (*traced in prefixes - - C , - -D, and - -E* ) | --- | £500 | £800 |

# SERIES "C" PORTRAIT £5 ERRORS

*N.B. All Series "C" £5 errors are rare*

E2b(i)

| | | VF | EF | UNC |
|---|---|---|---|---|
| **E2b(i)** | Missing colour—no mauve underprint on front.................. | £100 | £140 | £250 |
| **E3d(i)** | Missing digits—single.............................................................. | £50 | £85 | £125 |
| **E3d(ii)** | Missing digits—multiple .......................................................from £75 | £120 | £175 |

|  |  | VF | EF | UNC |
|---|---|---|---|---|
| **E5a(i)*** | Folds with extra paper (minor)............................................ from£50 | £80 | £150 |
| **E5a(i)**** | Folds with extra paper (major) ........................................... £150 | £275 | £400 |

*E5a(iii)*

| **E5a(iii)** | Folds with extra paper with part of adjoining note............from £150 | £275 | £400 |
|---|---|---|---|

# SERIES "D" PICTORIAL ISSUE
## (November 1971)
*Blue and multicoloured. 145.5 x78mm.*
*Reverse depicting the Duke of Wellington*
*Signature: J .B. Page*

*Prefix sequence: Letter/Number/Number*

BE108a

| | | VF | EF | UNC |
|---|---|---:|---:|---:|
| **BE108a** | Prefix A01 followed by serial number .................................. | £70 | £135 | £250 |
| **BE108b** | Prefix A- - ................................................................................. | £8 | £15 | £35 |
| **BE108c** | Prefix B- - to K- -...................................................................... | £7 | £12 | £25 |
| **BE108d** | Prefix L- -(*traced to L94*).......................................................... | £28 | £50 | £90 |
| **BE109a** | Prefix M01 Replacement note ................................................ | £150 | £280 | £500 |

BE109b

| | | | | |
|---|---|---:|---:|---:|
| **BE109b** | Prefix M- - Replacement note (*traced to M05*) ..................... | £80 | £150 | £285 |

## (August 1973)
*Blue and multicoloured. 145.5 x78mm. Reverse printed by lithography. Small "L" on reverse*
*Signature: J. B. Page*

*Prefix sequence: Number/Number/Letter*

*BE110 – BE117 all have a small "L" for Litho on reverse*

*BE110a*

| | | VF | EF | UNC |
|---|---|---|---|---|
| **BE110a** | Prefix 01A followed by serial number | £75 | £140 | £265 |
| **BE110b** | Prefix - -A | £8 | £15 | £35 |
| **BE110c** | Prefix - -B to - -Y | £6 | £12 | £25 |
| **BE110d** | Prefix - -Z | £12 | £25 | £45 |
| **BE110e** | Prefix 96Z | £120 | — | — |
| **BE111a** | Prefix 01M Replacement note.. | £150 | £280 | £500 |
| **BE111b** | Prefix - -M Replacement note (*traced to 08M*) | £80 | £150 | £285 |

*Prefix sequence: Letter/Letter/Number/Number*

*BE112a*

| | | VF | EF | UNC |
|---|---|---|---|---|
| **BE112a** | Prefix AN01 followed by serial number | £80 | £150 | £275 |
| **BE112b** | Prefix AN- - | £7 | £14 | £30 |
| **BE112c** | Prefix AR- - to CX- - | £6 | £12 | £20 |
| **BE112d** | Prefix EZ- - (*last series traced from EZ05-EZ56*) | £28 | £55 | £100 |

# (June 1980)

*Blue and multicoloured. 145.5 x78mm. Reverse printed by lithography. Small "L" on reverse*
*Signature: D. H. F. Somerset*

*Prefix sequence: Letter/Letter/Number/Number*

*BE113a*

|  |  | VF | EF | UNC |
|---|---|---|---|---|
| **BE113a** | Prefix DN01 followed by serial number............................... | £50 | £90 | £175 |
| **BE113b** | Prefix DN- -…....................................................... | £7 | £14 | £25 |
| **BE113c** | Prefix DR- - to LY- -................................................ | FV | £9 | £18 |
| **BE113d** | Prefix LZ- - (*last series traced to LZ90*)................................... | £12 | £25 | £50 |
| **BE113e** | Prefix NA- - (*not seen*)........................................... | — | — | — |
| **BE113f** | Prefix NB- - andNC- -.............................................. | FV | £10 | £20 |
| **BE113g** | Prefix NC90 ....................................................... | £12 | £25 | £45 |

*BE114*

| **BE114** | Prefix DU55 to DU77 Error note missing signature............ | £50 | £90 | £175 |
|---|---|---|---|---|

VF    EF    UNC

*Experimental notes for Optical Character Recognition (OCR)*
*Prefix sequence: Letter/Letter/Number/Number*

*BE115*

| | | | | |
|---|---|---|---|---|
| **BE115** | Prefix AN91, BR91, CS91, DT91, EU91, HW91, JX91, KY91 and LZ91 ................................. | £550 | £825 | £1100 |

## (July 1987)
*Blue and multicoloured. 145.5 x78mm. With 1mm wide security thread. Printed by web offset*
*Signature: D .H. F. Somerset*
*Prefix sequence: Letter/Letter/Number/Number*

| | | | | |
|---|---|---|---|---|
| **BE116a** | Prefix RA01 followed by serial number ............................. | £18 | £35 | £60 |
| **BE116b** | Prefix RA- - to RC- -............................................. | FV | £10 | £20 |
| **BE116c** | Prefix RC90 ........................................................ | £16 | £30 | £55 |

## (March 1988)
*Blue and multicoloured. 145.5 x78mm.*
*Signature: G .M.Gill*
*Prefix sequence: Letter/Letter/Number/Number*

| | | | | |
|---|---|---|---|---|
| **BE117a** | Prefix RD01 followed by serial number............................... | £14 | £28 | £55 |
| **BE117b** | Prefix RD- - ........................................................ | £7 | £14 | £25 |
| **BE117c** | Prefix RE- - to RL- -, SA- - to SE- - ........................................ | FV | £10 | £20 |
| **BE117d** | Prefix SE90 (*last prefix of Pictorial Series "D"£5 serial numbers below 998500 from circulation*)........................................... | £50 | £95 | £175 |

*BE117e*

| | | | | |
|---|---|---|---|---|
| **BE117e** | Prefix SE90 (*last prefix of Pictorial Series "D" £5*) (*serial numbers 998500 to 999999 from packs*)..................................... | — | — | £90 |

# SERIES "D" PICTORIAL £5 ERRORS

|  |  | VF | EF | UNC |
|---|---|---|---|---|
| **E1b(i)** | Security thread completely exposed ...................................... | £40 | £65 | £90 |

*E1b(ii)*

| **E1b(ii)** | Security thread partly exposed ............................................... | £30 | £50 | £75 |
|---|---|---|---|---|
| **E1c(ii)** | Paper join using red adhesive paper...................................... | £100 | £180 | £250 |
| **E2b(i)** | Missing battle scene—no m/c underprint on back ............ | £160 | £275 | £400 |

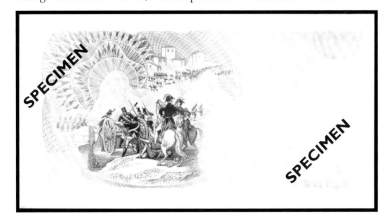

*E2b(ii)*

| **E2b(ii)** | Missing Wellington—no main blue on back ....................... | £120 | £200 | £275 |
|---|---|---|---|---|
| **E2b(iii)*** | Missing colours—dry print (minor) on front or back......... from£30 | | £50 | £75 |

*E2b(iii)***

| **E2b(iii)**** | Missing colours—dry print (major) on front or back ......... | £75 | £125 | £175 |
|---|---|---|---|---|

121

|  |  | VF | EF | UNC |
|---|---|---|---|---|
| **E2c(i)** | Extra colour—streak................................................................ | £18 | £30 | £45 |
| **E2c(ii)** | Extra colour—solid line........................................................ | £20 | £35 | £50 |
| **E2c(iii)\*** | Extra colour—blobs & blots (minor)....................................from£20 | | £35 | £50 |
| **E2c(iii)\*\*** | Extra colour— blobs & blots (major)................................... | £50 | £90 | £140 |
| **E2d(i)\*** | Offset—front on back (minor)..............................................from£40 | | £60 | £100 |
| **E2d(i)\*\*** | Offset—front on back (major)...................................... ....... | £75 | £140 | £250 |
| **E2d(iii)** | Offset—front on back, misaligned (major)......................... | £80 | £150 | £280 |
| **E2g** | Missing signature of D. H. F. Somerset............................... | | See BE114 | |

*E3a*

| **E3a** | No number, sometimes with number entered in pencil or ink £100 | | £175 | £250 |
|---|---|---|---|---|
| **E3b** | Only one number of two.......................................................... | £75 | £110 | £175 |
| **E3d(i)** | Missing digits—single ........................................................... | £25 | £40 | £60 |
| **E3d(ii)** | Missing digits—multiple ......................................................from £45 | | £70 | £100 |
| **E3f(ii)** | Different numbers— one different serial number.............. | £30 | £50 | £75 |
| **E3f(iii)** | Different numbers – two or more different serial numbers.from £50 | | £80 | £125 |
| **E4a(i)\*** | Design misplaced – vertically (minor)................................from £25 | | £40 | £60 |
| **E4a(i)\*\*** | Design misplaced – vertically (major) ................................ | £100 | £160 | £250 |
| **E4a(ii)\*** | Design misplaced – horizontally (minor)............................from £30 | | £50 | £75 |
| **E4a(ii)\*\*** | Designmisplaced – horizontally (major) ............................ | £125 | £200 | £300 |
| **E5a(i)\*** | Folds with extra paper (minor)............................................from £35 | | £50 | £75 |
| **E5a(i)\*\*** | Folds with extra paper (major) ............................................ | £75 | £120 | £180 |

| **E5a(ii)** | Folds with extra paper and colour bars................................ | £120 | £175 | £240 |
|---|---|---|---|---|
| **E5a(iii)** | Folds with extra paper with part of adjoining note............from £80 | | £130 | £200 |

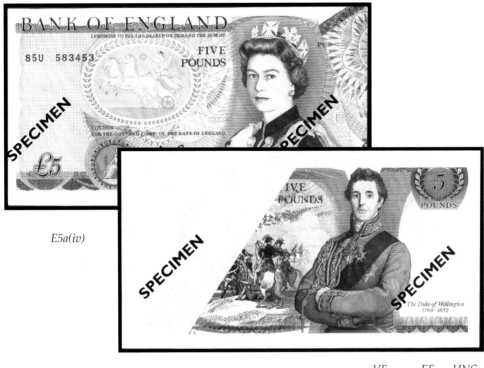

*E5a(iv)*

| | | VF | EF | UNC |
|---|---|---|---|---|
| **E5a(iv)** | Folds without extra paper, showing part back on front and blank area on back or vice versa ......................... | £175 | £275 | £400 |
| **E5b(i)** | Crease within the sheet—single............................................. | £35 | £60 | £90 |
| **E5b(ii)** | Crease within the sheet—multiple ........................................ | £75 | £130 | £200 |

# SERIES "E" HISTORICAL ISSUE
## (June 1990)
*Turquoise and multicoloured. With windowed security thread. 135x70mm.*
*Reverse depicting George Stephenson*
*Signature: G .M. Gill*

*Prefix sequence: Letter/Number/Number*

BE118a

|  | | VF | EF | UNC |
|---|---|---|---|---|
| **BE118a** | Prefix A01 followed by serial number ................................. | £6 | £14 | £30 |
| **BE118b** | Prefix A- - ................................................................. | FV | £10 | £22 |
| **BE118c** | Prefix B- - to L- - ...................................................... | FV | £8 | £18 |
| **BE118d** | Prefix N- -(*traced to N54 official last run*)............................. | £18 | £40 | £70 |
| **BE118e** | Prefix R- - to T- - (*overlaps with Kentfield BE119b and* | | | |
| | BE119c *below*) ........................................................ | £12 | £28 | £50 |
| **BE118f** | Prefix U- -(*last series overlap traced to U17*).......................... | £85 | £200 | — |

## (November 1991)
*Turquoise and multicoloured. 135x70mm. Printed on web presses.*
*Signature: G .E. A. Kentfield*

*Prefix sequence: Letter/Number/Number*

| **BE119a** | Prefix R01 followed by serial number ................................. | £8 | £18 | £40 |
|---|---|---|---|---|
| **BE119b** | Prefix R- - (*overlaps with Gill BE118e above*) ........................ | FV | £12 | £25 |
| **BE119c** | Prefix S- - to U- - (*overlaps with Gill BE118e and BE118f above*).. | FV | £8 | £18 |
| **BE119d** | Prefix W- - .............................................................. | £8 | £20 | £40 |
| **BE119f** | Prefix W18 (*serial numbers below998500 from circulation*) .... | £110 | £200 | — |

| | VF | EF | UNC |
|---|---|---|---|

BF119g

**BE119g**   Prefix W18 *(serial numbers 998500 to 999999 from packs)* .....   —   —   £95

## (March 1993)

*Turquoise and multicoloured. With darker £5 value tablet. 135x70mm.*
*Signature: G .E. A. Kentfield*

*Prefix sequence: Letter/Letter/Number/Number*

| | | VF | EF | UNC |
|---|---|---|---|---|
| **BE120a** | Prefix AA01 followed by serial number .............................. | £6 | £12 | £28 |
| **BE120b** | Prefix AA- -, AB- - ................................................... | FV | £8 | £16 |
| **BE120c** | Prefix AB18 *(serial numbers below 998500 from circulation)* .. | £125 | £225 | — |
| **BE120d** | Prefix AB18 *(serial numbers 998500 to 999999 from uncut trios)* | — | — | £80 |

*Printed by sheet fed offset litho*

BE121a

| | | VF | EF | UNC |
|---|---|---|---|---|
| **BE121a** | Prefix AC01 followed by serial number *(serial numbers 000001 to 001500 from uncut trios)* ........................................ | — | --- | £85 |
| **BE121b** | Prefix AC01 followed by serial number *(serial numbers above 001500 from circulation)* ........................................... | £65 | £120 | £225 |
| **BE121c** | Prefix AC- - to AL- -, BA- - to BL- -, CA- - to CK- - .............. | FV | £8 | £14 |
| **BE121d** | Prefix DA- -, DB- - ................................................... | FV | £8 | £16 |
| **BE121e** | Prefix DC- - *(traced to DC90)* ..................................... | FV | £10 | £20 |
| **BE121f** | Prefix DL99 *(special last run for collectors' packs)* ................. | — | — | £45 |
| **BE122a** | Prefix CL- -Column sort note *(traced to CL45)*..................... | £8 | £18 | £35 |
| **BE122b** | Prefix LL- -Replacement note *(traced to LL45 and overlaps with Lowther BE124b below)* ..................................... | £20 | £45 | £80 |

## (January 1999)
*Turquoise and multicoloured.135x70mm.*
*Signature: Merlyn Lowther*

*Prefix sequence: Letter/Letter/Number/Number*

|  |  | VF | EF | UNC |
|---|---|---|---|---|
| **BE123a** | Prefix EA01 followed by serial number.............................. | £7 | £14 | £30 |
| **BE123b** | Prefix EA- - to EJ- - (*traced to EJ45 last official run*).............. | FV | £6 | £10 |
| **BE123c** | Prefix EJ45 (*last official run*)...................................... | £65 | £120 | £225 |

*BE123d*

|  |  |  |  |  |
|---|---|---|---|---|
| **BE123d** | Prefix EJ90(*special last run for collectors' packs and last prefix of Historical Series "E" £5*)............................................. | — | --- | £75 |
| **BE124a** | Prefix CL- - Column sort note (*traced to CL45*) ................... | FV | £12 | £20 |

*BE124b*

|  |  |  |  |  |
|---|---|---|---|---|
| **BE124b** | Prefix LL- -Replacement note (*traced to LL45 and overlaps with Kentfield BE122b above*) ..................................... | £8 | £20 | £40 |

# SERIES "E" HISTORICAL £5 ERRORS

|  |  | VF | EF | UNC |
|---|---|---|---|---|
| **E2b(i)** | Missing orange, yellow and olive-green in underprint on back £40 | | £75 | £100 |

*E2b(iii)\**

| | | VF | EF | UNC |
|---|---|---|---|---|
| **E2b(iii)\*** | Missing colours—dry print (minor) on front or back........from £20 | | £40 | £60 |
| **E2b(iii)\*\*** | Missing colours—dry print (major) on front or back. ........ £85 | | £150 | £225 |
| **E2d(i)\*** | Offset—front on back (minor)................................from £40 | | £75 | £120 |
| **E2d(i)\*\*** | Offset—front on back (major) ................................ £120 | | £200 | £275 |
| **E3f(ii)** | Different numbers—one different serial number............... £25 | | £45 | £65 |
| **E3f(iii)** | Different numbers—two or more different serial numbersfrom £40 | | £65 | £100 |
| **E4a(i)\*** | Design misplaced—vertically (minor)................................from £25 | | £40 | £60 |
| **E4a(i)\*\*** | Design misplaced—vertically (major) ................................. £100 | | £175 | £250 |
| **E4a(ii)\*** | Design misplaced—horizontally (minor) ...........................from £30 | | £50 | £75 |
| **E4a(ii)\*\*** | Designmisplaced—horizontally (major) .............................. £140 | | £225 | £300 |
| **E5a(i)\*** | Folds with extra paper (minor)................................from £35 | | £50 | £75 |
| **E5a(i)\*\*** | Folds with extra paper (major) ............................................ £80 | | £130 | £180 |
| **E5a(ii)** | Folds with extra paper and colour bars.............................. £120 | | £200 | £275 |
| **E5a(iii)** | Folds with extra paper with part of adjoining note............from £100 | | £175 | £250 |

*E5a(iii)*

# SERIES "E" NEW HISTORICAL ISSUE
## (May 2002)
*Turquoise and multicoloured.135x70mm. Withdrawn issue with faulty varnish coating and full halo silver hologram*
*Reverse depicting Elizabeth Fry*
*Signature: Merlyn Lowther*

*Prefix sequence: Letter/Letter/Number/Number*

BE125a

|  |  | VF | EF | UNC |
|---|---|---|---|---|
| **BE125a** | Prefix HA01 followed by serial number | £6 | £10 | £22 |
| **BE125b** | Prefix HA- -, HB- -, JA- - | FV | £6 | £9 |
| **BE125c** | Prefix JA90 (*last prefix of withdrawn issue*) | £20 | £45 | £75 |
| **BE126a** | Prefix DL- - Column sort note (*traced to DL45 and overlaps with BE128a below*) | £6 | £9 | £20 |
| **BE126b** | Prefix LL- - Replacement note (*traced from LL46-LL90 and overlaps with BE128c below*) | £7 | £12 | £22 |

## (August 2002)
*Turquoise and multicoloured.135x70mm. Reissue with improved varnish coating and cut halo hologram*
*Signature: Merlyn Lowther*

*Prefix sequence: Letter/Letter/Number/Number*

| **BE127a** | Prefix HC01 followed by serial number | — | — | — |
|---|---|---|---|---|
| **BE127b** | Prefix HC- - to HK- - | FV | FV | £8 |
| **BE127c** | Prefix JB- - (*traced to JB90 and overlaps with Bailey BE129 below*) | FV | FV | £10 |

|  | VF | EF | UNC |
|---|---|---|---|

*BE127d*

| **BE127d** | Prefix XA- - to XE- -, XH- - to XK- - *(all traced from 01-45)*.. | £35 | £60 | £100 |
|---|---|---|---|---|
| **BE128a** | Prefix DL- - Column sort note *(traced to DL45 and overlaps with BE126a above)* ....................................................... | FV | £8 | £18 |
| **BE128b** | Prefix EL- - Column sort note *(traced to EL45 and overlaps with Bailey BE130a below)* ..................................... | FV | £8 | £18 |
| **BE128c** | Prefix LL- - Replacement note *(traced from LL46-LL90 and overlaps with Lowther BE126b above and Bailey B130b below)* | FV | £9 | £20 |

## (January 2004)
*Turquoise and multicoloured.135x70mm.*
*Signature: A. Bailey*

*Prefix sequence: Letter/Letter/Number/Number*

*BE129a*

| **BE129a** | Prefix JB46 followed by serial number ................................. | £18 | £35 | £60 |
|---|---|---|---|---|
| **BE129b** | Prefix JB- - *(overlaps with Lowther BE127c above)* ................. | FV | FV | £10 |
| **BE129c** | Prefix JC- - to JH- - *(continuing)*............................................. | FV | FV | £8 |
| **BE130a** | Prefix EL- - Column sort note *(traced to EL45 and overlaps with Lowther BE128b above)* ...................................... | FV | £7 | £15 |
| **BE130b** | Prefix LL- - Column sort note *(traced from LL46 to LL90 and overlaps with Lowther BE128c above)* ........................... | FV | £8 | £18 |
| **BE131– BE149** *[Held in reserve]* | | | | |

# TEN POUNDS
## BLACK AND WHITE SERIES (continued)

| | F | VF | EF |
|---|---|---|---|
| **(1925-29)** | | | |
| **BE150** *Signature: C. P. Mahon* | | | |
| London | £250 | £450 | £800 |

BE151

| | F | VF | EF |
|---|---|---|---|
| **(1929-34)** | | | |
| **BE151** *Signature: B. G. Catterns* | | | |
| London | £200 | £365 | £675 |

BE152

| | VF | EF | UNC |
|---|---|---|---|
| **(1934-44)** | | | |
| **BE152** *Signature: K. O. Peppiatt* | | | |
| London | £235 | £385 | £600 |

*NB. There are deceptive German World War II forgeries of the White £10 note, almost all of these being forgeries of BE151 and BE152.*

# SERIES "C" PORTRAIT ISSUE
## (February 1964)
*Brown 150 x 93mm.*
*Signature: J .Q. Hollom*

*Prefix sequence: Letter/Number/Number*

BE153a

| | | VF | EF | UNC |
|---|---|---|---|---|
| **BE153a** | Prefix A01 followed by serial number ................................. | £35 | £70 | £140 |
| **BE153b** | Prefix A- - ................................................................. | £15 | £30 | £50 |
| **BE153c** | Prefix A40 ................................................................. | £45 | £90 | £165 |

## (January 1967)
*Brown 150 x 93mm.*
*Signature: J. S. Fforde*

*Prefix sequence: Letter/Number/Number*

| | | VF | EF | UNC |
|---|---|---|---|---|
| **BE154a** | Prefix A41 followed by serial number ................................. | £50 | £95 | £175 |
| **BE154b** | Prefix A- - *(overlaps with Page BE155a, b below)*..................... | £15 | £30 | £50 |
| **BE154c** | Prefix A95 ................................................................. | £70 | £135 | £250 |

BE155a

## (1971 – date unknown)

*Brown 150 x 93mm.*
*Signature: J .B. Page*

*Prefix sequence: Letter/Number/Number*

|  |  | VF | EF | UNC |
|---|---|---|---|---|
| **BE155a** | Prefix A91 followed by serial number | £500 | £950 | £1750 |
| **BE155b** | Prefix A- -(*overlaps with Fforde BE154b, c above*) | £400 | £750 | £1350 |
| **BE155c** | Prefix B- -, C- - | £12 | £25 | £45 |
| **BE155d** | Prefix C90 (*last prefix of Portrait Series "C" £10*) | £185 | £350 | — |
| **BE156a** | Prefix M01 Replacement note | £55 | £100 | £185 |
| **BE156b** | Prefix M- - Replacement note (*traced to M17*) | £18 | £35 | £60 |

BE157

| **BE157** | Pair of consecutively numbered notes with signatures of J. S. Fforde and J. B. Page (*traced in prefixes A91 to A95 only*) | --- | £2200 | £3000 |
|---|---|---|---|---|

# SERIES "C" PORTRAIT £10 ERRORS

**N.B.** *All Series "C" £10 errors are very rare*

| | | VF | EF | UNC |
|---|---|---|---|---|
| **E2b(i)** | Missing colours—No underprint and multicolours on back... £350 | | £550 | £800 |
| **E2d(i)\*** | Offset—back on front (minor).....................................from £150 | | £275 | £400 |

*E2d(i)\*\**

| | | | | |
|---|---|---|---|---|
| **E2d(i)\*\*** | Offset—back on front (major) ................................. | £500 | £800 | £1200 |
| **E3d(i)** | Missing digits—single ............................................ | £75 | £110 | £150 |
| **E3d(ii)** | Missing digits—multiple .......................................from £100 | £175 | £250 |

*E5a(i)\**

| | | | | |
|---|---|---|---|---|
| **E5a(i)\*** | Folds with extra paper (minor) ............................from £90 | £140 | £200 |
| **E5a(i)\*\*** | Folds with extra paper (major) ...........................from £160 | £240 | £350 |
| **E5a(iii)** | Folds with extra paper with part of adjoining note...........from £220 | £350 | £450 |

# SERIES "D" PICTORIAL ISSUE
## (February 1975)
*Brown and multicoloured. 151 x 85mm.*
*Reverse depicting Florence Nightingale*
*Signature: J.B. Page*

*Prefix sequence: Letter/Number/Number*

*BE158a*

|  |  | *VF* | *EF* | *UNC* |
|---|---|---|---|---|
| **BE158a** | Prefix A01 followed by serial number ................................. | £50 | £90 | £175 |
| **BE158b** | Prefix A- - ................................................................. | £14 | £28 | £45 |
| **BE158c** | Prefix B- - to S- -........................................................ | FV | £22 | £40 |
| **BE158d** | Prefix T- - ................................................................. | £30 | £55 | £100 |
| **BE158e** | Prefix T20 ................................................................. | £225 | £400 | — |
| **BE158f** | Prefix U- - (*traced in U34, U35 and U39 with only 1 copy of each prefix known and overlaps with Somerset BE160b below*)........ | £1250 | £2500 | — |

BE158A

| | | VF | EF | UNC |
|---|---|---|---|---|
| **BE158A** | Pair of consecutively numbered notes with signatures of J. B. Page and D. H. F. Somerset (*traced in prefix U35 only*)….. | — | Unique | — |
| **BE159a** | Prefix M01 Replacement note ................................................ | £80 | £150 | £285 |

BE159a

| | | | | |
|---|---|---|---|---|
| **BE159b** | Prefix M- - Replacement note ................................................ | £40 | £85 | £150 |
| **BE159c** | Prefix M50 Replacement note ................................................ | £60 | £110 | £250 |

## (December 1980)

*Brown and multicoloured. 151 x 85mm.*
*Reverse depicting Florence Nightingale*
*Signature: D. H. F. Somerset*

*Prefix sequence: Letter/Number/Number*

|  |  | VF | EF | UNC |
|---|---|---|---|---|
| **BE160a** | Prefix U01 followed by serial number ................................. | £250 | £450 | £800 |
| **BE160b** | Prefix U- - *(overlaps with Page BE158f above)* ........................ | £20 | £45 | £80 |
| **BE160c** | Prefix W- - to Y- -.................................................................. | £15 | £35 | £60 |
| **BE160d** | Prefix Z- - ............................................................................. | £25 | £50 | £85 |
| **BE160e** | Prefix Z80 .............................................................................. | £200 | £375 | — |

*Prefix sequence: Number/Number/Letter*

*BE161a*

|  |  | VF | EF | UNC |
|---|---|---|---|---|
| **BE161a** | Prefix 01A followed by serial number ................................. | £90 | £165 | £325 |
| **BE161b** | Prefix - -A ............................................................................. | £15 | £35 | £65 |
| **BE161c** | Prefix - -B to - -K .................................................................. | £12 | £25 | £50 |
| **BE161d** | Prefix - -L.............................................................................. | £35 | £65 | £120 |
| **BE161e** | Prefix 40L.............................................................................. | £185 | £350 | — |

## (February 1984)

*Brown and multicoloured. 151 x 85mm. With 0.5mm wide security thread. Reverse printed by*
*lithography. Small 'L' on reverse*
*(see extract of note right)*
*Signature: D. H. F. Somerset*

*Prefix sequence: Letter/Letter/Number/Number*

*BE162, BE163, BE164 and BE165 all have a*
*small "L" for Litho at lower left on the reverse*

|  |  | VF | EF | UNC |
|---|---|---|---|---|
| **BE162a** | Prefix AN01 followed by serial number ............................. | £65 | £120 | £220 |
| **BE162b** | Prefix AN- - to AZ- -, BN- - to BZ- -, CN- - ......................... | FV | £18 | £35 |
|  |  | VF | EF | UNC |
| **BE162c** | Prefix CR- -............................................................................ | £18 | £35 | £65 |

BE162d

| | | | | |
|---|---|---|---|---|
| **BE162d** | Prefix CR90 ............................................................... | £90 | £175 | £300 |

## (July 1987)

*Brown and multicoloured. 151 x 85mm. With 1mm wide windowed security thread.*
*Signature: D. H. F. Somerset*

*Prefix sequence: Letter/Letter/Number/Number*

| | | | | |
|---|---|---|---|---|
| **BE163a** | Prefix CS01 followed by serial number ............................... | £28 | £55 | £120 |
| **BE163b** | Prefix CS- - to CZ- - ...................................................... | FV | `£22 | £40 |
| **BE163c** | Prefix DN (*traced to DN30*)........................................... | £20 | £40 | £70 |

## (March 1988)

*Brown and multicoloured. 151 x 85mm.*
*Signature: G. M. Gill*

*Prefix sequence: Letter/Letter/Number/Number*

BE164a

| | | | | |
|---|---|---|---|---|
| **BE164a** | Prefix DR01 followed by serial number ............................... | £22 | £40 | £70 |
| **BE164b** | Prefix DR- - to DZ- -, EN- -, ER- - to EZ- -, HN- -, HR- - to HZ- -, JN- - ................................................... | FV | £18 | £35 |
| **BE164c** | Prefix JR................................................................... | £18 | £40 | £75 |
| **BE164d** | Prefix JR60 ............................................................... | £185 | £350 | — |

## (November 1991)

*Brown and multicoloured. 151 x 85mm.*
*Signature: G. E. A. Kentfield*

*Prefix sequence: Letter/Letter/Number/Number*

|  |  | VF | EF | UNC |
|---|---|---|---|---|
| **BE165a** | Prefix KN01 followed by serial number ............................ | £28 | £50 | £90 |
| **BE165b** | Prefix KN- -, KR- - ................................................................. | £14 | £28 | £55 |

*BE165c*

| **BE165c** | Prefix KR30 (*last prefix of Pictorial Series "D" £10 serial numbers from circulation below998500 with the exception of 722501 to 723000* ....................................................................................... | £75 | £140 | £240 |
|---|---|---|---|---|
| **BE165d** | Prefix KR30 (*serial numbers 722501 to 723000 and 998500 to 999999 from packs*)........................................................................ | — | — | £120 |

## SERIES "D" PICTORIAL £10 ERRORS

| **E1a(i)** | Watermark misplaced ............................................................. | £60 | £100 | £150 |
|---|---|---|---|---|

*E1a(i)*

*E1a(ii)*

| **E1a(ii)** | Watermark exposed on surface—too dark on back ............ | £90 | £175 | £250 |
|---|---|---|---|---|
| **E1b(i)** | Security thread completely exposed ..................................... | £50 | £80 | £110 |
| **E1b(ii)** | Security thread partly exposed ............................................. | £45 | £70 | £95 |
| **E1c(ii)** | Paper join using red adhesive paper..................................... | £120 | £200 | £280 |

*E2b(i)*

|  | | VF | EF | UNC |
|---|---|---|---|---|
| **E2b(i)** | Missing hospital scene— no m/c underprint on back....... | £140 | £240 | £325 |

*E2b(ii)*

| | | VF | EF | UNC |
|---|---|---|---|---|
| **E2b(ii)** | Missing Nightingale—no main brown on back .................. | £120 | £200 | £280 |
| **E2b(iii)*** | Missing colours—dry print (minor) on front or back........from £45 | | £70 | £100 |
| **E2b(iii)**** | Missing colours—dry print (major) on front or back. ........ | £90 | £160 | £225 |
| **E2c(i)** | Extra colour—streak............................................................ | £35 | £60 | £80 |
| **E2c(ii)** | Extra colour—solid line ...................................................... | £35 | £60 | £80 |

*E2c(iii)\**

|  |  | VF | EF | UNC |
|---|---|---|---|---|
| **E2c(iii)\*** | Extra colour—blobs & blots (minor)........................from £40 | £65 | £90 |
| **E2c(iii)\*\*** | Extra colour—blobs & blots (major).................................... £75 | £140 | £200 |
| **E2d(i)\*** | Offset—front on back (minor)................................from £40 | £60 | £100 |

*E2d(i)\*\**

| **E2d(i)\*\*** | Offset—front on back (major) ................................. | £130 | £220 | £300 |
|---|---|---|---|---|
| **E2g** | Missing signature of J. B. Page............................ | £200 | £375 | £500 |
| **E3d(i)** | Missing digits—single ........................................ | £45 | £70 | £90 |
| **E3d(ii)** | Missing digits—multiple ....................................from £60 | £100 | £140 |
| **E3f(ii)** | Different numbers—one different serial number .............. | £40 | £65 | £100 |
| **E3f(iii)** | Different numbers—two or more different serial numbersfrom £60 | £100 | £140 |

*E2i(j)(i)*

| **E3i(j)(i)** | Double number—second (different) number over first serial number ....................................................................... | £85 | £140 | £250 |
|---|---|---|---|---|

|  |  | VF | EF | UNC |
|---|---|---|---|---|
| E4a(i)* | Design misplaced – vertically (minor) ...................... from £45 | £70 | £90 |  |
| E4a(i)** | Design misplaced – vertically (major) ................................ | £180 | £300 | £450 |
| E4a(ii)* | Design misplaced – horizontally (minor) ........................ from £45 | £75 | £100 |  |
| E4a(ii)** | Designmisplaced – horizontally (major) ............................. | £200 | £375 | £500 |
| E5a(i)* | Folds with extra paper (minor) ........................... from £40 | £65 | £100 |  |
| E5a(i)** | Folds with extra paper (major) ........................................ | £100 | £180 | £250 |
| E5a(ii) | Folds with extra paper and colour bars............................. | £130 | £240 | £325 |
| E5a(iii) | Folds with extra paper with part of adjoining note...........from £110 | £200 | £275 |  |
| E5b(i) | Crease within the sheet—single........................................ | £40 | £65 | £100 |
| E5b(ii) | Crease within the sheet—multiple .................................. | £85 | £140 | £225 |

# SERIES "F" HISTORICAL ISSUE
## (April 1992)
*Orange and multicoloured. With windowed security thread. 142x75mm.*
*Reverse depicting Charles Dickens*
*Signature: G .E. A. Kentfield*

*Prefix sequence: Letter/Number/Number*

BE166a

| BE166a | Prefix A01 followed by serial number ................................. | £14 | £25 | £45 |
|---|---|---|---|---|
| BE166b | Prefix A- - to E- -, H- - to L- -, N- -, R- - to X- - ..................... | FV | £15 | £28 |
| BE166c | Prefix X40(*last official run serial numbers from circulation below 998500*)...................... | £90 | £160 | — |
| BE166d | Prefix X40 (*serial numbers998500 to 999999 from packs*)........ | — | — | £85 |
| BE166e | Prefix Y- - (*extra run using unenhanced design traced from Y41 to Y96*) ...................... | £30 | £55 | £100 |
| BE167a | Prefix M01 Replacement note ............................................. | £35 | £65 | £125 |
| BE167b | Prefix M- - Replacement note ............................................. | £20 | £45 | £80 |
| BE167c | Prefix M40 Replacement note ............................................. | £40 | £75 | £140 |
| BE167d | Prefix Z90 Experimental note.............................................. | £30 | £55 | £100 |

## (October 1993)
*Orange and multicoloured but with enhanced and additional value tablets. 142x75mm.*
*Signature: G .E. A. Kentfield*

*Prefix sequence: Letter/Letter/Number/Number*

*BE168a*

| | | VF | EF | UNC |
|---|---|---|---|---|
| **BE168a** | Prefix AA00 followed by 000000 serial number (*Registration note issued in error*) | £350 | £650 | £1000 |
| **BE168b** | Prefix DA01 followed by serial number | £75 | £140 | £250 |
| **BE168c** | Prefix DA- - to DE- -, DH- - to DL- -, EA- - to EK- -, HA- - to HE- -, HH- - to HK- -, JA- - to JE- -, JH- - to JK- -, KA- - to KE- -, KH- - to KK- -… | FV | £12 | £25 |
| **BE168d** | Prefix KK80 (*last official run*) | £130 | £250 | — |
| **BE168e** | Prefix KK99 (*special last run for collectors' packs*) | — | — | £55 |
| **BE169a** | Prefix DL- - Column sort note (*traced from DL81-DL96*) | £14 | £30 | £70 |
| **BE169b** | Prefix EL- - Column sort note (*traced from EL01-EL40*) | FV | £20 | £40 |
| **BE169c** | Prefix LL- -Replacement note (*traced to LL40 and overlaps with Lowther BE171b below*) | £40 | £70 | £125 |

## (January 1999)
*Orange and multicoloured. 142x75mm.*
*Signature: Merlyn Lowther*

*Prefix sequence: Letter/Letter/Number/Number*

| | | | | |
|---|---|---|---|---|
| **BE170a** | Prefix KL01 followed by serial number | £14 | £25 | £45 |
| **BE170b** | Prefix KL- - and LA- - | FV | £14 | £25 |

*BE170c*

| | | VF | EF | UNC |
|---|---|---|---|---|
| **BE170c** | Prefix LA80 (*last prefix of Historical Series "E" £10 serial numbers below 999000 from circulation*) ................................. | £100 | £180 | — |
| **BE170d** | Prefix LA80 (*serial numbers 999000 to 999999 from packs*).... | — | — | £50 |
| **BE171a** | Prefix EL- - Column sort note (*traced to EL40*) ..................... | FV | £20 | £45 |
| **BE171b** | Prefix LL- -Replacement note (*traced to LL40 and overlaps with Kentfield BE169c above*) ..................................................... | £45 | £85 | £150 |

## SERIES "E" HISTORICAL £10 ERRORS

| | | | | |
|---|---|---|---|---|
| **E1b(i)** | Securitythread—completely exposed ................................... | £40 | £75 | £100 |
| **E1b(i)** | Securitythread—partly exposed ......................................... | £35 | £60 | £80 |
| **E2b(iii)\*** | Missing colours—dry print (minor) on front or back.........from £25 | £45 | £65 |
| **E2b(iii)\*\*** | Missing colours—dry print (major) on front or back. ........ | £75 | £120 | £175 |

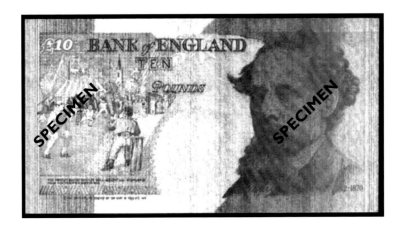

*E2c(iv)*

| | | | | |
|---|---|---|---|---|
| **E2c(iv)** | Excess brown (major) with Dickens blotted out on back... | £140 | £225 | £300 |
| **E2c(v)** | Wrong colour—all brown including Dickens in green on back | £140 | £225 | £300 |
| **E2d(i)*** | Offset—front on back (minor)............................... from £40 | £60 | £80 |
| **E2d(i)\*\*** | Offset—front on back (major) ............................................... | £90 | £150 | £200 |
| **E3a** | No number, sometimes with number entered in pencil or ink | £100 | £185 | £250 |
| **E3f(ii)** | Different numbers—one different serial number............... | £35 | £60 | £85 |
| **E3f(iii)** | Different numbers—two or more different serial numbers from £50 | £90 | £120 |
| **E4a(i)\*** | Design misplaced—vertically (minor)................................from £25 | £40 | £60 |

*E4a(i)\*\**

|                | | *VF* | *EF* | *UNC* |
|----------------|--------------------------------------------------------------|------|------|------|
| **E4a(i)\*\*** | Design misplaced – vertically (major) | £100 | £175 | £250 |
| **E4a(ii)\*** | Design misplaced – horizontally (minor) | from £35 | £55 | £80 |
| **E4a(ii)\*\*** | Designmisplaced – horizontally (major) | £150 | £240 | £325 |
| **E5a(i)\*** | Folds with extra paper (minor) | from £40 | £60 | £75 |
| **E5a(i)\*\*** | Folds with extra paper (major) | £70 | £120 | £160 |
| **E5a(ii)** | Folds with extra paper and colour bars | £90 | £150 | £200 |
| **E5a(iii)\*** | Folds with extra paper with part of adjoining note (minor) | from £40 | £75 | £100 |
| **E5a(iii)\*\*** | Folds with extra paper with two Queens or two Britannias (over 30% of adjoining note, major) | £250 | £450 | £600 |

# SERIES "E" NEW HISTORICAL ISSUE
## (November 2000)

*Orange and multicoloured.142x75mm.*
*Reverse depicting Charles Darwin*
*© 2000 wording incorrectly reads "The Governor and the Company of the Bank of England"*
*Signature: Merlyn Lowther*

*Prefix sequence: Letter/Letter/Number/Number*

BE172a

| | | VF | EF | UNC |
|---|---|---|---|---|
| **BE172a** | Prefix AA01 followed by serial number ............................... | FV | £18 | £35 |
| **BE172b** | Prefix AA- - to AE- -, AH- - (*AD- - overlaps with BE174b below*) | FV | £14 | £22 |
| **BE172c** | Prefix AH80.................................................................. | £100 | £180 | — |
| **BE173a** | Prefix EL- - Column sort note (*traced to EL40 and overlaps with BE175a below*) ............................................................. | FV | £18 | £30 |
| **BE173b** | Prefix LL- - Replacement note (*traced to LL40 and overlaps with BE175b below*) ................................................................. | £35 | £60 | £100 |

## (2000–date unknown)

*Orange and multicoloured.142x75mm.*
*© 2000 wording correctly reads "The Governor and Company of the Bank of England"*
*Signature: Merlyn Lowther*

*Prefix sequence: Letter/Letter/Number/Number*

*Copyright 2000 wording on front and back reads, "The Governor and the Company…"*

*Copyright 2000 wording on front and back reads, "The Governor and Company…"*

|  | | VF | EF | UNC |
|---|---|---|---|---|
| **BE174a** | Prefix AA01 (*special run for collectors' packs*) ........................ | — | — | £50 |
| **BE174b** | Prefix AD- - (*traced to AD40 and overlaps with AD- - BE172b above*) ........................................................................ | £20 | £40 | £85 |
| **BE174c** | Prefix AJ01 (*first official run*).................................................. | £45 | £80 | £150 |
| **BE174d** | Prefix AJ- -, AK- -, BA- - to BE- -, BH- - to BL- -, CA- - to CC- | FV | FV | £18 |

BE174e

| **BE174e** | Prefix CC40 ................................................................ | £85 | £160 | — |
|---|---|---|---|---|
| **BE175a** | Prefix EL- - Column sort note (*traced from EL01-EL80 and overlaps with BE173a above and Bailey BE178a below*)........... | FV | £14 | £24 |
| **BE175b** | Prefix LL- -Replacement note (*traced to LL40 and overlaps with BE173b above and Bailey BE178b below*)......................... | FV | £18 | £35 |

BE176

| | | VF | EF | UNC |
|---|---|---|---|---|
| **BE176** | Prefix MH- -, MJ- -, MK- -, MM- - Experimental note ........ | £90 | £165 | £300 |

## (January 2004)
*Orange and multicoloured.142x75mm.*
*Signature: A. Bailey*

*Prefix sequence: Letter/Letter/Number/Number*

BE177a

| | | | | |
|---|---|---|---|---|
| **BE177a** | Prefix CC41 ................................................................. | £45 | £85 | £150 |
| **BE177b** | Prefix CC- - to CE- -, CH- - to CK- -, DA- - to DE- -, DH- - to DK- -, EA- - (*continuing*) ........................................... | FV | FV | £16 |
| **BE178a** | Prefix EL- - Column sort note (*traced from EL41-EL80 and overlaps with BE175a above*)..................................... | FV | £12 | £22 |
| **BE178b** | Prefix LL- -Replacement note (*traced from LL01-LL40 and overlaps with BE175b above*)..................................... | FV | £14 | £25 |

**BE179– BE199** [*Held in reserve*]

# TWENTY POUNDS

## BLACK AND WHITE SERIES (continued) (1925-29)

| | F | VF | EF |
|---|---|---|---|
| **BE200** *Signature: C. P. Mahon* | | | |
| London ....................................................................... | £750 | £1350 | £2400 |

## (1929-34)

BE201

| | F | VF | EF |
|---|---|---|---|
| **BE201** *Signature: B. G. Catterns* | | | |
| London ..................................................................... | £600 | £1100 | £2000 |

## (1934-42)

| | F | VF | EF |
|---|---|---|---|
| **BE202** *Signature: K. O. Peppiatt* | | | |
| London ..................................................................... | £450 | £750 | £1350 |

*NB. There are deceptive German World War II forgeries of the White £20 note, almost all of these being forgeries of BE201 and BE202.*

# SERIES "D" PICTORIAL ISSUE
## (July 1970)
*Purple and multicoloured. 160 x 90mm.*
*Reverse depicting William Shakespeare*
*Signature: J .S. Fforde*

*Prefix sequence: Letter/Number/Number*

BE203a

|  |  | VF | EF | UNC |
|---|---|---|---|---|
| **BE203a** | Prefix A01 followed by serial number ................................ | £100 | £180 | £350 |
| **BE203b** | Prefix A- - . .................................................................. | £60 | £125 | £240 |
| **BE203c** | Prefix A05 ...................................................................... | £125 | £240 | £450 |

BE204

| **BE204** | Prefix M01 Replacement note .................................... | £120 | £225 | £425 |
|---|---|---|---|---|

## (1970–date unknown)

*Purple and multicoloured. 160 x 90mm.*
*Signature: J .B. Page*
*Prefix sequence: Letter/Number/Number*

*BE205a*

| | | VF | EF | UNC |
|---|---|---|---|---|
| **BE205a** | Prefix A06 followed by serial number ................................. | £140 | £265 | £500 |
| **BE205b** | Prefix A- - ................................................................ | £28 | £50 | £90 |
| **BE205c** | Prefix B- -(*not seen*)................................................. | — | — | — |
| **BE205d** | Prefix C- - ................................................................ | £25 | £45 | £80 |
| **BE205e** | Prefix D- - (*traced to D80*) ......................................... | £30 | £55 | £95 |

*BE206a*

| | | | | |
|---|---|---|---|---|
| **BE206a** | Prefix M01 Replacement note ............................................... | £140 | £265 | £475 |
| **BE206b** | Prefix M- - Replacement note............................................. | £65 | £125 | £225 |
| **BE206c** | Prefix M04 Replacement note ............................................... | £145 | £275 | £500 |

## (March 1981)

*Purple and multicoloured. 160 x 90mm.*
*Signature: D .H. F. Somerset*
*Prefix sequence: Letter/Number/Number*

| | | | | |
|---|---|---|---|---|
| **BE207a** | Prefix E01 followed by serial number ................................. | £225 | £400 | £650 |
| **BE207b** | Prefix E- - ................................................................. | £45 | £85 | £150 |
| **BE207c** | Prefix H- -.................................................................. | £30 | £55 | £100 |
| **BE207d** | Prefix J- -................................................................... | £40 | £70 | £125 |
| **BE207e** | Prefix J40.................................................................... | £260 | £480 | — |

## (November 1984)

*Purple and multicoloured with enhanced green and brown colouring*
*and windowed security thread. Watermark is changed from H.M.*
*Queen Elizabeth II to Shakespeare. 160 x 90mm.*
*Signature: D .H. F. Somerset*

*Prefix sequence: Number/Number/Letter*

BE208a

|  |  | VF | EF | UNC |
|---|---|---|---|---|
| **BE208a** | Prefix 01A followed by serial number .................................. | £50 | £95 | £185 |
| **BE208b** | Prefix - -A ................................................................................ | £28 | £50 | £90 |
| **BE208c** | Prefix - -B to - -J ................................................................... | £25 | £45 | £80 |
| **BE208d** | Prefix - -K(*traced to 40K*) ......................................................... | £30 | £55 | £110 |

## (March 1988)

*Purple and multicoloured. 160 x 90mm.*
*Signature: G. M. Gill*

*Prefix sequence: Number/Number/Letter*

| **BE209a** | Prefix 01L followed by serial number .................................. | £45 | £85 | £160 |
|---|---|---|---|---|
| **BE209b** | Prefix - -L ................................................................................. | £28 | £50 | £85 |
| **BE209c** | Prefix - -M to - -W ................................................................ | £24 | £40 | £75 |
| **BE209d** | Prefix - -X................................................................................ | £30 | £55 | £95 |

BE209e

|  | | VF | EF | UNC |
|---|---|---|---|---|
| **BE209e** | Prefix 20X (*last prefix of Pictorial Series "D" £20 serial numbers below 998500 from circulation*) ................................................. | £110 | £200 | — |
| **BE209f** | Prefix 20X (*serialnumbers 998500 to 999999 from packs*).......... | — | — | £180 |

## SERIES "D" PICTORIAL £20 ERRORS

*N.B. Errors on the first issues of the £20 note are much scarcer than those on the later notes with modified colours and are likely to attract a premium.*

E2b(i)

| | | | | |
|---|---|---|---|---|
| **E2b(i)** | Missing St George & dragon and underprint on front and Romeo & Juliet and underprint on back ............................. | £180 | £300 | £450 |

*E2b(ii)*

| | | VF | EF | UNC |
|---|---|---|---|---|
| **E2b(ii)** | Missing Shakespeare—no main purple on back | £140 | £220 | £300 |
| **E2c(iii)\*** | Extra colour—blobs & blots (minor) | from£50 | £85 | £120 |
| **E2c(iii)\*\*** | Extra colour—blobs & blots (major) | £100 | £160 | £250 |
| **E2c(iv)** | Extra colour—excess purple on front (major) | £100 | £160 | £250 |
| **E2d(i)** | Offset—front on back (major) | £80 | £140 | £225 |

*E2d(ii)*

| | | | | |
|---|---|---|---|---|
| **E2d(ii)** | Offset – back on front (major) | £100 | £180 | £275 |
| **E3d(i)** | Missing digits—single | £50 | £80 | £120 |
| **E3d(ii)** | Missing digits—multiple | from£60 | £125 | £200 |
| **E3f(ii)** | Different numbers—one different serial number | £50 | £80 | £110 |
| **E3f(iii)** | Different numbers—two or more different serial numbers | from£75 | £120 | £175 |
| **E4a(i)\*** | Design misplaced—vertically (minor) | from£50 | £80 | £110 |
| **E4a(i)\*\*** | Design misplaced—vertically (major) | £150 | £250 | £350 |
| **E4a(ii)\*** | Design misplaced—horizontally (minor) | from£50 | £85 | £125 |
| **E4a(ii)\*\*** | Designmisplaced—horizontally (major) | £160 | £275 | £400 |
| **E5a(i)\*** | Folds with extra paper (minor) | from£60 | £90 | £125 |
| **E5a(i)\*\*** | Folds with extra paper (major) | £100 | £180 | £275 |
| **E5a(ii)** | Folds with extra paper and colour bars | £150 | £250 | £350 |
| **E5a(iii)** | Folds with extra paper with part of adjoining note | from£120 | £225 | £300 |
| **E5b(i)** | Crease within the sheet—single narrow | £60 | £90 | £125 |

*E5b(ii)*

|  | | VF | EF | UNC |
|---|---|---|---|---|
| **E5b(ii)** | Crease within the sheet—single wide or multiple..............from | £100 | £180 | £275 |

# SERIES "E" HISTORICAL ISSUE
## (June 1991)
*Purple and multicoloured. With windowed security thread. 149x 80mm.*
*Reverse depicting Michael Faraday*
*Signature: G. M. Gill*

*Prefix sequence: Letter/Number/Number*

*BE210a*

| | | | | |
|---|---|---|---|---|
| **BE210a** | Prefix A01 followed by serial number ................................ | £24 | £40 | £75 |
| **BE210b** | Prefix A- - to D- -.................................................................... | FV | £30 | £55 |
| **BE210c** | Prefix D70 (last official run).................................................. | £90 | £175 | — |

BE210d

| | | VF | EF | UNC |
|---|---|---|---|---|
| **BE210d** | Prefix E- -, H- -, J- -, L- -, R- -, S- -, U- - (*overlaps with Kentfield BE212a, b below*) ......................................................... | £35 | £60 | £110 |
| **BE210e** | Prefix U19......................................................................... | £110 | £200 | — |
| **BE210f** | Prefix Z13 Experimental note............................................ | — | — | — |
| **BE211** | Prefix A- - to C- - Column sort note (*with control numbers above 70. Overlaps with Kentfield BE213a, b below*)................. | £25 | £45 | £85 |

## (November 1991)

*Purple and multicoloured.149x 80mm.*
*Signature: G .E. A. Kentfield*

*Prefix sequence: Letter/Number/Number*

BE212a

| | | | | |
|---|---|---|---|---|
| **BE212a** | Prefix E01 followed by serial number ................................. | £45 | £85 | £165 |
| **BE212b** | Prefix E- -, H- - to L- -, N- -, R- - to U- -, W- - (*overlaps with Gill BE210d above*)....................................................... | FV | £32 | £60 |
| **BE212c** | Prefix W35 (*last official run with serial numbers below 998500 from circulation*)..................................................................... | £80 | £150 | £275 |
| **BE212d** | Prefix W35 (*with serial numbers 998500 to 999999 from packs*) | — | — | £150 |
| **BE213a** | Prefix A- - Column sort note (*with control numbers above 70. Overlaps with Gill BE211 above*) ............................................... | £35 | £60 | £125 |
| **BE213b** | Prefix B- - and C- - Column sort note (*with control numbers above 70. Overlaps with Gill BE211 above*) ............................... | £40 | £70 | £140 |
| **BE214a** | Prefix M- - Replacement note (*traced from M01 to M31*) ..... | £45 | £85 | £150 |

| | | VF | EF | UNC |
|---|---|---|---|---|
| **BE214b** | Prefix Z- - Experimental note (*traced to Z35*)...................... | £45 | £85 | £150 |
| **BE214c** | Prefix Z90 Experimental note ............................................. | £60 | £110 | £200 |

## (September 1993)
Purple and multicoloured. With enhanced and additional value tablets.149x 80mm.
*Signature: G .E. A. Kentfield*

*Prefix sequence: Letter/Number/Number*

BE215a

| | | | | |
|---|---|---|---|---|
| **BE215a** | Prefix X01 followed by serial number.................................. | £30 | £55 | £100 |
| **BE215b** | Prefix X- - and Y- - (*traced to Y70*)................................... | FV | £40 | £70 |
| **BE216** | Prefix X- - and Y- - Column sort note (*with control numbers above 70*) ....................................................................... | £50 | £95 | £175 |

## (1994 – date unknown)
*Purple and multicoloured. 149x 80mm.*
*Signature: G .E. A. Kentfield*

*Prefix sequence: Letter/Letter/Number/Number*

BE217a

| | | | | |
|---|---|---|---|---|
| **BE217a** | Prefix AA01 followed by serial number ............................... | £70 | £135 | £250 |

|  | | *VF* | *EF* | *UNC* |
|---|---|---|---|---|
| **BE217b** | Prefix AA- - ............................................................. | FV | £32 | £60 |
| **BE217c** | Prefix AB- - to CJ- - .............................................. | FV | £25 | £45 |
| **BE217d** | Prefix CJ80 (*last official run*)................................. | £145 | £275 | — |
| **BE217e** | Prefix CJ99 (*special last run for collectors' packs*) ................... | — | — | £70 |
| **BE218a** | Prefix CL- - Column sort note ............................... | £35 | £60 | £125 |

*BE218b*

| **BE218b** | Prefix LL01 Replacement note ................................ | £55 | £100 | £185 |
|---|---|---|---|---|
| **BE218c** | Prefix LL- - Replacement note (*traced to LL40*) ................... | £40 | £70 | £130 |

## (January 1999)
*Purple and multicoloured. 149x 80mm.*
*Signature: Merlyn Lowther*

*Prefix sequence: Letter/Letter/Number/Number*

| **BE219a** | Prefix DA01 followed by serial number ............................. | £30 | £55 | £100 |
|---|---|---|---|---|
| **BE219b** | Prefix DA- - ........................................................... | FV | £40 | £75 |

*BE219c*

| **BE219c** | Prefix DA80 (*last prefix Historical Series "E" £20 with serial numbers below 999000 from circulation*)................................. | £110 | £200 | — |
|---|---|---|---|---|
| **BE219d** | Prefix DA80 ( *serial numbers 999000 to 999999 from packs*).. | — | — | £110 |

# SERIES "E" HISTORICAL £20 ERRORS

| | | VF | EF | UNC |
|---|---|---|---|---|
| **E1a(i)** | Watermark misplaced ............................................ | £75 | £120 | £175 |
| **E1b(i)** | Securitythread—completely exposed ............................... | £60 | £90 | £125 |
| **E1b(ii)** | Securitythread—partly exposed ........................................ | £50 | £70 | £90 |

]

*E2b(ii)*

| | | VF | EF | UNC |
|---|---|---|---|---|
| **E2b(ii)** | Missing portrait of Queen—no main black on front .......... | £85 | £140 | £200 |
| **E2b(iii)\*** | Missing colours—dry print (minor) on front or back.........from £40 | £65 | £90 |
| **E2b(iii)\*\*** | Missing colours—dry print (major) on front or back. ........ | £85 | £140 | £200 |

*E2c(iv)*

| | | VF | EF | UNC |
|---|---|---|---|---|
| **E2c(iv)** | Excess purple and violet (major) on front ............................ | £75 | £125 | £175 |
| **E2d(i)\*** | Offset—front on back (minor)...................................from £50 | £70 | £90 |
| **E2d(i)\*\*** | Offset—front on back (major) ........................................ | £100 | £160 | £200 |
| **E3b** | One number of two................................................................ | £75 | £125 | £175 |
| **E3f(ii)** | Different numbers— one different serial number............... | £45 | £75 | £100 |
| **E3f(iii)** | Different numbers—two or more different serial numbers. from £65 | £110 | £140 |
| **E3i(ii)** | Double number—second different number on both serial numbers........................................................................ | £125 | £200 | £275 |
| **E4a(i)\*** | Design misplaced—vertically (minor)...............................from £35 | £60 | £85 |
| **E4a(i)\*\*** | Design misplaced—vertically (major) ................................ | £100 | £175 | £225 |
| **E4a(ii)\*** | Design misplaced— horizontally (minor)...........................from £40 | £65 | £90 |
| **E4a(ii)\*\*** | Design misplaced—horizontally (major) ............................ | £125 | £200 | £275 |
| **E5a(i)\*** | Folds with extra paper (minor)..............................................from £35 | £60 | £85 |
| **E5a(i)\*\*** | Folds with extra paper (major) ........................................ | £75 | £120 | £160 |

*E5a(ii)*

| | VF | EF | UNC |
|---|---|---|---|
| **E5a(ii)** Folds with extra paper and colour bars............................. | £100 | £175 | £225 |
| **E5a(iii)*** Folds with extra paper with part of adjoining note (minor).................................................................from £40 | | £100 | £140 |

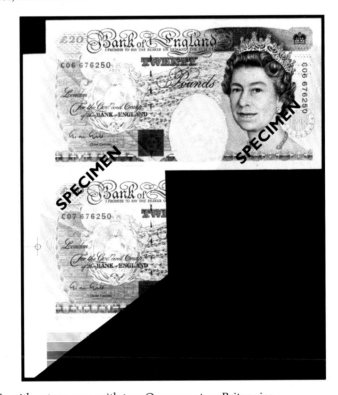

*E5a(iii)*

**E5a(iii)**** Folds with extra paper with two Queens or two Britannias (over 30% of adjoining note, major)....................£225 £375 £500

# SERIES "E" NEW HISTORICAL ISSUE
## (June 1999)
*Purple and multicoloured.149x80mm.*
*Reverse depicting Sir Edward Elgar*
*Signature: Merlyn Lowther*

*Prefix sequence: Letter/Letter/Number/Number*

BE220a

| | | VF | EF | UNC |
|---|---|---|---|---|
| **BE220a** | Prefix AA01 followed by serial number ............................ | FV | £30 | £55 |
| **BE220b** | Prefix AA- - ................................................................... | FV | FV | £35 |
| **BE220c** | Prefix AB- - to AE- -, AH- - to AK- -, BA- - to BE- -, BH- - to | | | |
| | BK- -, CA- - to CE- -, CH- -, CJ- -, DB- - to DD- - ............... | FV | FV | £30 |
| **BE220d** | Prefix DE- - (*overlaps with Bailey BE222a, b below*)............... | FV | FV | £35 |
| **BE220e** | Prefix DE80 (*overlaps with Bailey BE222b below*). ................. | £45 | £85 | £160 |

BE220e

| | | | | |
|---|---|---|---|---|
| **BE221a** | Prefix AL- - Column sort note (*traced to AL40*) ................... | FV | £25 | £40 |
| **BE221b** | Prefix BL- - Column sort note (*traced to BL80 and overlaps with* | | | |
| | *Bailey BE223a below*) ................................................................. | FV | £25 | £40 |
| **BE221c** | Prefix LL- - Replacement note (*overlaps with Bailey* | | | |
| | *BE223b below*) .......................................................................... | FV | £35 | £60 |

## (January 2004)
*Purple and multicoloured.149x 80mm.*
*Signature: A. Bailey*

*Prefix sequence: Letter/Letter/Number/Number*

*BE222a*

| | | VF | EF | UNC |
|---|---|---|---|---|
| **BE222a** | Prefix DE41 followed by serial number .............................. | £45 | £85 | £150 |
| **BE222b** | Prefix DE- - (*overlaps with Lowther BE220d above*) ............... | FV | FV | £35 |
| **BE222c** | Prefix DH- - to DK- -, EA- - to EE- - (*continuing*)................. | FV | FV | £28 |
| **BE223a** | Prefix BL- - Column sort note (*traced from BL01-BL40 overlaps with Lowther BE221b above*)...................................... | FV | FV | £35 |
| **BE223b** | Prefix LL- - Replacement note (*traced from LL01-LL40 and overlaps with Lowther BE221c above*) ....................................... | FV | £25 | £40 |

# SERIES "F" THIRD HISTORICAL ISSUE
## (March 2007)
*Purple and multicoloured.149x80mm.*
*Reverse depicting Adam Smith, Scottish economist*
*Signature: A. Bailey*

*Prefix sequence: Letter/Letter/Number/Number*

*BE224*

| | | | | |
|---|---|---|---|---|
| **BE224** | Prefix followed by serial number .......................................... | — | — | — |

**BE225–BE249** [*Held in reserve*]

# FIFTY POUNDS

## BLACK AND WHITE SERIES (continued)

|  | | F | VF | EF |
|---|---|---|---|---|
| **(1925-29)** | | | | |

**BE250**  *Signature: C. P. Mahon*
London ..................................................................... £700 £1250 £2200

**(1929-34)**

BE251

**BE251**  *Signature: B. G. Catterns*
London ..................................................................... £550 £950 £1600

**(1934-42)**

BE252

**BE252**  *Signature: K. O. Peppiatt*
London ..................................................................... £375 £600 £1100

*NB. There are deceptive German World War II forgeries of the White £50 note, almost all of these being forgeries of BE251 and BE252.*

# SERIES "D" PICTORIAL ISSUE
## (March 1981)
*Deep green and multicoloured. 169 x 95mm.*
*Reverse depicting Sir Christopher Wren*
*Signature: D. H. F. Somerset*

*Prefix sequence: Letter/Number/Number*

BE253a

| | | VF | EF | UNC |
|---|---|---|---|---|
| **BE253a** | Prefix A01 followed by serial number | £60 | £100 | £185 |
| **BE253b** | Prefix A- -, B- - . | FV | £70 | £125 |
| **BE253c** | Prefix B90 | £70 | £135 | £260 |

## (July 1988)

*Deep green and multicoloured with enhanced olive green colouring and windowed security thread. 169 x 95mm.*
*Signature: G. M. Gill*

*Prefix sequence: Letter/Number/Number*

BE254a

|  |  | VF | EF | UNC |
|---|---|---|---|---|
| **BE254a** | Prefix C01 followed by serial number ................................. | £100 | £185 | £350 |
| **BE254b** | Prefix C- -, D- - .................................................................. | FV | £95 | £140 |
| **BE254c** | Prefix D90 (*last official run*) ....................................... | £75 | £140 | £260 |
| **BE254d** | Prefix E- - (*overlaps with Kentfield BE256a, b below*) ............. | £65 | £120 | £235 |

BE254e

|  |  |  |  |  |
|---|---|---|---|---|
| **BE254e** | Prefix E30 (*overlaps with Kentfield BE256c below*) ................. | £90 | £165 | £300 |
| **BE255** | Prefix D- - Column sort note (*with control numbers above 90*) | £65 | £120 | £225 |

# (November 1991)

*Deep green and multicoloured. 169 x 95mm.*
*Signature: G. E. A. Kentfield*

*Prefix sequence: Letter/Number/Number*

BE256a

|  | | VF | EF | UNC |
|---|---|---|---|---|
| **BE256a** | Prefix E01 followed by serial number ................................. | £60 | £100 | £195 |
| **BE256b** | Prefix E- - (*overlaps with Gill BE254d, e above*)...................... | FV | £80 | £135 |
| **BE256c** | Prefix E30 (*last prefix of Pictorial Series "D" £50 serial numbers from circulation below 998500 with the exception of 722501 to 723000*) .............................................................. | £175 | £300 | — |
| **BE256d** | Prefix E30 (*last prefix of Pictorial Series "D" £50 (serial numbers 722501 to 723000 and 998500 to 999999 from packs*) ............ | — | — | £175 |

# SERIES "D" PICTORIAL £50 ERRORS

**N.B.** *All Series "D" £50 errors are very scarce*

*E2b(i)*

|  | VF | EF | UNC |
|---|---|---|---|

**E2b(i)**    Missing phoenix and underprint on front and St. Paul's
Cathedral and underprint on back....................................... £300    £500    £650

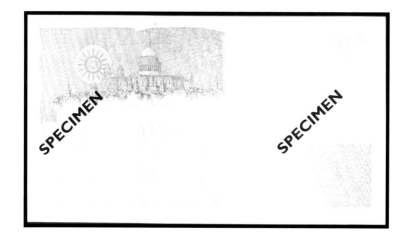

*E2b(ii)*

**E2b(ii)**    Missing Wren, plan of Cathedral and view of old London—no
main green and brown on back ............................................ £200    £375    £500
**E2c(iii)\*** Extra colour—blobs & blots (minor) .................................... from £90    £130    £160
**E2c(iii)\*\*** Extra colour—blobs & blots (major) .................................... £140    £275    £375

*E2d(i)*

|  |  | VF | EF | UNC |
|---|---|---|---|---|
| **E2d(i)** | Offset—front on back (major) ........................................... | £175 | £325 | £450 |
| **E3g** | Identical numbers on a pair of notes................................. | £500 | £800 | £1000 |
| **E4a(i)\*** | Design misplaced—vertically (minor)............................. | from £100 | £180 | £225 |
| **E4a(ii)\*** | Design misplaced—horizontally (minor)........................ | from £120 | £190 | £250 |
| **E5a(i)\*** | Folds with extra paper (minor)........................................ | from £100 | £180 | £225 |
| **E5a(i)\*\*** | Folds with extra paper (major) ......................................... | £175 | £300 | £400 |

*E5a(ii)\*\**

| | | | | |
|---|---|---|---|---|
| **E5a(ii)** | Folds with extra paper and colour bars................................ | £225 | £375 | £500 |

# SERIES "E" HISTORICAL ISSUE
## (April 1994)
*Red and multicoloured. 156x 85mm.*
*Reverse depicting Sir John Houblon*
*Signature: G. E. A. Kentfield*

*Prefix sequence: Letter/Number/Number*

*BE257a*

|  | *VF* | *EF* | *UNC* |
|---|---|---|---|
| **BE257a** Prefix A01 followed by serial number ................................. | £60 | £95 | £150 |
| **BE257b** Prefix A- - to E- -, H- - ............................................................ | FV | £60 | £95 |
| **BE257c** Prefix H70 *(last run from circulation)* ..................................... | £120 | £200 | — |
| **BE257d** Prefix H99 *(special last run for collectors' packs)* .................... | — | — | £130 |
| **BE258a** Prefix A- -, B- -, H- - Column sort note *(with control numbers above 70)*.............................................................. | FV | £80 | £130 |

*BE258b*

**BE258b** Prefix L- - Column sort note *(traced to L35 and overlaps with Lowther BE 261 below)* ......................................... | FV | £80 | £135

| | VF | EF | UNC |
|---|---|---|---|
| **BE258c** Prefix LL- - Replacement note *(traced to LL35)*..................... | £65 | £110 | £200 |
| **BE259a** Prefix A99 Experimental note ................................................. | FV | £75 | £140 |
| **BE259b** Prefix M- - Experimental note *(traced in M01 and M97 to M99)* | £110 | £200 | £375 |

## (January 1999)
*Red and multicoloured. 156x 85mm.*
*Signature: Merlyn Lowther*

*Prefix sequence: Letter/Number/Number*

BE260a

| | VF | EF | UNC |
|---|---|---|---|
| **BE260a** Prefix J01 followed by serial number ................................... | £55 | £95 | £150 |
| **BE260b** Prefix K- - , M- -....................................................................... | FV | FV | £90 |
| **BE260c** Prefix M35 ................................................................................. | £60 | £95 | £175 |
| **BE261** Prefix L- - Column sort note *(traced from L01 to L35 and* | | | |
| *overlaps with Kentfield BE258b above)* ...................................... | FV | £80 | £120 |

## (2006 Date unknown)
*Red and multicoloured. 156x 85mm.*
*Signature: Andrew Bailey*

*Prefix sequence: Letter/Number/Number*

| | VF | EF | UNC |
|---|---|---|---|
| **BE262a** Prefix M- - followed by serial number *(traced from M01-M70* | | | |
| *And overlaps with Lowther BE260b above)* ............................. | FV | FV | £85 |
| **BE263** Prefix L- - Column sort note *(traced from L36-L70)* .............. | FV | FV | £95 |

**BE264– BE274** [*Held in reserve*]

# SERIES "E" HISTORICAL £50 ERRORS

**N.B.** *All Series "E" £50 errors are very scarce*

|  |  | VF | EF | UNC |
|---|---|---|---|---|
| **E1b(iv)** | Missing silver rose on front................................................. | £100 | £150 | £200 |
| **E2b(iii)*** | Missing colours—dry print (minor) on front or back.........from £75 | £100 | £125 |

*E2b(iii)\*\**

| **E2b(iii)\*\*** | Missing colours—dry print (major) on front or back.........from £100 | £160 | £225 |
|---|---|---|---|
| **E4a(i)*** | Design misplaced—vertically (minor) ................................. from £80 | £120 | £160 |
| **E4a(ii)*** | Design misplaced—horizontally (minor) ........................... from £90 | £130 | £175 |
| **E5a(i)*** | Folds with extra paper (minor).............................................from £100 | £180 | £225 |
| **E5a(i)\*\*** | Folds with extra paper (major) ............................................ £175 | £300 | £400 |

*E5a(ii)*

| **E5a(ii)** | Folds with extra paper and colour bars............................... £225 | £375 | £500 |
|---|---|---|---|

# ONE HUNDRED POUNDS

## BLACK AND WHITE SERIES (continued)

|  | F | VF | EF |
|---|---|---|---|

### (1925-29)
**BE275** *Signature: C. P. Mahon*

| London | £1100 | £2000 | £3500 |
|---|---|---|---|

### (1929-34)
**BE276** *Signature: B. G. Catterns*

| London | £700 | £1350 | £2400 |
|---|---|---|---|

### (1934-42)
**BE277a** *Signature: K. O. Peppiatt*

| London | £525 | £900 | £1600 |
|---|---|---|---|

*BE277b*

| **BE277b** Liverpool | £500 | £850 | £1500 |
|---|---|---|---|

*In addition to the notes listed there is also a series including £200, £500 and £1,000 white notes bearing various cashiers' signatures issued up to 1941. However as these are seldom seen on the market, it has been decided to omit them from this publication.*

# Isle of Man

The Isle of Man has a very long history of paper money with the first banknote issues appearing during the latter part of the 18th. Century. Over the next 150 years there were numerous mergers and acquisitions as the fortunes of the different banks rose and fell. By the early part of the 20th century the banknote issues were in the hands of five Commercial Banks—The Isle of Man Bank Limited, Westminster Bank Limited, Martins Bank Limited, Lloyds Bank Limited and Barclays Bank Limited.

In 1961 the Isle of Man Government Notes Act was passed and the note issuing licences of all of the commercial banks were revoked. The first Government note issues, comprising denominations of 10 Shillings, one Pound and five Pounds were put into circulation during July of this same year.

## ISLE OF MAN BANK LIMITED

The Isle of Man Banking Company was established in Douglas in 1865 and subsequently set up branches in the other main towns in the Island. The name was changed to Isle of Man Bank Limited in 1925, and in 1961 the bank merged with the National Provincial Bank. Since 1969 the Isle of Man Bank has been part of the National Westminster Group.

## ONE POUND NOTES

Size 168 mm x 120 mm approximately

*Obverse – black with "ONE" in brown at the centre. Vignette of Douglas bay and harbour at the top*
*Reverse – blue. Triune and Isle of Man motto at the centre*

|  | F | VF |
|---|---|---|
| **IM1** *Signatories: Handsigned by Manager and Assistant Manager* Prefix P dated 9.6.1915 to prefix O/1 dated 1.3.1926.................. |  | Rare |

Size 158 mm x 90 mm approximately

*Obverse – black with "ONE" in pink geometric design at the centre. Vignette of Douglas bay and harbour at the top*
*Reverse – green panel. Triune and Isle of Man motto at the centre*

|  | F | VF |
|---|---|---|

**IM2**    *Signatories: Handsigned by Manager and Assistant Manager*
Prefix O/1 dated 1.5.1926 to prefix L/2 dated 1.3.1926 ............... Rare

Size 150 mm x 84 mm approximately

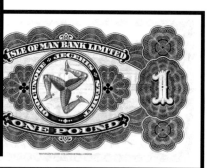

*Obverse – blue on a pale green underprint with brown geometric design at the centre. Vignette of Douglas bay and harbour at the top*
*Reverse – blue on a pale green underprint. Triune and Isle of Man motto at the centre*

**IM3a**    *Signatories: J. R. Quayle (Manager) and J. N. Ronan (Assistant Manager)*
Prefix N/2 dated 1.10.1934 to prefix W/2 dated 5.5.1937 ........... Rare

**IM3b**    *Signatories: J. N. Ronan ( Manager) and C. M. Watterson (Assistant Manager), or*
*J. N. Ronan ( Manager) and Edw. Corteen (per pro Assistant Manager)*
Prefix X/2 dated 4.2.1938 to prefix L/3 dated 16.12.1942 ........... £90    £160

**IM3c**    *Signatories: J. N. Ronan ( Manager) and W. E. Quirk (Assistant Manager)*
Prefix L/3 dated 16.12.1942 to prefix P/3 dated 7.1.1948 ........... £90    £160

**IM3d**    *Signatories: J. N. Ronan ( Manager) and R. H. Kelly (Assistant Manager)*
Prefix P/3 dated 7.1.1948 to prefix B/4 dated 29.11.1954............ £80    £150

**IM3e**    *Signatories: J. N. Ronan ( Manager) and W. E. Quirk (Assistant Manager), or*
*J. N. Ronan ( Manager) and J. E. Cashin (Assistant Manager)*
Prefix B/4 dated 29.11.1954 ............................................................. Rare

**IM3f**    *Signatories: J. E. Cashin (Manager) and W. E. Quirk (Assistant Manager)*
Prefix C/4 dated 5.1.1956 to prefix O/4 dated 24.10.1960 .......... £80    £150

# FIVE POUND NOTES

Size 176 mm x 92 mm approximately

*Obverse – blue on a pale green and pink underprint. Vignette of Douglas bay and harbour at the centre.*
*Reverse – blue on a pale green underprint. Triune and Isle of Man motto at the centre*

| | | F | VF |
|---|---|---|---|
| **IM4** | *Signatories: Handsigned by Manager and Assistant Manager* | | |
| | No prefix letters; dated 1.11.1927 ................................................... | £220 | £380 |

*Obverse – brown on a pale pink and green underprint. Vignette of Douglas bay and harbour at the centre*
*Reverse – brown on a pale pink underprint. Triune and Isle of Man motto at the centre*

| | | | |
|---|---|---|---|
| **IM5** | *Signatories: Handsigned by Manager and Assistant Manager* | | |
| | No prefix letters; dated 1.12.1936 to 7.4.1960.............................. | £280 | £550 |

# WESTMINSTER BANK LIMITED

## ONE POUND NOTES

In 1918 the London County & Westminster Bank merged with Parr's Bank Limited to form the London County Westminster & Parr's Bank Limited. A few years later in 1923, the decision was taken to shorten the name to Westminster Bank Limited.

Size 176 mm x 92 mm approximately

Overprint on banknote stock of Parr's Bank Limited
*Obverse – black on a pale blue underprint. Triune flanked by a lion and unicorn at the top.*
*Overprinted in the top margin; "LONDON COUNTY WESTMINSTER"*
*Reverse –blue panel with the Isle of Man triune and motto at the centre*

| | | F | VF |
|---|---|---|---|
| **IM7** | *Signatories: Handsigned by Manager and Accountant* | | |
| | No prefix letters; dated 28.3.1918 to 22.11.1918 .......................... | | Rare |

From 1919 to 1921 there were issues of £1 notes with a similar design to the earlier Parr's Bank notes but with the new title of London County Westminster & Parr's Bank Limited. Only 5000 notes were printed and none are known to have survived. Following the adoption of the new Bank name in 1923, these notes were issued overprinted "WESTMINSTER BANK LIMITED" in the top margin.

Overprint on banknote stock of London County Westminster & Parr's Bank Limited
*Obverse – black on a pale blue/grey underprint. Triune flanked by a lion and unicorn at the top*
*Overprinted in the top margin; "WESTMINSTER BANK LIMITED - formerly"*
*Reverse –blue panel with the Isle of Man triune and motto at the centre*

**IM9**   Signatories: Handsigned by Manager and Assistant Manager.
No prefix letters; dated 4.7.1923 to 4.4.1927.................................... Rare

Size 176 mm x 92 mm approximate

*Obverse – black on a pale yellow underprint. Triune flanked by a lion and unicorn at the top*
*Reverse –blue panel with the Isle of Man triune and motto at the centre*

|  |  | F | VF |
|---|---|---|---|
| **IM10a** | *Signatories: F. Proud (Manager) and A. O. Christian (Assistant Manager)* | | |
| | No prefix letters; dated 9.1.1929 to 14.11.1933 .............................. | | Rare |
| **IM10b** | *Signatories: A. O. Christian (Manager) and R. E. Callin (Chief Clerk)* | | |
| | No prefix letters; dated 22.1.1935 to 4.2.1943............................... | | from £180 |
| **IM10c** | *Signatories: R. E. Callin (Manager) and W. G. Flinn (Chief Clerk)* | | |
| | No prefix letters; dated 11.2.1944 to 18.3.1949 .............................. | | Rare |
| **IM10d** | *Signatories: R. E. Callin (Manager) and G. D. Radcliffe (Chief Clerk)* | | |
| | No prefix letters; dated 7.11.1950 to 23.11.1955 ............................ | £110 | £200 |
| **IM10e** | *Signatories: P. F. Barlow (Manager) and G. D. Radcliffe (Chief Clerk)* | VF | EF |
| | No prefix letters; dated 4.4.1956 to 3.3.1959.................................. | £150 | £280 |
| **IM10e** | *Signatories: P. F. Barlow (Manager) and T. D. Russell (Chief Clerk)* | | |
| | No prefix letters; dated 8.12.1959 to 10.3.1961.............................. | £150 | £280 |

# MARTINS BANK LIMITED

## ONE POUND NOTES

Martins Bank Limited acquired a foothold in the Isle of Man following a merger with the
Lancashire & Yorkshire Bank Limited in 1928. This latter bank had already absorbed the
Mercantile Bank of Lancashire Limited which previously had purchased the Manx Bank in
1900. Thus the Lancashire and Yorkshire Bank Limited had been issuing banknotes in the Isle
of Man since 1920. The initial banknotes of Martins Bank Limited were overprints on existing
stock of Lancashire & Yorkshire Bank.

Size 165 mm x 85 mm approximately

Overprint on notes of The Lancashire & Yorkshire Bank Limited
*Obverse – black. Bank's Coat of Arms to the left and the Tower of Refuge to the right. Overprinted at*
*the top: "MARTINS BANK LIMITED" in black, and "WITH WHICH IS INCORPORATED" in*
*red.*
*Reverse – black. Isle of Man Triune at the centre with vignettes of Castle Rushen and the Laxey Wheel*
*to the left and right*

|  | *F* | *VF* |
|---|---|---|
| **IM12** *Signatories: Handsigned by the Manager and Assistant Manager* | | |
| No prefix letters; dated 9.10.1928 and 3.11.1928.......................... | | Rare |

Size 150 mm x 84 mm approximately

*Obverse – dark grey. Bank's Coat of Arms depicting a grasshopper and Liver bird to the left, and the Tower of Refuge to the right*
*Reverse – black. Isle of Man Triune at the centre with vignettes of Castle Rushen and the Laxey Wheel to the left and right*

|  |  | F | VF |
|---|---|---|---|
| **IM13a** | *Signatories: R. H. Milner (Manager) and E. S. Oldham (Assistant Manager)* | | |
|  | No prefix letters, dated 2.4.1929      no notes are known to have survived | | |
| **IM13b** | *Signatories: A. F. Shawyer (General Manager) and E. S. Oldham (District Manager)* | | |
|  | No prefix letters, dated 1.12.1931 and 31.12.1932 ...................... | | Rare |
| **IM13c** | *Signatory: J. M. Furniss (General Manager)* | | |
|  | No prefix letters, dated 1.8.1934 and 1.10.1938 ........................... | £110 | £200 |
| **IM13d** | *Signatory: Jas. McKendrick (Chief General Manager)* | | |
|  | No prefix letters, dated 1.3.1946 .................................................. | £120 | £180 |
| **IM13e** | *Signatory: C. J. Verity (Chief General Manager)* | | |
|  | No prefix letters, dated 1.6.1950 and 1.5.1953 ........................... | £90 | £150 |
| **IM13f** | *Signatory: M. Conacher (Chief General Manager)* | VF | EF |
|  | No prefix letters, dated 1.2.1957 .................................................. | £110 | £180 |

# LLOYDS BANK LIMITED

Lloyds Bank Limited opened its first branch in the Isle of Man in Douglas in 1896 and acquired a licence to issue banknotes to a limit of £15,000 in about 1918. The first notes were issued in 1919, but the first known to have survived are dated 1921.

## ONE POUND NOTES

Size 156 mm x 114 mm approximately

*Obverse – black on a green and pale pink underprint. Black horse in panel towards top centre. Vignette of Viking ship at bottom centre*
*Reverse – blue. Isle of Man Triune and motto at centre*

|  | | F | VF |
|---|---|---|---|
| **IM15** | *Signatories: handsigned by the Manager and Accountant* | | |
| | Prefix A dated 23.4.1919 to prefix B dated 21.1.1927 ................. | | Rare |

Size 150 mm x 84 mm approximately

*Obverse – black on a pale green and pink underprint. Black horse in panel with vignette of Viking ship at bottom centre*
*Reverse – blue on a pink sunburst underprint. Isle of Man Triune and motto at centre*

|  |  | F | VF |
|---|---|---|---|
| **IM16a** | *Signatories: H. Towler (Manager) and R. A. Hodder (Accountant)*<br>Prefix C dated 1.8.1929 to 14.2.1934 .............................................. |  | Rare |
| **IM16b** | *Signatories: H. Towler (Manager) and J. Greenwood (Accountant)*<br>Prefix C dated 28.1.1935 to prefix D dated 12.3.1941 ................. | £350 | — |
| **IM16c** | *Signatories: J. Greenwood (Manager) and C. R. Collister (Accountant)*<br>Prefix D dated 20.11.1942 to 6.3.1946 ............................................ |  | Rare |
| **IM16d** | *Signatories: J. Greenwood (Manager) and R. C. Sale (Accountant)*<br>Prefix D dated 25.2.1948 and 27.4.1949 ........................................ |  | Rare |
| **IM16e** | *Signatories: J. Greenwood (Manager) and C. R. Collister (Accountant)*<br>Prefix D dated 27.2.1951 to 25.2.1957 ............................................ | £350 | — |
| **IM16e** | *Signatories: D. Berry (Manager) and C. R. Collister (Accountant)*<br>Prefix D dated 28.2.1958 to 14.3.1961 ............................................ | £250 | £380 |

# BARCLAYS BANK LIMITED

Barclays Bank Limited established a presence in the Isle of Man when it opened a branch in Douglas in 1922. The one Pound notes which it issued from 1924 onwards were all of the same size and design.

## ONE POUND NOTES

Size 150 mm x 84 mm approximately

*Obverse – brown on a yellow and green underprint*
*Reverse – brown. Vignette of Douglas Bay and harbour*

|  |  | F | VF |
|---|---|---|---|
| **IM18a** | *Signatories: E. E. Swan (Manager) and J. E. Callister (Accountant)* No prefix letters; dated from 7.6.1924 to 7.4.1926 ...................... |  | Rare |
| **IM18b** | *Signatories: E. E. Swan (Manager) and M. Pullman (Accountant)* No prefix letters; dated from 28.8.1926 to 19.4.1929 ................... |  | Rare |
| **IM18c** | *Signatories: E. E. Swan (Manager) and A. Tranter (Accountant)* No prefix letters; dated from 10.12.1929 to 7.4.1937 ................... |  | Rare |
| **IM18d** | *Signatories: T. H. Hall (Manager) and A. Tranter (Accountant)* No prefix letters; dated from 17.12.1937 to 20.3.1950 ................. |  | from £350 |
| **IM18e** | *Signatories: T. H. Hall (Manager) and J. A. Butterworth (Accountant)* No prefix letters; dated from 13.11.1950 to 4.12.1953................. | £280 | £480 |
| **IM18f** | *Signatories: T. H. Hall (Manager) and J. A. Butterworth (Chief Clerk)* No prefix letters; dated from 10.4.1954 to 25.3.1958 ................... | £280 | £480 |
| **IM18e** | *Signatories: J. A. Butterworth (Manager) and A. Smith (Chief Clerk)* No prefix letters; dated from 25.3.1958 to 30.3.1960 ................... |  | Rare |

# ISLE OF MAN GOVERNMENT ISSUES

## TEN SHILLING NOTES

Size 140 mm x 67 mm approximately

First issued in 1961.
*Obverse – mainly red. Portrait of Queen Elizabeth II to the right; Triune and motto at the centre*
*Reverse – red. Picture of a Viking ship under sail*

|  |  | EF | UNC |
|---|---|---|---|
| **IM21a** | Signatory: R. H. Garvey (Lieutenant Governor) No prefix letter (000001 to 1000000) and Prefix A (000001 to 250000) ............................................................ | £35 | £45 |
| **IM21b** | Signatory: P. G. H. Stallard (Lieutenant Governor) Prefix A (250001 to 517000) ............................................................ | £35 | £45 |

## FIFTY PENCE NOTES

Size 140 mm x 67 mm approximately

First issued in 1969
*Obverse – mainly blue. Portrait of Queen Elizabeth II to the right; Triune and motto at the centre*
*Reverse – blue. Picture of a Viking ship under sail*

| **IM22** | Signatory: P. G. H. Stallard (Lieutenant Governor) No prefix letter (000001 to 679000) ................................................ | £16 | £25 |
|---|---|---|---|

Size 127 mm x 61 mm approximately

First issued in 1972
*Obverse – mainly blue. Portrait of Queen Elizabeth II to the right;  Triune and motto at the centre*
*Reverse – blue. Picture of a Viking ship under sail*

|  |  | EF | UNC |
|---|---|---|---|
| **IM23a** | *Signatory: P. G. H. Stallard (Lieutenant Governor)* Prefix A  (200001 to 800000) ............................................................ | £20 | £30 |
| **IM23b** | *Signatory: John Paul (Lieutenant Governor) – large signature* Prefix A  (800001 to 1000000) and Prefix B  (000001 to 370000)............................................................. | £14 | £20 |
| **IM23c** | *Signatory: John Paul (Lieutenant Governor) – small signature* Prefix B  (370001 to 1000000) and Prefix C  (000001 to 200000) ............................................................ | £10 | £15 |

First issued in 1979. Similar to previous issue but for change of title of signatory
*Obverse – mainly blue. Portrait of Queen Elizabeth II to the right;  Triune and motto at the centre*
*Reverse – blue. Picture of a Viking ship under sail*

| **IM24** | Signatory: W. Dawson (Treasurer of the Isle of Man) Prefix C  (200001 to 750000) ......................................................... | £4 | £7 |
|---|---|---|---|

# ONE POUND NOTES

Size 151 mm x 72 mm approximately

First issued in 1961
*Obverse – mainly violet. Portrait of Queen Elizabeth II to the right; Triune and motto at the centre*
*Reverse – violet. View of Tynwald Hill and St. John's church*

|  |  | EF | UNC |
|---|---|---|---|
| **IM31a** | *Signatory: R. H. Garvey (Lieutenant Governor)* | | |
| | No prefix letter (000001 to 1000000), | | |
| | Prefix A and prefix B (000001 to 200000)...................................... | £40 | £55 |
| | | | |
| **IM31b** | *Signatory: P. G. H. Stallard (Lieutenant Governor)* | | |
| | Prefix B (200001 to 1000000) and prefix C (000001 to 745000).... | £40 | £55 |

Size 135 mm x 67 mm approximately

First issued in 1972
*Obverse – mainly violet. Portrait of Queen Elizabeth II to the right; Triune and motto at the centre*
*Reverse – violet. View of Tynwald Hill and St. John's church*

| | | | |
|---|---|---|---|
| **IM32a** | *Signatory: P. G. H. Stallard (Lieutenant Governor)* | | |
| | Prefix C (050001 to 1000000) and | | |
| | Prefix D (000001 to 970000) ......................................................... | £35 | £50 |
| | | | |
| **IM32b** | *Signatory: John Paul (Lieutenant Governor) – large signature* | | |
| | Prefix D (970001 to 1000000) ...................................................... | | Rare |
| | Prefix E ....................................................................................... | £250 | £350 |
| | | | |
| **IM32c** | *Signatory: John Paul (Lieutenant Governor) – small signature* | | |
| | Prefix F, G and H (000001 to 440000) ......................................... | £14 | £20 |

First issued in 1979. Similar to previous issue but for change of title of signatory
*Obverse – mainly violet. Portrait of Queen Elizabeth II to the right; Triune and motto at the centre*
*Reverse – violet. View of Tynwald Hill and St. John's church*

|  |  | EF | UNC |
|---|---|---|---|
| **IM33a** | *Signatory: W. Dawson (Treasurer of the Isle of Man)* | | |
| | Prefix H (440001 to 1000000) to prefix K..................................... | £6 | £10 |
| | (issued before the Tyvek notes – ref. IM34) | | |
| **IM33b** | *Signatory: W. Dawson (Treasurer of the Isle of Man)* | | |
| | Prefix P (500001 to 1000000) to prefix R (000001 to 500000)....... | £6 | £10 |
| | (issued after the Tyvek notes – ref. IM34, circa 1988) | | |

First issued in 1979.
*Obverse – green on a light multicoloured underprint. Portrait of Queen Elizabeth II to the right;*
*Triune and motto at the centre*
*Reverse – green. View of Tynwald Hill and St. John's church*

|  |  | | |
|---|---|---|---|
| **IM34** | *Signatory: W. Dawson (Treasurer of the Isle of Man)* | | |
| | Prefix M, N and P (000001 to 500000).......................................... | £10 | £15 |

Size 128 mm x 65 mm approximately

First issued in 1990
*Obverse – mainly violet. Portrait of Queen Elizabeth II to the right; Triune and motto at the centre*
*Reverse – violet. View of Tynwald Hill and St. John's church*

|  |  | EF | UNC |
|---|---|---|---|
| **IM35a** | *Signatory: W. Dawson (Chief Financial Officer)* |  |  |
|  | Prefix R, S and T  (500001 to 1000000) ....................................... | £8 | £12 |
|  | Prefix Z – replacement note............................................................ | £120 | £200 |
| **IM35b** | *Signatory: J. A. Cashen (Chief Financial Officer)* |  |  |
|  | Prefix U to prefix Y ......................................................... | — | £2 |
|  | Prefix Z – replacement note........................................................ | £15 | £22 |

# FIVE POUND NOTES

Size 139 mm x 84 mm approximately

First issued in 1961
*Obverse – blue and green on a multicoloured underprint. Portrait of Queen Elizabeth II to the right;*
*Triune and motto at the centre*
*Reverse – dark grey. View of Castle Rushen, 1775*

|  |  | VF | EF |
|---|---|---|---|
| **IM41a** | *Signatory: R. H. Garvey (Lieutenant Governor)* |  |  |
|  | No prefix letter (000001 to 250000),................................. | £160 | £350 |
| **IM41b** | *Signatory: P. G. H. Stallard (Lieutenant Governor)* |  |  |
|  | No prefix letter (250001 to 500000).................................. | £160 | £350 |

Size 147 mm x 78 mm approximately

First issued in 1972
*Obverse – blue and maroon on a multicoloured underprint. Portrait of Queen Elizabeth II to the right;*
*Triune and motto at the centre*
*Reverse – dark grey. View of Castle Rushen, 1775*

|  |  | EF | UNC |
|---|---|---|---|
| **IM42a** | *Signatory: P. G. H. Stallard (Lieutenant Governor)* | | |
| | No prefix letter (500001 to 950000) .................................................... | £160 | £240 |
| **IM42b** | *Signatory: John Paul (Lieutenant Governor)* | | |
| | No prefix letter (950001 to 1000000) ................................................. | £180 | — |
| | Prefix A and B (000001 to 600000) ...................................................... | £85 | £120 |

First issued in 1979. Similar to previous issue but for change of title of signatory
*Obverse – blue and maroon on a multicoloured underprint. Portrait of Queen Elizabeth II to the right;*
*Triune and motto at the centre*
*Reverse – dark grey. View of Castle Rushen, 1775*

| **IM43a** | *Signatory: W. Dawson (Treasurer of the Isle of Man)* | | |
|---|---|---|---|
| | Prefix B (600001 to 1000000), C and D (000001 to 100000 approx.) | £45 | £75 |
| | Prefix letters are in Serif script | | |
| **IM43b** | *Signatory: W. Dawson (Treasurer of the Isle of Man)* | | |
| | Prefix D (100000 approximately to 1000000) ................................ | £45 | £75 |
| | Prefix letters are in Sans Serif script | | |

Size 135 mm x 69 mm approximately.

First issued in 1991
*Obverse – blue and maroon on a multicoloured underprint. Portrait of Queen Elizabeth II to the right; Triune and motto at the centre*
*Reverse – dark grey on a multicoloured underprint. View of Castle Rushen, 1775*

|  |  | EF | UNC |
|---|---|---|---|
| **IM44a** | *Signatory: W. Dawson (Chief Financial Officer)* | | |
| | Prefix E and .................................................................... | £25 | £40 |
| | Prefix F (000001 to 100000) ............................................. | £80 | Rare |
| | Prefix Z – replacement note .............................................. | | Rare |
| **IM44b** | *Signatory: J. A. Cashen (Chief Financial Officer)* | | |
| | Prefix F (100001 to prefix K and ongoing) ................................... | --- | £10 |
| | Prefix Z – replacement note .............................................. | £15 | £25 |

# TEN POUND NOTES

Size 151 mm x 85 mm approximately

First issued in 1972
*Obverse – brown and green on a multicoloured underprint. Portrait of Queen Elizabeth II to the right; Triune and motto at the centre*
*Reverse – shades of brown. View of Peel Castle, circa 1830*

|  |  | | |
|---|---|---|---|
| **IM51a** | *Signatory: P. G. H. Stallard (Lieutenant Governor)* | | |
| | No prefix letter (000001 to 050000) .................................. | | Rare |
| **IM51b** | *Signatory: John Paul (Lieutenant Governor)* | | |
| | No prefix letter (050001 to 360000) .................................. | £100 | £150 |

Size 150 mm x 85 mm approximately

First issued in 1972. Similar to previous issue but for change of title of signatory.
*Obverse – brown and green on a multicoloured underprint. Portrait of Queen Elizabeth II to the right;*
*Triune and motto at the centre*
*Reverse – shades of brown. View of Peel Castle, circa 1830*

|  |  | EF | UNC |
|---|---|---|---|
| **IM52a** | Signatory: W. Dawson (Treasurer of the Isle of Man) | | |
|  | No prefix letter (360001 to 1000000) and prefix A ..................... | £80 | £130 |
| **IM52b** | Signatory: W. Dawson (Chief Financial Officer) | | |
|  | Prefix B (000001 to 010000) ......................................................... | | Rare |

First issued in 1991
*Obverse – brown and green on a multicoloured underprint. Portrait of Queen Elizabeth II to the right;*
*Triune and motto at the centre. The clause under the title at the top of the note reads: "promise to pay*
*the bearer on demand at any office of Isle of Man Bank Limited"*
*Reverse – shades of brown. View of Peel Castle, circa 1830*

| **IM53** | Signatory: J. A. Cashen (Chief Financial Officer) | | |
|---|---|---|---|
|  | Prefix C to prefix G ......................................................... | £14 | £22 |
|  | Prefix Z – replacement note......................................... | £35 | £50 |

First issued in 2002
*Obverse – brown and green on a multicoloured underprint. Portrait of Queen Elizabeth II to the right; Triune and motto at the centre. The clause under the title at the top of the note reads: "promise to pay the bearer on demand at any office of Isle of Man Bank"*
*Reverse – shades of brown. View of Peel Castle, circa 1830*

|         |                                                          | EF   | UNC  |
|---------|----------------------------------------------------------|------|------|
| **IM54a** | *Signatory: J. A. Cashen (Chief Financial Officer)*    |      |      |
|         | Prefix H to prefix M...................................... | —    | £20  |
|         | Prefix Z – replacement note.............................. | £25  | £35  |
|         |                                                          |      |      |
| **IM54b** | *Signatory: P. M. Shimmin (Chief Financial Officer)*   |      |      |
|         | Prefix N and ongoing...................................... | —    | £20  |
|         | Prefix Z – replacement note.............................. | £25  | £35  |

# TWENTY POUND NOTES

Size 160 mm x 90 mm approximately

First issued 1979. Commemorating the millennium year of the Isle of Man
*Obverse – red and brown on a multicoloured underprint. Portrait of Queen Elizabeth II to the right; Triune and motto at the centre. Clause below Queen's portrait reads: "ISSUED DURING MILLENNIUM YEAR 1979"*
*Reverse – red, yellow and multicoloured. View of the Laxey Wheel, 1854*

|         |                                                          | | |
|---------|----------------------------------------------------------|------|------|
| **IM61** | *Signatory: W. Dawson (Treasurer of the Isle of Man)*   |      |      |
|         | No prefix letter (000001 to 005000). ................... | £170 | £250 |

First issued 1979. Similar to above but without commemorative clause
*Obverse – red and brown on a multicoloured underprint. Portrait of Queen Elizabeth II to the right;*
*Triune and motto at the centre*
*Reverse – red, yellow and multicoloured. View of the LaxeyWheel, 1854*

|  | | EF | UNC |
|---|---|---|---|
| **IM62** | *Signatory: W. Dawson (Treasurer of the Isle of Man)* | | |
|  | No prefix letter (005001 to 150000)................................................ | £160 | £240 |

Size 150 mm x 80 mm approximately

First issued 1991
*Obverse – red and brown on a multicoloured underprint. Portrait of Queen Elizabeth II to the right;*
*Triune and motto at the centre. The clause under the title at the top of the note reads: "promise to pay*
*the bearer on demand at any office of Isle of Man Bank Limited"*
*Reverse – lilac and orange brown. View of the Laxey Wheel, 1854*

| **IM63a** | *Signatory: W. Dawson (Chief Financial Officer)* | | |
|---|---|---|---|
|  | No prefix letter (150001 to 450000)................................. | £120 | £200 |
| **IM63b** | *Signatory: J. A. Cashen (Chief Financial Officer)* | | |
|  | No prefix letter (450001 to 1000000) and prefix B to prefix D .... | £30 | £45 |
|  | Prefix Z – replacement note ........................................... | £60 | £90 |

First issued 2002
*Obverse – red and brown on a multicoloured underprint. Portrait of Queen Elizabeth II to the right; Triune and motto at the centre. The clause under the title at the top of the note reads: "promise to pay the bearer on demand at any office of Isle of Man Bank"*
*Reverse – lilac and orange brown. View of the Laxey Wheel, 1854*

|  |  | EF | UNC |
|---|---|---|---|
| **IM64** | *Signatory: J. A. Cashen (Chief Financial Officer)* | | |
| | Prefix E to G (ongoing) | — | £40 |
| | Prefix Z – replacement note | £50 | £80 |

# FIFTY POUND NOTES

Size 170 mm x 95 mm approximately

First issued 1983
*Obverse blue and green on a multicoloured underprint. Portrait of Queen Elizabeth II to the right; Triune and motto at the centre*
*Reverse – blue green and multicoloured. View of Douglas Bay 1841*

| **IM62** | *Signatory: W. Dawson (Treasurer of the Isle of Man)* | | |
|---|---|---|---|
| | No prefix letter (000001 to 250000) | — | £100 |

# Guernsey

## SOME EXAMPLES OF BANKNOTES IN CIRCULATION IN GUERNSEY PRIOR TO WWII

Guernsey banknotes issued before the outbreak of WWII are all scarce; quantities issued were small and relatively few have survived. Many note types are true rarities with just a handful being known in private collections. For this reason no attempt has been made to fully catalogue, or ascribe values to these issues, but a number of notes are illustrated below.

Size 140 mm x 85 mm approximately

*Obverse—pale blue with 10/- in red/orange at the centre*
*Reverse—red panel with the Guernsey seal at the centre*

| | | *F* | *VF* |
|---|---|---|---|
| **GU21** | **Ten Shillings**—*Signatory: H. E. Marquand (Treasurer)* | | |
| | Prefix B/R (circa 1932) to prefix G/H dated 9.3.1940 ................ from £400 | | £750 |

Size 150 mm x 87 mm approximately

*Obverse—black with £1 in a red panel at the centre.*
*Reverse—blue panel with the Guernsey seal at the centre.*

| | | | |
|---|---|---|---|
| **GU22** | **One Pound**—*Signatory: H. E. Marquand (Treasurer)* | | |
| | Prefix K/G (circa 1933) to prefix S/L dated 9.3.1940 ................ from £450 | | £800 |

# GUERNSEY WORLD WAR II ISSUES

Following the occupation of the Channel Island by Germany during WWII there was an acute shortage of coinage in the Island and permission was given by the Germans for the printing and distribution of small denomination banknotes, subject to the withdrawal from circulation of an equivalent amount of Guernsey and Bank of England notes. These Bank of England notes were overstamped "Withdrawn from Circulation September 18th, 1941." and "Withdrawn from Circulation November 10th, 1941." Some 5,000 Bank of England £1 notes and a similar amount of Guernsey 10 shilling and £1 notes (there is some doubt about the exact figure) were withdrawn to balance the introduction of notes of 6 pence, 1 shilling, 1 shilling and 3 pence, 2 shillings and 6 pence, and 5 shillings.

During the occupation, notes of 10 shillings, 1 pound and 5 pounds (references GU29 to GU31) were also printed covertly on the island and issued immediately following the liberation on Wednesday, May 9, 1945. They were used to redeem the small denomination occupation notes and were quickly superceded by the post War issue dated 1.8.1945.

Bank of England notes (above) were withdrawn from circulation in Guernsey prior to the issue of the small denomination notes below. For full information and values on these notes, see catalogue references BE48 to BE50 in the Bank of England section.

Size 90 mm x 60 mm approximately

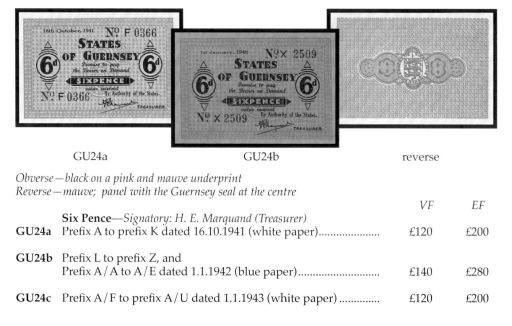

| GU24a | GU24b | reverse |

*Obverse—black on a pink and mauve underprint*
*Reverse—mauve; panel with the Guernsey seal at the centre*

| | | VF | EF |
|---|---|---|---|
| **Six Pence**—*Signatory: H. E. Marquand (Treasurer)* | | | |
| **GU24a** Prefix A to prefix K dated 16.10.1941 (white paper).................... | | £120 | £200 |
| **GU24b** Prefix L to prefix Z, and | | | |
| Prefix A/A to A/E dated 1.1.1942 (blue paper)........................... | | £140 | £280 |
| **GU24c** Prefix A/F to prefix A/U dated 1.1.1943 (white paper).............. | | £120 | £200 |

Size 90 mm x 60 mm approximately

*Obverse—1 Shilling overprint in red/brown on a note for 1 Shilling and 3 Pence*
*Printed on white or blue paper; black on a yellow and brown underprint*
*Reverse—brown; panel with the Guernsey seal at the centre*

|  |  | VF | EF |
|---|---|---|---|
| **One Shilling**—*Signatory: H. E. Marquand (Treasurer)* | | | |
| **GU25a** Prefix G to prefix M dated 18.7.1942 (blue paper).................... | | £250 | £400 |
| **GU25b** Prefix N to prefix Z dated 1.1.1943 (white paper) ...................... | | £140 | £220 |

Size 90 mm x 60 mm approximately

| GU26a | GU26b | reverse |
|---|---|---|

*Obverse—Printed on white or blue paper; black on a yellow and brown underprint*
*Reverse—brown; panel with the Guernsey seal at the centre*

**One Shilling and Three Pence**—*Signatory: H. E. Marquand (Treasurer)*
**GU26a**   Prefix A to prefix F dated 16.10.1941 (white paper) .................   £120   £240
**GU26b**   Prefix G dated 18.7.1942 (blue paper – only 500 notes printed)   Rare

Size 90 mm x 60 mm approximately

| GU27a | GU27c | reverse |
|---|---|---|

*Obverse—Printed on white or blue paper; blue, with "2/6" in brown at the centre*
*Reverse—blue; panel with the Guernsey seal at the centre*

|  |  | | |
|---|---|---|---|
| **Two Shillings and Six Pence**—*Signatory: H. E. Marquand (Treasurer)* | | | |
| **GU27a** | Prefix A/A to prefix A/E dated 25.3.1941 (white paper) ........... | £160 | £260 |
| **GU27b** | Prefix A/F to prefix A/K dated 17.5.1941 (white paper) ........... | £160 | £260 |
| **GU27c** | Prefix A/L to prefix B/A dated 1.1.1942 (blue paper) ................ | £160 | £260 |
| **GU27d** | Prefix B/B to prefix B/J dated 1.1.1943 (white paper)............... | £150 | £250 |

Size 100 mm x 65 mm approximately

*Obverse — Black with "5/-" in red at the centre*
*Reverse — red; panel with the Guernsey seal at the centre*

|  | | *VF* | *EF* |
|---|---|---|---|
| **Five Shillings**—*Signatory: H. E. Marquand (Treasurer)* | | | |
| **GU28a** | Prefix A/F to prefix A/H dated 25.3.1941 ..................................... | £170 | £280 |
| **GU28b** | Prefix A/H to prefix A/K dated 1.1.1942...................................... | £260 | £380 |
| **GU28c** | Prefix A/L to prefix A/T dated 1.1.1943 ...................................... | £190 | £320 |

Notes issued immediately following the liberation of Guernsey on May 9, 1945

Size 135 mm x 80 mm approximately

*Obverse — Blue with "10/-" in red at the centre*
*Reverse — red; panel with the Guernsey seal at the centre*

|  | | | |
|---|---|---|---|
| **Ten Shillings**—*Signatory: H. E. Marquand (Treasurer)* | | | |
| **GU29** | Prefix A/1 to prefix W/1 dated 1.1.1943 ...................................... | £400 | £650 |

Size 150 mm x 87 mm approximately

*Obverse—Printed on white or blue paper; black, with "£1" in red at the centre*
*Reverse—blue; panel with the Guernsey seal at the centre*

| | | VF | EF |
|---|---|---|---|
| | **One Pound**—*Signatory: H. E. Marquand (Treasurer)* | | |
| **GU30a** | Prefix A/1 to prefix Z/1, and | | |
| | Prefix A/2 to prefix N/2 dated 1.1.1943 (white paper) .............. | £500 | £850 |
| **GU30b** | Prefix O/2 to prefix S/2 dated 1.1.1945 (blue paper) ................. | | Rare |

Size 165 mm x 95 mm approximately

*Obverse—Printed on blue paper; green with red date and serial numbers*
*Reverse—green; panel with the Guernsey seal at the centre*

| | **Five Pounds**—*Signatory: H. E. Marquand (Treasurer)* | |
|---|---|---|
| **GU31** | Prefix 1/A to prefix 1/H dated 1.1.1945 ....................................... | Rare |
| | (only 53 notes are outstanding) | |

# GUERNSEY POST WAR ISSUES

## TEN SHILLING NOTES

*Obverse—Lilac on a light green underprint.*
*Reverse—purple; panel with the Guernsey seal at the centre*

| | | VF | EF |
|---|---|---|---|
| **GU32a** | *Signatory: H. E. Marquand (Treasurer)* Prefix 1/A to prefix 2/Z dated 1.8.1945. ..................................... | £180 | £250 |
| **GU32b** | *Signatory: L. A. Guillemette (Treasurer)* Prefix 2/Z dated 1.1.1950 to prefix 24/G dated 1.7.1966 ............ from £35 | | £55 |
| | (Some dates are scarce and worth considerably more) | | |

## ONE POUND NOTES

Size 155 mm x 87 mm approximately

*Obverse—purple on a green underprint. "£1" in a green panel at centre.*
*Reverse—green; panel with the Guernsey seal at the centre*

| | | | |
|---|---|---|---|
| **GU33a** | *Signatory: H. E. Marquand (Treasurer)* Prefix 1/A dated 1.8.1945 to prefix 5/X dated 1.4.1948 .............. | £180 | £250 |
| **GU33b** | *Signatory: L. A. Guillemette (Treasurer)* Prefix 5/Y dated 1.1.1950 to prefix 49/W dated 1.7.1966 ........... from £70 | | £140 |
| | (Some dates are scarce and worth considerably more) | | |

Size 135 mm x 75 mm approximately

First issued 1969
*Obverse—olive on a pink and yellow underprint. Guernsey seal at the centre*
*Reverse—olive; illustration of Castle Cornet*

|  | | *EF* | *UNC* |
|---|---|---|---|
| **GU34a** | *Signatory: L. A. Guillemette (Treasurer)* | | |
| | Prefix A to prefix C 100000 ............................................................ | £35 | £50 |
| **GU34b** | *Signatory: C. H. Hodder (Treasurer)* | | |
| | Prefix C 100001 to prefix G 630000 ................................................. | £14 | £20 |
| **GU34c** | *Signatory: W. C. Bull (Treasurer)* | | |
| | Prefix G 630001 to prefix H 860000 ................................................ | £16 | £22 |

Size 135 mm x 67 mm approximately

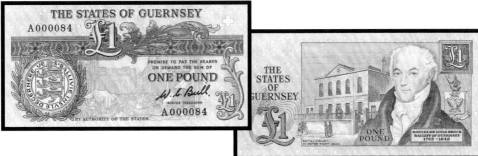

First issued 1980
*Obverse—green on a multicoloured underprint. Guernsey seal at bottom left; picture of the old market square circa 1830 in underprint at the centre*
*Reverse—green; portrait of Daniel de Lisle Brock to the right with illustration of Royal Court, St. Peter Port 1840, in the background*

| **GU35a** | *Signatory: W. C. Bull (States Treasurer)* | | |
|---|---|---|---|
| | Prefix A to prefix G............................................................................ | £6 | £10 |
| | Prefix Z—replacement note. ............................................................. | £15 | £25 |
| **GU35b** | *Signatory: M. J. Brown (States Treasurer)* | | |
| | Prefix H only ...................................................................................... | £9 | £15 |
| | Prefix Z—replacement note. ............................................................. | | Rare |

Size 129 mm x 65 mm approximately

Similar to previous issue, but reduced size. First issued 1991
*Obverse—green on a multicoloured underprint. Guernsey seal at bottom left; picture of the old market square circa 1830 in underprint at the centre.*
*Reverse—green; portrait of Daniel de Lisle Brock to the right with illustration of Royal Court, St. Peter Port 1840, in the background.*

|  |  | EF | UNC |
|---|---|---|---|
| **GU36a** | *Signatory: M. J. Brown (States Treasurer)* | | |
| | Prefix J to prefix L ............................................................ | £3 | £6 |
| | Prefix Z—replacement note. ......................................... | £10 | £15 |
| **GU36b** | *Signatory: D. P. Trestain (States Treasurer)* | | |
| | Prefix M to prefix S............................................................ | -- | £3 |
| | Prefix Z—replacement note. ......................................... | £6 | £10 |
| **GU36c** | *Signatory: D. M. Clark (States Treasurer)* | | |
| | Prefix T and U (ongoing)................................................. | -- | £2 |
| | Prefix Z—replacement note. ......................................... | £6 | £10 |

# FIVE POUND NOTES

Size 155 mm x 90 mm approximately

*Obverse—green on a multicoloured underprint*
*Reverse—light green; Guernsey seal at the centre*

|  |  | F | VF |
|---|---|---|---|
| **GU41** | *Signatory: L. A. Guillemette (Treasurer)* | | |
| | Prefix 1/J dated 1.12.1956 to prefix 4/C dated 1.7.1966 ............. | £250 | £400 |

Size 145 mm x 85 mm approximately

First issued 1969
*Obverse—purple on a light brown underprint. Guernsey seal to the lower right*
*Reverse—mainly purple; town sea front and harbour scene*

|  |  | EF | UNC |
|---|---|---|---|
| **GU42a** | *Signatory: L. A. Guillemette (Treasurer)* | | |
| | Prefix A (to 400000) ........................................................... | £70 | £120 |
| **GU42b** | *Signatory: C. H. Hodder (Treasurer)* | | |
| | Prefix A and prefix B (to 850000)....................................... | £50 | £75 |
| **GU42c** | *Signatory:  W. C. Bull (Treasurer)* | | |
| | Prefix B (from B850001) and C ......................................... | £45 | £65 |

Size 145 mm x 78 mm approximately

First issued 1980
*Obverse—brown and multicoloured. Guernsey seal at bottom left; Fort Grey in underprint at the centre*
*Reverse—mainly brown; portrait of Thomas de la Rue with illustrations of Fountain Street, St. Peter Port 1977, and an envelope making machine, 1851*

| **GU43** | *Signatory: W. C. Bull (States Treasurer)* | | |
|---|---|---|---|
| | Prefix A to prefix F........................................................... | £16 | £25 |
| | Prefix Z—replacement note. .......................................... | £40 | £60 |

Size 135 mm x 70 mm approximately

Similar to earlier issue but reduced size. First issued 1991
*Obverse—brown and multicoloured. Guernsey seal at bottom left; Fort Grey in underprint at the centre*
*Reverse—mainly brown; portrait of Thomas de la Rue with illustrations of Fountain Street, St. Peter Port 1977, and an envelope making machine, 1851*

|  | | EF | UNC |
|---|---|---|---|
| **GU44a** | *Signatory: M. J. Brown (States Treasurer)* | | |
| | Prefix G and prefix H (to 500000) ................................................. | £14 | £22 |
| | Prefix Z—replacement note. ......................................................... | £25 | £35 |
| **GU44b** | *Signatory: D. P. Trestain (States Treasurer)* | | |
| | Prefix H 500001 and prefix J............................................................ | £12 | £20 |
| | Prefix Z—replacement note. ......................................................... | £25 | £35 |

First issued 1996.
*Obverse—brown and multicoloured. Portrait of Queen Elizabeth II to the right; Guernsey seal at bottom centre.*
*Reverse—multicoloured, illustrations of Fort Grey and Hanois Lighthouse, 1862*

| **GU45a** | *Signatory: D. P. Trestain (States Treasurer)* | | |
|---|---|---|---|
| | Prefix A and prefix B ......................................................... | — | £12 |
| | Prefix Z—replacement note. ......................................................... | £20 | £30 |
| **GU45b** | *Signatory: D. M. Clark (States Treasurer)* | | |
| | Prefix C and ongoing ......................................................... | — | £10 |
| | Prefix Z—replacement note. ....................................................... | probably exists | |

*Similar to previous issue.* Issued in 2000 to commemorate the Millennium
*Obverse—multicoloured. Portrait of Queen Elizabeth II to the right; Guernsey seal at bottom centre
Commemorative overprint to the left*
*Reverse—multicoloured, illustrations of Fort Grey and Hanois Lighthouse, 1862*

|  | EF | UNC |
|---|---|---|
| **GU46** Signatory: D. P. Trestain (States Treasurer) |  |  |
| Prefix M only. ...................................................................................... | — | £12 |

# TEN POUND NOTES

Size 150 mm x 90 mm approximately

First issued 1975
*Obverse—blue and multicoloured; Britannia at left centre holding a spear and the Guernsey seal
Reverse—blue; an illustration of the Battle of Queenston Heights 1812, with a portrait of Major
General Sir Isaac Brock KB, to the right*

| | | |
|---|---|---|
| **GU51** Signatory: C. H. Hodder (States Treasurer) | | |
| Prefix A (to 571400) .......................................................................... | £160 | £250 |

Size 150 mm x 85 mm approximately

First issued 1980.
*Obverse—blue on a multicoloured underprint. Guernsey seal at bottom left; Castle Cornet in underprint at the centre*
*Reverse—blue; an illustration of the Battle of Queenston Heights 1812, with a portrait of Major General Sir Isaac Brock KB, to the right*

|  |  | EF | UNC |
|---|---|---|---|
| **GU52a** | *Signatory: W. C. Bull (States Treasurer)* | | |
| | Prefix A and prefix B .......................................................... | £35 | £50 |
| | Prefix Z—replacement note. ............................................... | £60 | £90 |
| **GU52b** | *Signatory: M. J. Brown (States Treasurer)* | | |
| | Prefix C and prefix D........................................................... | £30 | £40 |
| | Prefix Z— replacement note. .............................................. | £60 | £90 |

Size 143 mm x 75 mm approximately

Similar to above but smaller size. First issued 1990
*Obverse—blue on a multicoloured underprint. Guernsey seal at bottom left; Castle Cornet in underprint at the centre.*
*Reverse—blue; an illustration of the Battle of Queenston Heights 1812, with a portrait of Major General Sir Isaac Brock KB, to the right*

|  |  | | |
|---|---|---|---|
| **GU53** | *Signatory: M. J. Brown (States Treasurer)* | | |
| | Prefix E and prefix F. ....................................................... | £18 | £25 |
| | Prefix Z—replacement note. ............................................. | £30 | £50 |

First issued 1995

*Obverse—blue and multicoloured. Portrait of Queen Elizabeth II to the right; Picture of Elizabeth College to the left of Guernsey seal, lower centre*
*Reverse—blue and multicoloured; illustrations of Saumarez Park, Le Trepied Dolman and Les Niaux Waterwheel*

|  |  | EF | UNC |
|---|---|---|---|
| **GU54a** | *Signatory: D. P. Trestain (States Treasurer)* | | |
| | Prefix A to prefix C . . . . . . . . . . . . . . . . . . . . . . . . . . . . . . . . . . . . | — | £20 |
| | Prefix Z—replacement note. . . . . . . . . . . . . . . . . . . . . . . . . . . . . | £25 | £40 |
| | | | |
| **GU54b** | *Signatory: D. M. Clark (States Treasurer)* | | |
| | Prefix D and ongoing . . . . . . . . . . . . . . . . . . . . . . . . . . . . . . . . . . . | — | £18 |
| | Prefix Z—replacement note. . . . . . . . . . . . . . . . . . . . . . . . . . . . . | £22 | £35 |

# TWENTY POUND NOTES

Size 160 mm x 90 mm approximately

First issued 1980
*Obverse—red on a multicoloured underprint. Guernsey seal at bottom left; Saumarez Park, 1815 in underprint at the centre*
*Reverse—red on a multicoloured underprint; an illustration of British ships in Gibraltar Bay 1801 with a portrait of Admiral Lord de Saumarez to the right*

|  |  | | |
|---|---|---|---|
| **GU61a** | Signatory: W. C. Bull (States Treasurer). | | |
| | Prefix A (to 500000) . . . . . . . . . . . . . . . . . . . . . . . . . . . . . . . . . . . | £60 | £95 |
| | Prefix Z—replacement note. . . . . . . . . . . . . . . . . . . . . . . . . . . . . . | £130 | — |
| | | | |
| **GU61b** | Signatory: M. J. Brown (States Treasurer). | | |
| | Prefix A (500001–813000) . . . . . . . . . . . . . . . . . . . . . . . . . . . . . | £60 | £95 |
| | Prefix Z—replacement note. . . . . . . . . . . . . . . . . . . . . . . . . . . . . . | £130 | — |

Size 150 mm x 80 mm approximately

Similar to above but smaller size. First issued 1990
*Obverse—red on a multicoloured underprint. Guernsey seal at bottom left; Saumarez Park, 1815 in underprint at the centre*
*Reverse—red on a multicoloured underprint; an illustration of British ships in Gibraltar Bay 1801 with a portrait of Admiral Lord de Saumarez to the right*

|  |  | EF | UNC |
|---|---|---|---|
| **GU62a** | *Signatory: M. J. Brown (States Treasurer)* | | |
| | Prefix B (to 500000)............................................. | £35 | £50 |
| | Prefix Z— replacement note........................................... | £60 | £80 |
| **GU62b** | *Signatory: D. P. Trestain (States Treasurer)* | | |
| | Prefix B (500001 upwards). .............................................. | £35 | £45 |
| | Prefix Z—replacement note............................................ | £60 | £80 |

First issued 1995
*Obverse—red and multicoloured. Portrait of Queen Elizabeth II to the right; Picture of St. James Concert Hall to the left of Guernsey seal, lower centre*
*Reverse—red and multicoloured; illustrations of St. Sampson's Church with Sailing dinghies in the foreground and Vale Castle in the background*

| | | | |
|---|---|---|---|
| **GU63a** | *Signatory: D. P. Trestain (States Treasurer)* | | |
| | Prefix A and prefix B.......................................... | — | £40 |
| | Prefix Z—replacement note........................................... | £35 | £50 |
| **GU63b** | *Signatory: D. M. Clark (States Treasurer)* | | |
| | Prefix C and ongoing.......................................... | — | £35 |
| | Prefix Z— replacement note........................................... | £35 | £50 |

# FIFTY POUND NOTES

Size 155 mm x 85 mm approximately

First issued 1994
*Obverse—brown and multicoloured. Portrait of Queen Elizabeth II to the right; Picture of The Royal Court House to the left of Guernsey seal, lower centre*
*Reverse—multicoloured; illustrations of St. Andrew's Church, La Gran'mere, the Letter of Marque and the Pointe de la Moye*

|  | | *EF* | *UNC* |
|---|---|---|---|
| **GU71a** | *Signatory: D. P. Trestain (States Treasurer)* | | |
| | Prefix A ............................................................................................ | — | £90 |
| | Prefix Z—replacement note ............................................................ | probably exists | |

# Jersey

Prior to the Jersey States banknote issues of 1963, Bank of England notes were used in Jersey. During the German occupation of the Channel Islands during WWII, permission was given for the printing and circulation of banknotes from six Pence to one Pound (reference JE1 to JE6 below). This was to alleviate a shortage of cash, particularly coinage, in the island.

## JERSEY WORLD WAR II ISSUES

Size 110 mm x 70 mm approximately

*Obverse—black on a red/brown underprint which has "six pence" in large script. Jersey Shield to the left*
*Reverse—red/brown with "six pence" in large script, exactly as the underprint on the obverse*

|  |  | VF | EF |
|---|---|---|---|
| **JE1** | **Six Pence**—*Signatory: H. F. Ereaut (Treasurer of the States of Jersey)* Prefix JN only, issued from April 1942 to February 1945.............. | £35 | £60 |

Size 110 mm x 70 mm approximately

*Obverse—brown on a blue underprint of a silhouette of two old people chatting. Jersey Shield to the left*
*Reverse—brown; silhouette of two old people chatting—same as obverse underprint*

|  |  | VF | EF |
|---|---|---|---|
| **JE2** | **One Shilling**—*Signatory: H. F. Ereaut (Treasurer of the States of Jersey)* Prefix JN only, issued in April 1942 and June 1942........................ | £35 | £60 |

Size 108 mm x 70 mm approximately.

*Obverse—blue on a salmon pink underprint; Jersey Shield to the left*
*Reverse—large "2/-" in blue on a salmon pink underprint*

|  | | VF | EF |
|---|---|---|---|
| **JE3** | **Two Shillings**—*Signatory: H. F. Ereaut (Treasurer of the States of Jersey)* | | |
| | Prefix JN only, issued in June 1941 .................................................... | £85 | £160 |

Size 108 mm x 70 mm approximately

*Obverse—blue on a light brown and blue underprint depicting a cart and two horses in silhouette Jersey Shield to the left*
*Reverse—blue; silhouette of a cart and horses, same as obverse underprint*

| **JE4** | **Two Shillings**—*Signatory: H. F. Ereaut (Treasurer of the States of Jersey)* | | |
|---|---|---|---|
| | Prefix JN only, issued in April 1942 .................................................... | £45 | £80 |

Size 130 mm x 85 mm approximately

*Obverse—green on a pale green and brown underprint. Jersey Shield to the left*
*Reverse—green; picture of a milkmaid with three cows*

|  | | VF | EF |
|---|---|---|---|
| **JE5** | **Ten Shillings**—*Signatory: H. F. Ereaut (Treasurer of the States of Jersey)* | | |
| | Prefix JN only, issued in April 1942 and June 1942.......................... | £130 | £220 |

Size 130 mm x 85 mm approximately

*Obverse—mauve on a pale mauve and green underprint. Jersey Shield to the left*
*Obverse—picture of a cart and horses on the sea shore*

| | | | |
|---|---|---|---|
| **JE6** | **One Pound**—*Signatory: H. F. Ereaut (Treasurer of the States of Jersey)* | | |
| | Prefix JN only, issued in April 1942 and June 1942.......................... | £160 | £300 |

# JERSEY STATES ISSUES FROM 1963

## TEN SHILLING NOTES

Size 140 mm x 70 mm approximately

First issued 1963
*Obverse—brown on a multicoloured underprint. Portrait of Queen Elizabeth II to the right*
*Reverse—brown on a pale blue underprint. Illustration of St. Ouen's Manor*

| | | EF | UNC |
|---|---|---|---|
| **JE10** | *Signatory: F. N. Padgham (Treasurer of the States)* | | |
| | Prefix A, B and C first issued 1963 ..................................................... | £15 | £25 |

## ONE POUND NOTES

Size 154 mm x 77 mm approximately

First issued 1963
*Obverse—green on a multicoloured underprint. Portrait of Queen Elizabeth II to the right*
*Reverse—green. Illustration of Mont Orgueil Castle*

| | | EF | UNC |
|---|---|---|---|
| **JE11a** | *Signatory: F. N. Padgham (Treasurer of the States)* | | |
| | Prefix A to prefix E, first issued 1963 ............................................... | £40 | £55 |
| **JE11b** | *Signatory: J. Clennett (Treasurer of the States)* | | |
| | Prefix F to prefix K, first issued 1972 ............................................... | £35 | £50 |
| | Prefix Z—replacement note.................................................................. | | Rare |

Size 135 mm x 67 mm approximately

First issued 1976
*Obverse—blue on a pink and blue underprint. Portrait of Queen Elizabeth II to the right*
*Reverse—mainly blue. Picture of the death of Major Peirson at the Battle of Jersey*

|  |  | EF | UNC |
|---|---|---|---|
| **JE12a** | *Signatory: J. Clennett (Treasurer of the States)* |  |  |
|  | Prefix AB to prefix LB, first issued 1976 | £6 | £10 |
|  | Prefix ZB—replacement note. | £17 | £25 |
| **JE12b** | *Signatory: L. May (Treasurer of the States)* |  |  |
|  | Prefix MB to prefix TB, first issued 1985 | £6 | £9 |
|  | Prefix ZB—replacement note. | £15 | £22 |

Size 128 mm x 66 mm approximately

First issued 1989
*Obverse—green on a multicoloured underprint. Portrait of Queen Elizabeth II to the right*
*"£1" at top right in outline print*
*Reverse—mainly green. Illustration of St. Helier Parish Church*

|  |  | EF | UNC |
|---|---|---|---|
| **JE13** | *Signatory: L. May (Treasurer of the States)* |  |  |
|  | Prefix AC to prefix GC, first issued 1989 | £4 | £7 |
|  | Prefix CZ—replacement note. | £15 | £25 |

First issued 1993

First issued 1993.
*Obverse—green on a multicoloured underprint. Portrait of Queen Elizabeth II to the right. "£1" at top right in solid print*
*Reverse—mainly green. Illustration of St. Helier Parish Church*

|  | EF | UNC |
|---|---|---|
| **JE14a** *Signatory: G. Baird (Treasurer of the States)* | | |
| Prefix GC to prefix RC, first issued 1993 | — | £3 |
| Prefix CZ—replacement note | £8 | £15 |
| | | |
| **JE14b** *Signatory: I. Black (Treasurer of the States)* | | |
| Prefix SC and ongoing | — | £2 |
| Prefix CZ—replacement note | £8 | £15 |

Issued to commemorate the 50th. Anniversary of the liberation of Jersey, 9th. May 1995
*Obverse—green on a multicoloured underprint. Similar to regular issue notes , with a commemorative overprint to the left*
*Reverse—mauve, green and yellow with a reproduction of the front and back of the German occupation £1 note, ref. JE6*

**JE15** *Signatory: G. Baird (Treasurer of the States)*
Prefix LJ only, issued in 1995............................................................... — £6

Issued to commemorate the 800th anniversary of the States of Jersey, 1204–2004
*Obverse—green on a multicoloured underprint. Similar to regular issue notes with*
*"Jersey 1204–2004" overprint to the left.*
*Reverse—green, brown and multicoloured. Illustration of Mont Orgueil Castle.*

|  | EF | UNC |
|---|---|---|
| **JE16** *Signatory: I. Black (Treasurer of the States)* | | |
| Prefix J8C, issued in 2004. | — | £3 |

# FIVE POUND NOTES

Size 140 mm x 91 mm approximately

First issued 1963
*Obverse—red on a multicoloured underprint. Portrait of Queen Elizabeth II to the right*
*Reverse—red. Illustration of St. Aubin's Fort*

| | | EF | UNC |
|---|---|---|---|
| **JE21a** *Signatory: F. N. Padgham (Treasurer of the States)* | | | |
| Prefix A only, first issued 1963 | | £80 | £130 |
| **JE21b** *Signatory: J. Clennett (Treasurer of the States)* | | | |
| Prefix B and prefix C, first issued 1972. | | £40 | £55 |
| Prefix Z—replacement note | | £65 | £100 |

Size 145 mm x 78 mm approximately

First issued 1976
*Obverse—brown on a multicoloured underprint. Portrait of Queen Elizabeth II to the right*
*Reverse—brown and mauve. Beach scene with old ships and Elizabeth Castle in the background*

|  |  | EF | UNC |
|---|---|---|---|
| **JE22a** | *Signatory: J. Clennett (Treasurer of the States)* | | |
| | Prefix AB and prefix GB, first issued 1976 | £25 | £35 |
| | Prefix ZB—replacement note. | £40 | £55 |
| **JE22b** | *Signatory: L. May (Treasurer of the States)* | | |
| | Prefix GB to prefix KB, first issued 1983 | £20 | £30 |
| | Prefix ZB—replacement note. | £30 | £45 |

Size 135 mm x 70 mm approximately

First issued 1989
*Obverse—maroon on a multicoloured underprint. Portrait of Queen Elizabeth II to the right. "£5" at top right in outline print*
*Reverse—mainly purple. Illustration of La Corbiere lighthouse*

| **JE23** | *Signatory: L. May (Treasurer of the States)* | | |
|---|---|---|---|
| | Prefix AC and prefix BC, first issued 1989 | £10 | £15 |
| | Prefix CZ—replacement note | £18 | £25 |

First issued 1993
*Obverse—maroon on a multicoloured underprint. Portrait of Queen Elizabeth II to the right. "£5" at top right in solid print*
*Reverse—mainly purple. Illustration of La Corbiere lighthouse*

|  |  | EF | UNC |
|---|---|---|---|
| **JE24** | *Signatory: G. Baird (Treasurer of the States)* | | |
|  | Prefix CC to prefix JC, first issued 1993............................................ | — | £12 |
|  | Prefix CZ—replacement note............................................................... | £15 | £25 |

# TEN POUND NOTES

Size 151 mm x 86 mm approximately

First issued 1963
*Obverse—purple on a multicoloured underprint. Portrait of Queen Elizabeth II to the right*
*Reverse—purple. Illustration of St. Ouen's Manor*

| | | | |
|---|---|---|---|
| **JE31** | *Signatory: J. Clennett (Treasurer of the States)* | | |
| | Prefix A only, first issued 1972 ........................................................ | £55 | £75 |
| | Prefix Z—replacement note............................................................... | £90 | £130 |

Size 150 mm x 85 mm approximately

First issued 1976
*Obverse—green on a multicoloured underprint. Portrait of Queen Elizabeth II to the right*
*Reverse—mainly green. Picture of Victoria College*

|  |  | EF | UNC |
|---|---|---|---|
| **JE32a** | *Signatory: J. Clennett (Treasurer of the States)* | | |
| | Prefix AB and prefix DB, first issued 1976 ....................................... | £40 | £55 |
| | Prefix ZB—replacement note. ........................................................... | £65 | £90 |
| | | | |
| **JE32b** | *Signatory: L. May (Treasurer of the States)* | | |
| | Prefix DB to prefix GB, first issued 1983............................................ | £35 | £50 |
| | Prefix ZB—replacement note. ........................................................... | £60 | £80 |

Size 143 mm x 75 mm approximately

First issued 1989
*Obverse—orange and brown on a multicoloured underprint. Portrait of Queen Elizabeth II to the right*
*"£10" at top right in outline print*
*Reverse—mainly red/brown. Picture of the death of Major Peirson at the Battle of Jersey*

| **JE33** | *Signatory: L. May (Treasurer of the States)* | | |
|---|---|---|---|
| | Prefix AC to prefix CC, first issued 1989 ......................................... | £15 | £25 |
| | Prefix CZ—replacement note............................................................ | £30 | £45 |

First issued 1993
*Obverse—orange and brown on a multicoloured underprint. Portrait of Queen Elizabeth II to the right.*
*"£10" at top right in solid print*
*Reverse—mainly red/brown. Picture of the death of Major Peirson at the Battle of Jersey*

|  |  | EF | UNC |
|---|---|---|---|
| **JE34a** | *Signatory: G. Baird (Treasurer of the States)* |  |  |
|  | Prefix DC to prefix MC, first issued 1993 ........................................ | -- | £20 |
|  | Prefix CZ—replacement note ........................................................... | £25 | £40 |
| **JE34b** | *Signatory: I. Black (Treasurer of the States)* |  |  |
|  | Prefix NC and ongoing ..................................................................... | -- | £18 |
|  | Prefix CZ—replacement note ........................................................... | £25 | £40 |

# TWENTY POUND NOTES

Size 160 mm x 90 mm approximately

First issued 1976
*Obverse—Orange and red on a multicoloured underprint. Portrait of Queen Elizabeth II to the right*
*Reverse—mainly red. Picture of Corey Castle*

|  |  | EF | UNC |
|---|---|---|---|
| **JE41a** | *Signatory: J. Clennett (Treasurer of the States)* |  |  |
|  | Prefix AB only, first issued 1976 ........................................................ | £60 | £85 |
|  | Prefix ZB—replacement note. ........................................................... | £100 | £160 |
| **JE41b** | *Signatory: L. May (Treasurer of the States)* |  |  |
|  | Prefix AB and prefix AC, first issued 1983 ...................................... | £55 | £80 |
|  | Prefix ZB—replacement note. ........................................................... | £100 | £160 |

Size 150 mm x 80 mm approximately

First issued 1989
*Obverse—mainly blue on a multicoloured underprint. Portrait of Queen Elizabeth II to the right*
*"£20" at top right in outline print*
*Reverse—blue on a multicoloured underprint. Illustration of St. Ouen's Manor*

|  |  | EF | UNC |
|---|---|---|---|
| **JE42** | *Signatory: L. May (Treasurer of the States)* | | |
| | Prefix AC and prefix BC, first issued 1989 ...................................... | £50 | £70 |
| | Prefix CZ—replacement note........................................................... | £65 | £90 |

First issued 1993
*Obverse—mainly blue on a multicoloured underprint. Portrait of Queen Elizabeth II to the right*
*"£20" at top right in solid print*
*Reverse – blue on a multicoloured underprint. Illustration of St. Ouen's Manor*

| **JE43a** | *Signatory: G. Baird (Treasurer of the States)* | | |
|---|---|---|---|
| | Prefix BC to prefix JC, first issued 1993 ............................................. | — | £45 |
| | Prefix CZ—replacement note........................................................... | £40 | £55 |
| **JE43b** | *Signatory: I. Black (Treasurer of the States)* | | |
| | Prefix KC and ongoing.......................................................... | — | £35 |
| | Prefix CZ—replacement note........................................................... | £35 | £50 |

# FIFTY POUND NOTES

Size 155 mm x 85 mm approximately

*Obverse dark grey on a multicoloured underprint. Portrait of Queen Elizabeth II to the right*
*"£50" at top right in outline print*
*Reverse—mainly dark grey. Picture of Government House with the Jersey flag to the left*

|  |  | EF | UNC |
|---|---|---|---|
| **JE51** | Signatory: L. May (Treasurer of the States) |  |  |
|  | Prefix AC only, first issued 1989 ......................................................... | £100 | £150 |
|  | Prefix CZ—replacement note............................................................. |  | Rare |

First issued 1993
*Obverse—dark grey on a multicoloured underprint. Portrait of Queen Elizabeth II to the right*
*"£50" at top right in solid print*
*Reverse—mainly dark grey. Picture of Government House with the Jersey flag to the left*

|  |  | EF | UNC |
|---|---|---|---|
| **JE52a** | Signatory: G. Baird (Treasurer of the States) |  |  |
|  | Prefix AC only, first issued 1993 ......................................................... | — | £110 |
|  | Prefix CZ—replacement note............................................................. | £110 | £160 |
| **JE52b** | Signatory: I. Black (Treasurer of the States) |  |  |
|  | Prefix AC and ongoing......................................................................... | — | £85 |
|  | Prefix CZ—replacement note............................................................. | £100 | £150 |

# Ireland

Ireland was a relative latecomer to banking, the first notes of the Bank of Ireland being introduced in 1783. Thereafter the history of banking paralleled that of Scotland, with a number of private banks in the early 19th century which, as a result of mergers and amalgamations, resulted in half a dozen major banks still producing distinctive notes at the turn of the century.

The situation was complicated by the political developments which led to the establishment of the Irish Free State and the province of Northern Ireland in 1921. The Belfast Banking Company, whose notes circulated through the whole of Ireland, confined its activities to Northern Ireland from 1922 onwards. On the other hand, the Bank of Ireland, which was traditionally based in Dublin, was obliged to produce separate issues from 1929 onwards for Northern Ireland and the Irish Free State, while both the Provincial Bank of Ireland and the Ulster Bank likewise had distinctive issues for the Free State and Northern Ireland in the same period.

In the Irish Free State, the government established a Currency Commission in 1927 under whose auspices notes, inscribed in English and Irish, were issued from 1928 onwards, notable on account of the portrait of Hazel, Lady Lavery in the guise of an Irish colleen. The inscriptions in these notes were altered in 1938 from Irish Free State (Saorstát Éireann) to Ireland (Eire), following the constitutional changes of that year. In addition the Currency Commission produced distinctive notes, showing a farmer ploughing, with the names of one or other of the eight "shareholder" banks inscribed at the foot: the Bank of Ireland, the Hibernian Bank, the Munster & Leinster Bank, the National Bank, the Northern Bank, the Provincial Bank, the Royal Bank and the Ulster Bank. These notes were replaced from 1943 onwards by the notes of the Central Bank of Ireland, which at first retained the Lady Lavery portrait, but since 1976 have used historic scenes and personalities.

Distinctive notes for circulation in Northern Ireland have been produced by the Bank of Ireland, the Belfast Banking Company and the National, Northern, Provincial and Ulster banks and it is interesting to note that the Bank of Ireland even produced a commemorative £20 in 1983 to celebrate its bicentenary. Generally speaking, the notes of Northern Ireland have always been much more varied in their designs and subject matter. Bank amalgamations led to the formation of the Allied Irish Banks Limited whose notes, similar to the last issue of the Provincial Bank, were introduced in January 1982.

# REPUBLIC OF IRELAND
## CURRENCY COMMISSION
## (Consolidated banknotes) (1929–41)

Designs for the notes issued by the eight Banks under the auspices of the Currency Commission are virtually identical except for the values, titles and signatures. Notes representative of the design, are illustrated below. (In keeping with the current regulations for the reproduction of banknote illustrations, the serial numbers have been obscured.)

**ONE POUND**
Size: 151 x 84mm

*Obverse—Green on orange and mauve underprint; "Ploughman"*
*Reverse—The Customs House, Dublin*

**FIVE POUNDS**
Size 165 x 92mm

*Obverse—Brown on green and mauve underprint; "Ploughman"*
*Reverse—St Patrick's Bridge, Cork city*

**TEN POUNDS**
Size 189 x 107mm

*Obverse—Blue on green and mauve underprint; "Ploughman"*
*Reverse—Currency Commission Building, Foster Place, Dublin*

**TWENTY POUNDS**
Size 203 x 114mm

*Obverse—Red on yellow and mauve underprint; "Ploughman"*
*Reverse—Ruined Monastery on the Rock of Cashel, Co. Tipperary*

**FIFTY POUNDS**
Size 203 x 114mm

*Obverse—Mauve on yellow underprint; "Ploughman"*
*Reverse—View of Croagh Patrick Mountain, Co. Mayo*

**ONE HUNDRED POUNDS**
Size 203 x 114mm

*Obverse—Brown on mauve and yellow underprint; "Ploughman"*
*Reverse—View of Killiney Bay, Co. Dublin*

> **NB. £20, £50 and £100 notes exist only as Bank of Ireland Specimens. No issued notes remain. We illustrate them here but have not included them in the listings that follow.**

The catalogue numbering used in this section is as the standard work on the subject: *Irish Banknotes—Irish Paper Money from 1928* by Mártan Mac Devitt.

# THE BANK OF IRELAND

|  |  | VF | EF |
|---|---|---|---|

## ONE POUND

| | | VF | EF |
|---|---|---|---|
| E001 | *Signatures: Joseph Brennan and J. A. Gargan* <br> 1929–38. Prefix 01BA–89BA | £200 | £300 |
| E002 | *Signatures:: Joseph Brennan and H. J. Johnston* <br> 1939–40. Prefix 89BA–09BB | £200 | £350 |

## FIVE POUNDS

| | | VF | EF |
|---|---|---|---|
| E003 | *Signatures: Joseph Brennan and J. A. Gargan* <br> 1929–31. Prefix 01BK–02BK | £600 | £1000 |
| E004 | *Signatures: Joseph Brennan and H. J. Johnston* <br> 1939. 02BK–03BK | £600 | £1000 |

## TEN POUNDS

| | | VF | EF |
|---|---|---|---|
| E005 | *Signatures: Joseph Brennan and J. A. Gargan* <br> 1929. Prefix 01BT | £1400 | £2300 |

# HIBERNIAN BANK LTD.

## ONE POUND

| | | VF | EF |
|---|---|---|---|
| E009 | *Signatures: Joseph Brennan and H. J. Campbell*<br>1929–39. Prefix 01HA–22HA | £225 | £400 |
| E010 | *Joseph Brennan and A. K. Hodges*<br>1939–40. Prefix 23HA–24HA | £250 | £450 |

## FIVE POUNDS

| | | VF | EF |
|---|---|---|---|
| E011 | *Signatures: Joseph Brennan and H. J. Campbell*<br>1929–May 1939. Prefix 01HK–03HK | £700 | £1200 |

## TEN POUNDS

| | | VF | EF |
|---|---|---|---|
| E013 | *Signatures: Joseph Brennan and H. J. Campbell*<br>1929–31. Prefix 01HT | £1800 | £2500 |

# MUNSTER & LEINSTER BANK LTD.

## ONE POUND

| | | VF | EF |
|---|---|---|---|
| E016 | *Signatures: Joseph Brennan and J. L. Gubbins*<br>1929–35. Prefix 01MA–24MA | £200 | £300 |
| E017 | *Signatures: Joseph Brennan and A. E. Hosford*<br>1936–40. Prefix 26MA–50MA | £225 | £350 |

## FIVE POUNDS

| | | VF | EF |
|---|---|---|---|
| E018 | *Signatures: Joseph Brennan and J. L. Gubbins*<br>1929–33. Prefix 01MK–03MK | £600 | £1000 |
| E019 | *Signatures: Joseph Brennan and A. E. Hosford*<br>1938–39. Prefix 03MK | £600 | £1000 |

## TEN POUNDS

| | | VF | EF |
|---|---|---|---|
| E020 | *Signatures: Joseph Brennan and J. L. Gubbins*<br>1929–31. Prefix 01MT | £1200 | £2000 |
| E021 | *Signatures: Joseph Brennan and A. E. Hosford*<br>1938–39. Prefix 01MT | £1400 | £2300 |

# NATIONAL BANK LTD.

## ONE POUND

E025   *Signatures: Joseph Brennan and H. A. Russell*
1929–39. Prefix 01NA–44NA .................................................. £200      £300

## FIVE POUNDS

E026   *Signatures: Joseph Brennan and H. A. Russell*
1929–1939. Prefix 01NK–04NK ......................................... £480      £1000

## TEN POUNDS

E027   *Signatures: Joseph Brennan and J. L. Gubbins*
1929–39. Prefix 01NT ...................................................... £1200      £2000

# NORTHERN BANK LTD.

## ONE POUND

E028   *Signatures: Joseph Brennan and S. W. Knox*
1929. Prefix 01OA ................................................................ £1500      £1800
E029   *Signatures: Joseph Brennan and H. H. Stewart*
1931–33. Prefix 03EA–04EA............................................. £1000      £1500

## FIVE POUNDS

E032   *Signatures: Joseph Brennan and S. W. Knox*
1929. Prefix 01OK.............................................................. £2000      £3000
E033   *Signatures: Joseph Brennan and H. H. Stewart*
1931–33. Prefix 01EK ....................................................... £1500      £2000

## TEN POUNDS

E034   *Signatures: Joseph Brennan and S. W. Knox*
1929. Prefix 01OT ............................................... Rare      Rare

# PROVINCIAL BANK OF IRELAND LTD.

## ONE POUND

**E036**  *Signatures: Joseph Brennan and Hume Robertson*
1929. Prefix 01PA–06PA ............................................................ £250    £400
**E037**  *Signatures: Joseph Brennan and F. S. Forde*
1931–36. Prefix 07PA–13PA ...................................................... £215    £400
**E038**  *Signatures: Joseph Brennan and G. A. Kennedy*
1937–40. Prefix 13PA–23PA ...................................................... £215    £400

## FIVE POUNDS

**E039**  *Signatures: Joseph Brennan and Hume Robertson*
1929. Prefix 01PK.................................................................... £1000    £1500
**E040**  *Signatures: Joseph Brennan and F. S. Forde*
1931. Prefix 01PK–02PK............................................................ £600    £1000
**E041**  *Signatures: Joseph Brennan and G. A. Kennedy*
1939. Prefix 02PK.................................................................... £600    £1000

## TEN POUNDS

**E042**  *Signatures: Joseph Brennan and Hume Robertson*
*1929.* Prefix 01PT ................................................................. £1200    £2000
**E043**  *Signatures: Joseph Brennan and F. S. Forde*
*1931.* Prefix 01PT ................................................................. £1200    £2000
**E044**  *Signatures: Joseph Brennan and G. A. Kennedy*
*1939.* Prefix 01PT ................................................................. £1200    £2000

# ROYAL BANK OF IRELAND LTD.

## ONE POUND

**E046**  *Signatures: Joseph Brennan and G. A. Stanley*
1929. Prefix 01RA–08RA ........................................................... £350    £500
**E047**  *Signatures: Joseph Brennan and D. R. Mack*
1931–39. Prefix 009RA–26RA ..................................................... £285    £400
**E048**  *Signatures: Joseph Brennan and J. Wilson*
1939. Prefix 26RA–28RA ........................................................... £350    £500

## FIVE POUNDS

**E049**  *Signatures: Joseph Brennan and G. A. Stanley*
1929. Prefix 01RK.................................................................... £950    £1500
**E050**  *Signatures: Joseph Brennan and D. R. Mack*
1931. Prefix 01RK.................................................................... £950    £1500

## TEN POUNDS

**E052**  *Signatures: Joseph Brennan and G. A. Stanley*
1929. Prefix 01RT ................................................................... £2000    £3000

# ULSTER BANK LTD.

## ONE POUND

**E056** *Signatures: Joseph Brennan and C. W. Patton*
1929–39. Prefix 01UA–07UA.................................................................. £400　　　£500
**E057** *Signatures: Joseph Brennan and C. W. Lester*
1939–40. Prefix 08UA–12UA................................................................. £400　　　£500

## FIVE POUNDS

**E058** *Signatures: Joseph Brennan and C. W. Patton*
1929–33. Prefix 01UK.......................................................................... £900　　£1500
**E059** *Signatures: Joseph Brennan and C. W. Lester*
1938–39. Prefix 01UK–02UK................................................................ £950　　£1500

## TEN POUNDS

**E060** *Signatures: Joseph Brennan and C. W. Patton*
1929–39. Prefix 01UT......................................................................... £2000　£3000
**E061** *Signatures: Joseph Brennan and C. W. Lester*
1938–39. Prefix 01UT......................................................................... £2000　£3000

**For example illustrations of the "Ploughman" notes see pages 229–231.**

# SERIES A
# "LADY LAVERY" NOTES (1928–77)

Designs for the notes issued under the auspices of the Currency Commission
Irish Free State, the Currency Commission of Ireland and the Central Bank of
Ireland are virtually identical except for the values, titles and signatures. Notes
representative of the design, are illustrated below. (In keeping with the current
regulations for the reproduction of banknote illustrations, the serial numbers
have been obscured.)

**TEN SHILLINGS**
Size: 138 x 78mm

*Orange on green and mauve underprint.*

**ONE POUND**
Size: 151 x 84mm

*Green on pink and yellow underprint.*

**FIVE POUNDS**
Size: 166 x 92mm

*Brown on yellow and mauve underprint.*

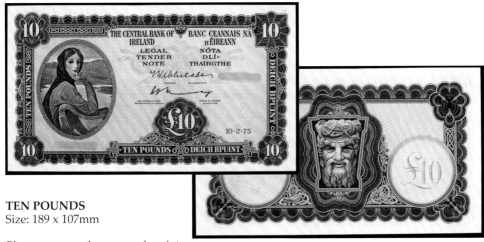

**TEN POUNDS**
Size: 189 x 107mm

*Blue on green and mauve underprint.*

**TWENTY POUNDS**
Size: 203 x 114mm

*Red on orange and mauve underprint.*

**FIFTY POUNDS**
Size: 203 x 114mm

*Mauve on yellow underprint.*

**ONE HUNDRED POUNDS**
Size: 203 x 114mm

*Black on yellow and mauve underprint.*

# CURRENCY COMMISSION IRISH FREE STATE

## TEN SHILLINGS

|  |  | *VF* | *EF* |
|---|---|---|---|
| *Signatures: Joseph Brennan and J. J. McElligott* | | | |
| E065 | Fractional prefix—Letter over Number (1928) | £250 | £1000 |
| E066 | Straight prefix—Number/Number/Letter (1929–37) | £100 | £175 |

## ONE POUND

| | *Signatures: Joseph Brennan and J. J. McElligott* | | |
|---|---|---|---|
| E075 | Fractional prefix—Letter over Number (1928) | £150 | £300 |
| E076 | Straight prefix—Number/Number/Letter (1930–37) | £70 | £150 |

## FIVE POUNDS

| | *Signatures: Joseph Brennan and J. J. McElligott* | | |
|---|---|---|---|
| E088 | Fractional prefix—Letter over Number (1928) | £175 | £500 |
| E089 | Straight prefix—Number/Number/Letter (1932–37) | £145 | £275 |

*Series A, "Lady Lavery". Currency Commission Irish Free State (continued)*   VF   EF

## TEN POUNDS

*Signatures: Joseph Brennan and J. J. McElligott*
E100  Fractional prefix—Letter over Number (1928)............................... £350  £1200
E101  Straight prefix—Number/Number/Letter (1932–33).................... £200  £1000

## TWENTY POUNDS

*Signatures: Joseph Brennan and J. J. McElligott*
E113  Fractional prefix—Letter over Number (1928)............................... £1200  £2500

## FIFTY POUNDS

*Signatures: Joseph Brennan and J. J. McElligott*
E121  Fractional prefix—Letter over Number (1928)............................... £1600  £4000

## ONE HUNDRED POUNDS

*Signatures: Joseph Brennan and J. J. McElligott*
E128  Fractional prefix—Letter over Number (1928)............................... £1600  £4000
E129  Straight prefix—Number/Number/Letter (1937).......................... £1250  £3000

# CURRENCY COMMISSION IRELAND

## TEN SHILLINGS

E067  *Signatures: Joseph Brennan and J. J. McElligott. With title of
Secretary of the Department of Finance as "Rúnaidhe na Roinne
Airgedais" (1938–39)* ..........................................................................  £100  £175
E068  *Signatures: Joseph Brennan and J. J. McElligott. With Emergency
Tracer Overprint codes H, K, J in circles (1940–41)* .............................  £50  £75

## ONE POUND

E077  *Signatures: Joseph Brennan and J. J. McElligott. "Rúnaidhe na Roinne
Airgedais" (1939)* ..........................................................................  £45  £75
E078  *Signatures: Joseph Brennan and J. J. McElligott. With ETO codes T,
B, P, V in circles (1941–42)* ................................................................  £45  £75

## FIVE POUNDS

E090  *Signatures: Joseph Brennan and J. J. McElligott "Rúnaidhe na Roinne
Airgedais" (1938–39)* ..........................................................................  £80  £140
E091  *Signatures: Joseph Brennan and J. J. McElligott. With ETO codes A,
C, D in circles (1940–42)*................................................................  £80  £140

         *VF*         *EF*

## TEN POUNDS

| | | | |
|---|---|---|---|
| **E102** | *Signatures: Joseph Brennan and J. J. McElligott. "Rúnaidhe na Roinne Airgedais"(1938–40)* ................................. | £120 | £285 |
| **E103** | *Signatures: Joseph Brennan and J. J. McElligott. With ETO codes E, F in circles (1941–42)* ................................. | £120 | £180 |

# CENTRAL BANK OF IRELAND

## TEN SHILLINGS

| | | | |
|---|---|---|---|
| **E069** | *Signatures: Joseph Brennan and J. J. McElligott. With ETO codes L, M, R, E in circles (1943–44)* ................................. | £55 | £75 |
| **E070** | *Signatures: Joseph Brennan and J. J. McElligott. ETO codes discontinued (1945–50)* ................................. | £25 | £40 |
| **E071** | *Signatures: Joseph Brennan and J. J. McElligott. Serial nos. extended (1951–52)* ................................. | £15 | £30 |
| **E072** | *Signatures: J. J. McElligott and O. J. Redmond (1955)* ................. | £25 | £65 |
| **E073** | *Signatures: J. J. McElligott and T. K. Whitaker (1957–59)* ............. | £10 | £20 |
| **E074** | *Signatures: M. Ó Muimhneacháin and T. K. Whitaker (1962–68)* ...... | £5 | £15 |

## ONE POUND

| | | | |
|---|---|---|---|
| **E079** | *Signatures: Joseph Brennan and J. J. McElligott. With ETO codes G, Y, E, F in circles (1943–44)* ................................. | £50 | £70 |
| **E080** | *Signatures: Joseph Brennan and J. J. McElligott. ETO codes discontinued (1945–50)* ................................. | £15 | £30 |
| **E081** | *Signatures: Joseph Brennan and J. J. McElligott. Serial nos. extended (1951–52)* ................................. | £5 | £20 |
| **E082** | *Signatures: J. J. McElligott and O. J. Redmond (1954–55)* ............. | £5 | £25 |
| **E083** | *Signatures: J. J. McElligott and T. K. Whitaker (1957–60)* ............. | £5 | £10 |
| **E084** | *Signatures: M. Ó Muimhneacháin and T. K. Whitaker (1962–68)* ...... | £5 | £10 |
| **E085** | *Signatures: T. K. Whitaker and C. H. Murray (1969–70)* ................. | £5 | £10 |
| **E086** | *Signatures: T. K. Whitaker and C. H. Murray. Metallic security thread introduced (1971–75)* ................................. | FV | £10 |
| **E087** | *Signatures: C. H. Murray and M. O. Murchú (1976)* ................... | FV | £5 |

## FIVE POUNDS

| | | | |
|---|---|---|---|
| **E092** | *Signatures: Joseph Brennan and J. J. McElligott. With ETO codes N, R, M in circles (1943–44)* ................................. | £80 | £140 |
| **E093** | *Signatures: Joseph Brennan and J. J. McElligott. ETO codes discontinued (1945–51)* ................................. | £35 | £60 |
| **E094** | *Signatures: Joseph Brennan and J. J. McElligott. Serial nos. extended (1952–53)* ................................. | £20 | £35 |
| **E095** | *Signatures: J. J. McElligott and O. J. Redmond (1954–55)* ............. | £20 | £55 |
| **E096** | *Signatures: J. J. McElligott and T. K. Whitaker (1957–60)* ............. | £20 | £35 |
| **E097** | *Signatures: M. Ó Muimhneacháin and T. K. Whitaker (1961–68)* ...... | £10 | £20 |
| **E098** | *Signatures: T. K. Whitaker and C. H. Murray (1969–70)* ................. | £10 | £20 |
| **E099** | *Signatures: T. K. Whitaker and C. H. Murray. Metallic security thread introduced (1971–75)* ................................. | £5 | £20 |

*Series A, "Lady Lavery". Central Bank of Ireland (continued)*          VF          EF

## TEN POUNDS

| | | | |
|---|---|---|---|
| E104 | Signatures: Joseph Brennan and J. J. McElligott. With ETO codes S, W, B, G in circles (1943–44) | £120 | £180 |
| E105 | Signatures: Joseph Brennan and J. J. McElligott. ETO codes discontinued (1945–52) | £30 | £75 |
| E106 | Signatures: J. J. McElligott and O. J. Redmond (1954–55) | £50 | £120 |
| E107 | Signatures: J. J. McElligott and T. K. Whitaker (1957–1960) | £30 | £60 |
| E108 | Signatures: J. J. McElligott and T. K. Whitaker. Serial numbers extended (1960) | £30 | £60 |
| E109 | Signatures: M. Ó Muimhneacháin and T. K. Whitaker (1962–1968) | £30 | £60 |
| E110 | Signatures: T. K. Whitaker and C. H. Murray (1969–1970) | £30 | £60 |
| E111 | Signatures: T. K. Whitaker and C. H. Murray. Metallic security thread introduced (1971–1974) | £45 | £75 |
| E112 | Signatures: C. H. Murray and M. O. Murchú (1976) | £50 | £75 |

## TWENTY POUNDS

| | | | |
|---|---|---|---|
| E114 | Signatures: Joseph Brennan and J. J. McElligott. With ETO code A in circle (1943–44) | £1400 | £2500 |
| E115 | Signatures: Joseph Brennan and J. J. McElligott. ETO codes discontinued (1945–52) | £150 | £250 |
| E116 | Signatures: J. J. McElligott and O. J. Redmond (1954–55) | £100 | £250 |
| E117 | Signatures: J. J. McElligott and T. K. Whitaker (1957) | £100 | £180 |
| E118 | Signatures: M. Ó Muimhneacháin and T. K. Whitaker (1961–65) | £30 | £100 |
| E119 | Signatures: T. K. Whitaker and C. H. Murray (1969–75) | £30 | £50 |
| E120 | Signatures: T. K. Whitaker and M. O. Murchú (1976) | £30 | £50 |

## FIFTY POUNDS

| | | | |
|---|---|---|---|
| E122 | Signatures: Joseph Brennan and J. J. McElligott (1943–51) | £250 | £600 |
| E123 | Signatures: J. J. McElligott and O. J. Redmond (1954–55) | £250 | £600 |
| E124 | Signatures: J. J. McElligott and T. K. Whitaker (1957–60) | £175 | £400 |
| E125 | Signatures: M. Ó Muimhneacháin and T. K. Whitaker (1962–68) | £100 | £200 |
| E126 | Signatures: T. K. Whitaker and C. H. Murray (1970–75) | £90 | £175 |
| E127 | Signatures: C. H. Murray and M. O. Murchú (1977) | £70 | £130 |

## ONE HUNDRED POUNDS

| | | | |
|---|---|---|---|
| E130 | Signatures: Joseph Brennan and J. J. McElligott (1943–49) | £285 | £600 |
| E131 | Signatures: J. J. McElligott and O. J. Redmond (1954) | £250 | £600 |
| E132 | Signatures: J. J. McElligott and T. K. Whitaker (1959) | £200 | £400 |
| E133 | Signatures: M. Ó Muimhneacháin and T. K. Whitaker (1963–68) | £150 | £275 |
| E134 | Signatures: T. K. Whitaker and C. H. Murray (1970–75) | £130 | £220 |
| E135 | Signatures: C. H. Murray and M. O. Murchú (1977) | £120 | £200 |

For a concise and complete study of the notes of Ireland
visit the website
**www.irishpapermoney.com**

# CENTRAL BANK OF IRELAND
# SERIES B NOTES, 1976–93

## ONE POUND

**1976–93 ISSUE**

*Green on multicoloured underprint. Obverse—Portrait of Queen Medb, legendary Queen of Connaught. Next to portrait is an early Irish geometric design.*
*Reverse—Decorated excerpt from Lebor na hUidre.*
*Size 150 x 78mm*

|  |  | EF | UNC |
|---|---|---|---|
| **E136** | *Signatures: C. H. Murray and M. O. Murchú (1977)* ......................... | £3 | £8 |
| **E137** | *Signatures: C. H. Murray and Tomás F. Ó Cofaigh (1978–81)* ............. | £3 | £8 |
| **E138** | *Signatures: Tomás F. Ó Cofaigh and Maurice F. Doyle (1982–87)* ....... | £3 | £8 |
| **E139** | *Signatures: Maurice F. Doyle and S. P. Cromien (1988–89)* ................ | £3 | £8 |

## FIVE POUNDS

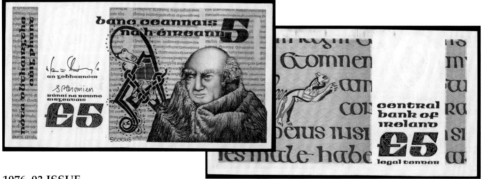

**1976–93 ISSUE**

*Brown on multicoloured underprint. Obverse—Portrait of philosopher John Scots Eriugena (c. 828–878).*
*Reverse—Extract from the Book of Kells.*
*Size 156 x 83mm*

| **E140** | *Signatures: T. K. Whitaker and C. H. Murray (1976)* ......................... | £15 | £30 |
|---|---|---|---|
| **E141** | *Signatures: C. H. Murray and M. O Murchú (1976–77)* ..................... | £8 | £20 |
| **E142** | *Signatures: C. H. Murray and Tomás F. Ó Cofaigh (1979–81)* ............ | £8 | £20 |
| **E143** | *Signatures: Tomás F. Ó Cofaigh and Maurice F. Doyle (1983–87)* ....... | £8 | £20 |
| **E144** | *Signatures: Maurice F. Doyle and S. P. Cromien (1988–93)* ................ | £8 | £20 |

*Central Bank of Ireland. Series B (continued)*       *EF*      *UNC*

# TEN POUNDS

### 1976–93 ISSUE
*Purple on multicoloured underprint. Obverse—Portrait of Jonathan Swift (1667–1745), Dean of St Patrick's Cathedral, Dublin.*
*Reverse—Famous map of Dublin by John Rocques, first published 1756.*
*Size 164 x 86mm*

| | | | |
|---|---|---|---|
| **E145** | *Signatures: C. H. Murray and Tomás F. Ó Cofaigh (1978–81)*............ | £15 | £40 |
| **E146** | *Signatures: Tomás F. Ó Cofaigh and Maurice F. Doyle (1983–87)* ...... | £15 | £30 |
| **E147** | *Signatures: Maurice F. Doyle and S. P. Cromien (1987–93)*............... | £15 | £30 |

# TWENTY POUNDS

### 1976–93 ISSUE
*Blue on multicoloured underprint. Obverse—Portrait of poet and writer William Butler Yeats (1865–1939).*
*Reverse—Group of the Blasket Islands of the Kerry coast.*
*Size 172 x 90mm*

| | | | |
|---|---|---|---|
| **E148** | *Signatures: C. H. Murray and Tomás F. Ó Cofaigh (1980–81)*............. | £25 | £70 |
| **E149** | *Signatures: Tomás F. Ó Cofaigh and Maurice F. Doyle (1983–86)* ....... | £25 | £60 |
| **E150** | *Signatures: Maurice F. Doyle and S. P. Cromien (1988–89)*................ | £22 | £45 |

## FIFTY POUNDS

**1976–93 ISSUE**
*Brown on multicoloured underprint. Obverse—Portrait of harpist and composer Turlough Ó Carolan (1670–1738).*
*Reverse—Design based on the wood carving in the organ loft of St Michans Church, Dublin.*
*Size 180 x 94mm*

| | | EF | UNC |
|---|---|---|---|
| **E151** | *Signatures: Tomás F. Ó Cofaigh and Maurice F. Doyle (1982)*............. | £65 | £130 |
| **E152** | *Signatures: Maurice F. Doyle and S. P. Cromien (1991)* ..................... | £60 | £100 |

EF          UNC

# CENTRAL BANK OF IRELAND
# SERIES C NOTES, 1992–2001

## FIVE POUNDS

**1992–2001 ISSUE**
*Brown and blue on multicoloured underprint. Obverse—Catherine Macauley (1778–1841), foundress*
*of the Catholic Order of the Sisters of Mercy.*
*Reverse—A classroom scene.*
*Size 120 x 64mm*

| | | | | |
|---|---|---|---|---|
| **E153** | *Signatures: Maurice F. Doyle and S. P. Cromien (1994)* ...................... | — | £20 |
| **E154** | *Signatures: Muiris S. Ó Conaill and P. Mullarkey (Dec. 1994–97)* ..... | — | £20 |
| **E155** | *Signatures: Muiris S. Ó Conaill and P. Mullarkey (Dec. 1998)* ........... | — | £10 |

## TEN POUNDS

**1992–2001 ISSUE**
*Brown, blue and green on multicoloured underprint. Obverse—James Joyce (1882–1941).*
*Reverse— River mask sculpture from the Dublin Custom House.*
*Size 128 x 68mm*

| | | | | |
|---|---|---|---|---|
| **E156** | *Signatures: Maurice F. Doyle and S. P. Cromien (1993–94)* ................ | — | £20 |
| **E157** | *Signatures: Muiris S. Ó Conaill and P. Mullarkey (1995–97)* ............. | — | £20 |
| **E158** | *Signatures: Muiris S. Ó Conaill and P. Mullarkey (Dec. 1997–98)* ..... | — | £15 |

*Central Bank of Ireland. Series C (continued)*                              EF        UNC

# TWENTY POUNDS

**1992–2001 ISSUE**
*Mauve and brown on multicoloured underprint. Obverse—Daniel O'Connell (1775–1847).*
*Reverse—Four Courts Building, Dublin.*
*Size 136 x 72mm*

E159  *Signatures: Maurice F. Doyle and S. P. Cromien (1992–94)* .................    —          £40
E160  *Signatures: Muiris S. Ó Conaill and P. Mullarkey (1995–97)* ...............    —          £35
E161  *Signatures: Muiris S. Ó Conaill and P. Mullarkey. With prefix letters*
       *M–Z (O and Q not used) (1997–98)* ......................................................    —          £30

# FIFTY POUNDS

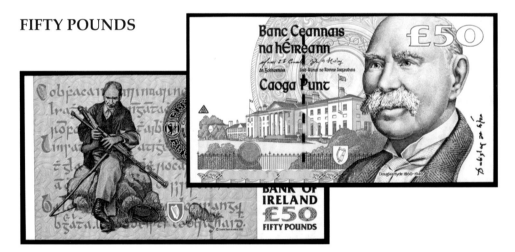

**1992–2001 ISSUE**
*Blue and green on multicoloured underprint. Obverse—Douglas Hyde (1860–1949).*
*Reverse—An uillean piper.*
*Size 144 x 76mm*

E162  *Signatures: Muiris S. Ó Conaill and P. Mullarkey  (1995–96)* ..............    —          £85
E164  *Signatures: Muiris S. Ó Conaill and P. Mullarkey. New design security*
       *thread introduced  (1999)* ........................................................................    —          £85
E165  *Signatures: Muiris S. Ó Conaill and John A. Hurley  (2001)* ................    —          £85

# ONE HUNDRED POUNDS

**1992–2001 ISSUE**
*Purple, red and blue on multicoloured underprint. Obverse— Charles Stewart Parnell (1846–1891).*
*Reverse—Parnell Monument, O'Connell Street, Dublin.*
*Size 152 x 80mm*

**E163**  *Signatures: Muiris S. Ó Conaill and P. Mullarkey (1996)*....................  £110          £160

# NORTHERN IRELAND
## ALLIED IRISH BANKS LIMITED

Formed in 1966 as a result of a merger of the Provincial Bank of Ireland Ltd. with the Munster & Leinster Bank and The Royal Bank of Ireland. The Banknotes share a common design with the last issues of the Provincial Bank. In the early 1990's the Allied Irish Banks plc merged with the Trustee Savings Bank to form the First Trust Bank.

## ONE POUND

Size 134 mm x 67 mm approximately

*Obverse—green and brown on a multicoloured underprint. Portrait of a teenage boy to the right*
*Reverse—mainly green. Illustration of the Spanish galleass "The Girona" at the centre*

| | | *EF* | *UNC* |
|---|---|---|---|
| **NI.101** | *Signatory: P. O'Keiffe (Group Chief Executive).* | | |
| | Prefix PN dated 1.1.1982............................................... | £15 | £22 |
| | Prefix ZY—replacement note........................................ | £45 | £70 |

# FIVE POUNDS

Size 146 mm x 78 mm approximately

*Obverse—blue and purple on a multicoloured underprint. Portrait of a young lady to the right*
*Reverse—mainly blue. Illustration of Dunluce Castle at the centre*

| | | EF | UNC |
|---|---|---|---|
| **NI.102** | Signatory: P. O'Keiffe (Group Chief Executive). | | |
| | Prefix QN dated 1.1.1982; 1.7.1983 and 1.12.1984 ...................... | £25 | £40 |
| | Prefix ZY—replacement note........................................................ | £45 | £85 |

# TEN POUNDS

Size 150 mm x 84 mm approximately

*Obverse—brown and purple on a multicoloured underprint. Portrait of a young man to the right*
*Reverse—mainly brown. Illustration of the sinking of the Spanish galleass The Girona at the centre*

| | | | |
|---|---|---|---|
| **NI.103** | Signatory: P. O'Keiffe (Group Chief Executive). | | |
| | Prefix RN dated 1.1.1982; 1.7.1983 and 1.12.1984...................... | £40 | £60 |
| | Prefix ZY—replacement note........................................................ | £75 | £120 |

# TWENTY POUNDS

Size 160 mm x 90 mm approximately

*Obverse—mauve on a multicoloured underprint. Portrait of a mature lady to the right*
*Reverse—mauve on a multicoloured underprint. Illustration of rock chimney at Lacada Point at the centre*

| **NI.104** | Signatory: P. O'Keiffe (Group Chief Executive). | *EF* | *UNC* |
|---|---|---|---|
| | Prefix SN dated 1.1.1982; 1.7.1983 and 1.12.1984 ........................ | £80 | £120 |
| | Prefix ZY—replacement note........................................................ | | probably exists |

# ONE HUNDRED POUNDS

Size 160 mm x 90 mm approximately

*Obverse—black green and olive on a multicoloured underprint. Portrait of an older man to the right*
*Reverse—black on a mainly green underprint. Illustration of the Spanish Armada at the centre*

| **NI.105** | Signatory: P. O'Keiffe (Group Chief Executive). | | |
|---|---|---|---|
| | Prefix TN dated 1.1.1982................................................... | £320 | £450 |
| | Prefix ZY—replacement note........................................................ | | probably exists |

# ALLIED IRISH BANKS P.L.C.

## FIVE POUNDS

Size 146 mm x 78 mm approximately

*Obverse—blue and purple on a multicoloured underprint. Portrait of a young lady to the right
Reverse—mainly blue. Illustration of Dunluce Castle at the centre*

| | | EF | UNC |
|---|---|---|---|
| **NI.106** | *Signatory: G. B. Scanlon (Group Chief Executive).* | | |
| | Prefix QN and UN dated 1.1.1987 and 1.1.1990......................... | £22 | £35 |
| | Prefix ZY—replacement note........................................................ | £50 | £80 |

# TEN POUNDS

Size 150 mm x 84 mm approximately

*Obverse—brown and purple on a multicoloured underprint. Portrait of a young man to the right*
*Reverse—mainly brown. Illustration of the sinking of the Spanish galleon The Girona at the centre*

| | | EF | UNC |
|---|---|---|---|
| **NI.107** | Signatory: G. B. Scanlon (Group Chief Executive). | | |
| | Prefix RN dated 1.1.1986 to prefix WN dated 18.5.1993 ........... | £35 | £45 |
| | Prefix ZY—replacement note...................................................... | £65 | £95 |

# TWENTY POUNDS

Size 160 mm x 90 mm approximately

*Obverse—red and maroon on a multicoloured underprint. Portrait of an older woman to the right*
*Reverse—maroon on a multicoloured underprint. Illustration of rock chimney at Lacada Point at the centre*

| | | | |
|---|---|---|---|
| **NI.108** | Signatory: G. B. Scanlon (Group Chief Executive). | | |
| | Prefix SN dated 1.1.1987, 1.4.1987 and 1.1.1990 ......................... | £55 | £70 |
| | Prefix ZY—replacement note...................................................... | | probably exists |

# ONE HUNDRED POUNDS

Size 160 mm x 90 mm approximately

*Obverse—black, green and olive on a multicoloured underprint. Portrait of an older man to the right*
*Reverse—black on a mainly green underprint. Illustration of the Spanish Armada at the centre*

| | | EF | UNC |
|---|---|---|---|
| **NI.109** | *Signatory: G. B. Scanlon (Group Chief Executive).* | | |
| | Prefix TN dated 1.12.1988............................................................ | £260 | £370 |
| | Prefix ZY—replacement note........................................................ | | probably exists |

# BANK OF IRELAND

Established in Dublin by royal charter in 1783, the Bank of Ireland quickly became the dominant force in Irish banking despite having no branch offices. For many years no rival bank was permitted by law to have more than six partners or shareholders, which led to the setting up of a large number of small and inadequately capitalised banks throughout Ireland.

Around 1820 many of these banks failed, but still the Bank of Ireland refused to establish branches outside Dublin, leading to an amendment in the law to permit the establishment of joint stock banking companies in Ireland from 1824 onwards. This change persuaded the Bank of Ireland to immediately open branch offices in order to compete with its new rivals.

For a time the Bank of Ireland retained some privileges, in that prior to 1845 no note-issuing joint stock bank was permitted to carry on business anywhere within a 65 mile radius of Dublin. Even after it lost that advantage, the Bank of Ireland remained by far the largest Irish bank until recent years. It was the Government banker and acted in a similar capacity to the Bank of England, whilst at the same time offering a full range of clearing bank services through a widespread branch network. Until 1929 it had a dominant share of the Irish note issue.

The Bank of Ireland's position was further strengthened when it took over the Hibernian Bank in 1958, and seven years later acquired the Irish business of the National Bank. However, Allied Irish Banks has recently come to rival it in size and profitability.

## ONE POUND

Size 150 mm x 83 mm approximately

*Obverse — black and green on a blue underprint. Statues of Hibernia to the left and right*
*Reverse — blue and green; Hibernia seated in a round panel with sunburst effect*

| | | | F | VF |
|---|---|---|---|---|
| **NI.201a** | *Signatory: J. H. Craig.* | | | |
| | Prefix B/10 dated 6.5.1929 and prefix B/11 dated 8.5.1929..... | | £70 | £120 |
| | | | | |
| **NI.201b** | *Signatory: G. W. Frazer.* | | | |
| | Prefix B/12 dated 3.4.1933 and prefix B/13 dated 9.3.1936..... | | £50 | £85 |

*Obverse—black and blue on a green underprint. Statues of Hibernia to the left and right*
*Reverse—Hibernia seated in a blue panel with green underprint*

|  |  | VF | EF |
|---|---|---|---|
| **NI.202a** | *Signatory: G. W. Frazer.* | | |
| | Prefix B/13 dated 9.3.1936 to prefix B17 dated 1.11.1940......... | £70 | £120 |
| **NI.202b** | *Signatory: H. J. Adams.* | | |
| | Prefix B/18 dated 23.2.1942 to prefix B/21 dated 15.11.1943 .. | £400 | £700 |

Size 150 mm x 70 mm approximately

First issued in 1967
*Obverse—blue grey on a multicoloured underprint. Hibernia to the right*
*Reverse—blue grey; Bank of Ireland building surrounded by images representing industry in Northern Ireland*

| | | EF | UNC |
|---|---|---|---|
| **NI.203** | *Signatory: W. E. Guthrie (Agent)* | | |
| | Prefix A to prefix C ........................................................ | £28 | £40 |

Size 135 mm x 66mm approximately

Design similar to previous issue. First issued in 1972. Value sign at top right and bottom left is shown as "1".
*Obverse – blue grey on a multicoloured underprint. Hibernia to the right*
*Reverse – blue grey; Bank of Ireland building surrounded by images representing industry in Northern Ireland*

| | | | |
|---|---|---|---|
| **NI.204a** | *Signatory: H. H. M. Chestnutt (Manager)* | | |
| | Prefix D and E................................................................ | £20 | £30 |
| | Prefix Z—replacement note ...................................... | | Rare |
| | | | |
| **NI.204b** | *Signatory: A. S. J. O'Neill (Manager)* | | |
| | Prefix E and F................................................................ | £10 | £18 |
| | Prefix Z—replacement note ...................................... | £55 | — |

"Sterling" added at centre and value sign at top right and bottom left is now shown as "£1". (From 1984)

| NI.205 | Signatory: A. S. J. O'Neill (Manager) | EF | UNC |
|---|---|---|---|
| | Prefix G and H ............................................................................ | £8 | £12 |
| | Prefix Z—replacement note ....................................................... | £8 | £12 |

## FIVE POUNDS

Size 178 mm x 97 mm approximately

*Obverse—black and red on an orange/yellow underprint. Statues of Hibernia to the left and right*
*Reverse—red panel on an orange underprint. Hibernia seated at the centre*

| NI.211a | Signatory: J. H. Craig. | F | VF |
|---|---|---|---|
| | Prefix S/10 dated 5.5.1929 and 15.5.1929 .................................. | £75 | £140 |
| | Prefix S/11 dated 7.5.1929 ........................................................ | £75 | £140 |
| | | | |
| NI.211b | Signatory: G. W. Frazer. | | |
| | Prefix S/12 dated 15.8.1935 to prefix S/15 dated 2.12.1940..... | £50 | £95 |
| | | | |
| NI.211c | Signatory: H. J. Adams. | VF | EF |
| | Prefix S/16 dated 16.2.1942 to prefix S/23 dated 20.12.1943... | £60 | £110 |
| | | | |
| NI.211d | Signatory: S. G. Skuce. | | |
| | Prefix S/24 dated 1.9.1958 and prefix S/25 dated 1.10.1958 ... | £55 | £100 |

Size 140 mm x 85 mm approximately

First issued in 1967
*Obverse—blue grey on a brown/violet underprint. Hibernia to the right*
*Reverse—blue grey; Bank of Ireland building surrounded by images representing industry in Northern Ireland*

|  |  | VF | EF |
|---|---|---|---|
| **NI.212a** | *Signatory: W. E. Guthrie (Agent)* | | |
| | Prefix M ......................................................................... | £120 | £220 |
| **NI.212b** | *Signatory: H. H. M. Chestnutt (Agent)* | | |
| | Prefix M....................................................................... | £120 | £220 |

Size 146 mm x 77 mm approximately

Design similar to previous issue. First issued in 1972. Value sign at top right and bottom left is shown as "5".
*Obverse—blue grey on a multicoloured underprint. Hibernia to the right*
*Reverse—blue grey; Bank of Ireland building surrounded by images representing industry in Northern Ireland*

|  |  | EF | UNC |
|---|---|---|---|
| **NI.213a** | *Signatory: H. H. M. Chestnutt (Manager)* | | |
| | Prefix N and prefix P.................................................... | £50 | £90 |
| | Prefix Z—replacement note ......................................... | | Rare |
| **NI.213b** | *Signatory: A. S. J. O'Neill (Manager)* | | |
| | Prefix Q and prefix R.................................................... | £40 | £80 |
| | Prefix Z—replacement note ......................................... | | Rare |

"Sterling" added at centre and value sign at top right and bottom left is now shown as "£5". (From 1984)

| | | EF | UNC |
|---|---|---|---|
| **NI.214a** | *Signatory: A. S. J. O'Neill (Manager)* | | |
| | Prefix R and S................................................................. | £45 | £85 |
| | Prefix Z—replacement note ........................................ | £110 | ---- |
| | | | |
| **NI.214b** | *Signatory: D. J. Harrison (Manager)* | | |
| | Prefix S to prefix V...................................................... | £25 | £40 |
| | Prefix Z—replacement note ........................................ | £80 | ----- |

Size 136 mm x 70 mm approximately

*Obverse—blue and violet on a multicoloured underprint. Hibernia to the left*
*Reverse—blue and multicoloured. Illustration of the Queen's University of Belfast*

| | | | |
|---|---|---|---|
| **NI.215** | *Signatory: D. J. Harrison (Manager)* | | |
| | Prefix A dated 28.8.1990 to prefix U dated 1.7.1994.................. | £14 | £22 |
| | Prefix Z—replacement note ........................................ | £40 | £60 |

Similar to previous issue with bolder colours.
*Obverse—blue and purple on a multicoloured underprint. Hibernia to the left*
*Reverse—blue and multicoloured. Illustration of the Queen's University of Belfast*

| | | | EF | UNC |
|---|---|---|---|---|
| **NI.216a** | *Signatory: G. McGinn (Chief Executive N.I.)* | | | |
| | Prefix U dated 1.7.1997 to prefix Y dated 4.8.1998, and | | | |
| | Prefix AA dated 4.8.1998 to prefix AY dated 5.9.2000............... | | ------ | £12 |
| | Prefix Z—replacement note ......................................................... | | £18 | £25 |
| | | | | |
| **NI.216b** | *Signatory: M. S. Soden (Group Chief Executive).* | | | |
| | Prefix AY to prefix BL dated 1.3.2003 and ongoing. ................. | | ------ | £10 |
| | Prefix Z—replacement note ......................................................... | | £18 | £25 |

# TEN POUNDS

Size 200 mm x 108 mm approximately

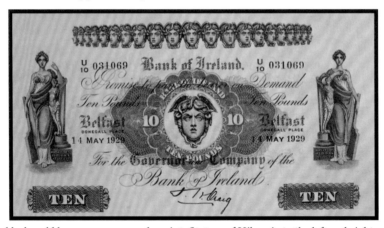

*Obverse—black and blue on an green underprint. Statues of Hibernia to the left and right*
*Reverse—blue panel on a green underprint. Hibernia seated at the centre*

| | | F | VF |
|---|---|---|---|
| **NI.221a** | *Signatory: J. H. Craig.* | | |
| | Prefix U/10 dated 4.5.1929 and 14.5.1929. .................................. | £140 | £280 |
| | | VF | EF |
| **NI.221b** | *Signatory: H. J. Adams.* | | |
| | Prefix U/11 dated 26.1.1942 and prefix U/12 dated 19.1.1943 | £80 | £150 |

Size 150 mm x 93 mm approximately

First issued in 1967
*Obverse—brown on a multicoloured underprint. Hibernia to the right*
*Reverse—brown and grey; Bank of Ireland building surrounded by images representing industry in Northern Ireland*

|  |  | VF | EF |
|---|---|---|---|
| **NI.222** | *Signatory: W. E. Guthrie (Agent)* |  |  |
|  | Prefix T ......................................................................................... | £200 | £400 |

Size 152 mm x 85 mm approximately

Design similar to previous issue. First issued in 1972. Value sign at top right and bottom left is shown as "10".
*Obverse—brown on a multicoloured underprint. Hibernia to the right*
*Reverse—brown on a green underprint; Bank of Ireland building surrounded by images representing industry in Northern Ireland*

|  |  | EF | UNC |
|---|---|---|---|
| **NI.223a** | *Signatory: H. H. M. Chestnutt (Manager)* |  |  |
|  | Prefix U........................................................................................ | £220 | £320 |
| **NI.223b** | *Signatory: A. S. J. O'Neill (Manager)* |  |  |
|  | Prefix U and prefix V.................................................................. | £120 | £180 |
|  | Prefix Z—replacement note .......................................................... |  | Rare |

"Sterling" added at centre and value sign at top right and bottom left is now shown as "£10". (From 1984)

| **NI.224a** | Signatory: A. S. J. O'Neill (Manager) | EF | UNC |
|---|---|---|---|
| | Prefix V and prefix W................................................................. | £60 | £90 |
| | Prefix Z—replacement ................................................................. | | Rare |
| | | | |
| **NI.224b** | Signatory: D. J. Harrison (Manager) | | |
| | Prefix X and prefix Y, and............................................................ | £45 | £65 |
| | Prefix AA to AF | | |
| | Prefix Z—replacement note ........................................................ | £130 | --- |

Size 142 mm x 75 mm approximately

*Obverse—purple and maroon on a multicoloured underprint. Hibernia to the left*
*Reverse—maroon and multicoloured. Illustration of the Queen's University of Belfast*

| **NI.225** | Signatory: D. J. Harrison (Manager) | | |
|---|---|---|---|
| | Prefix A dated 14.5.1991 to prefix P dated 28.5.1992.................. | £28 | £45 |
| | Prefix Z—replacement note ........................................................ | £50 | £80 |

Similar to previous design.
*Obverse—blue and brown on a multicoloured underprint. Hibernia to the left*
*Reverse—maroon and multicoloured. Illustration of the Queen's University of Belfast*

| | | EF | UNC |
|---|---|---|---|
| **NI.226a** | *Signatory: G. McGinn (Chief Executive N. I.)*................................ | | |
| | Prefix R dated 1.7.1995 to prefix BB dated 5.9.2000 and ongoing. | --- | £26 |
| | Prefix Z—replacement note. ........................................................ | | £50 |
| | | | |
| **NI.226b** | *Signatory: D. McGowan (Chief Executive N. I.)* ........................... | | |
| | Prefix BE to prefix BM dated 1.5.2005 and ongoing. ................ | --- | £20 |
| | Prefix Z—replacement note. ........................................................ | | £40 |

# TWENTY POUNDS

Size 200 mm x 108 mm approximately

*Obverse—black on an orange/brown and pale green underprint. Statues of Hibernia to the left and right*
*Reverse—orange/brown panel on a pale green underprint. Hibernia seated at the centre*

| | | F | VF |
|---|---|---|---|
| **NI.231** | *Signatory: J. H. Craig.* | | |
| | Prefix X/10 dated 9.5.1929 (print run of just 2,500 notes). ...... | | Rare |

Size 160 mm x 90 mm approximately

Issued in 1983 to commemorate the bicentenary anniversary of the Bank of Ireland 1783–1983.
*Obverse—green on a multicoloured underprint. Hibernia to the right*
*Reverse—mainly green; Bank of Ireland building surrounded by images representing industry in Northern Ireland*

| **NI.232** | Signatory: A. S. J. O'Neill (Manager) | *VF* | *EF* |
|---|---|---|---|
| | Prefix A.................................................................... | £250 | £400 |
| | Prefix Z—replacement note ...................................................... | | Rare |

Similar to the above note but without the commemorative text near the top. (From 1984)
*Obverse—green on a multicoloured underprint. Hibernia to the right*
*Reverse—mainly green; Bank of Ireland building surrounded by images representing industry in Northern Ireland*

| **NI.233a** | Signatory: A. S. J. O'Neill (Manager) | *EF* | *UNC* |
|---|---|---|---|
| | Prefix A and prefix B ...................................... | £110 | £160 |
| | Prefix Z—replacement note ...................................................... | | Rare |
| | | | |
| **NI.233b** | Signatory: D. J. Harrison (Manager) | | |
| | Prefix B to prefix F ........................................ | £70 | £100 |
| | Prefix Z—replacement note. ...................................................... | £130 | £180 |

Size 150 mm x 80 mm approximately

*Obverse—green and brown on a multicoloured underprint. Hibernia seated in a roundel to the left*
*Reverse—mainly green on a multicoloured underprint. Illustration of the Queen's University of Belfast*

| | | *EF* | *UNC* |
|---|---|---|---|
| **NI.234** | *Signatory: D. J. Harrison (Manager)* | | |
| | Prefix A dated 9.5.1991 to prefix K dated 28.5.1993. ................. | £45 | £70 |
| | Prefix Z – replacement note ........................................................ | £90 | £140 |

Similar to previous issue with some design and colour changes.
*Obverse—green, brown and purple on a multicoloured underprint. Hibernia seated in a roundel to the left*
*Reverse—mainly green on a multicoloured underprint. Illustration of the Queen's University of Belfast*

| | | | |
|---|---|---|---|
| **NI.235** | *Signatory: G. McGinn (Chief Executive N. I.)* | | |
| | Prefix L dated 1.7.1995 to prefix V dated 1.7.1997 ................... | £35 | £50 |
| | Prefix Z – replacement note. ........................................................ | | £80 |
| **NI.236a** | *Signatory: G. McGinn (Chief Executive N. I.)* | | |
| | Prefix W dated 1.1.1999 to prefix BC dated 5.9.2000 ............... | --- | £45 |
| | Prefix Z – replacement note ........................................................ | £50 | £70 |
| **NI.236b** | *Signatory: D. McGowan (Chief Executive N. I.)* | | |
| | Prefix BD dated 1.1.2003 to prefix CJ dated 1.3.2005............... | --- | £35 |
| | Prefix Z – replacement note. ........................................................ | --- | £60 |

# FIFTY POUNDS

Size 156 mm x 85 mm approximately

*Obverse—green, brown and blue on a multicoloured underprint. Hibernia seated in a roundel to the left*
*Reverse—mainly brown on a multicoloured underprint. Illustration of the Queen's University of Belfast*

|  |  | EF | UNC |
|---|---|---|---|
| **NI.241a** | Signatory: G. McGinn (Chief Executive N. I.)................................ | | |
| | Prefix A dated 1.7.1995................................................................ | £90 | £110 |
| **NI.241b** | Signatory: R. Keenan (Chief Executive U.K.).................................. | | |
| | Prefix A dated 5.4.2004 (starting from A 200001) ...................... | ---- | £95 |

# ONE HUNDRED POUNDS

Size 160 mm x 90 mm approximately

First issued in 1974. Value sign at top right and bottom left is shown as "100".
*Obverse—red on a multicoloured underprint. Hibernia to the right*
*Reverse—mainly red; Bank of Ireland building surrounded by images representing industry in Northern Ireland*

|  |  | VF | EF |
|---|---|---|---|
| **NI.251a** | Signatory: H. H. M. Chestnutt (Manager) | | |
| | Prefix A........................................................................................ | £450 | ------ |
| **NI.251b** | Signatory: A. S. J. O'Neill (Manager) | | |
| | Prefix A........................................................................................ | £350 | ------- |

"Sterling" added at centre and value sign at top right and bottom left is now shown as "£100". (From 1984)

| | | EF | UNC |
|---|---|---|---|
| **NI.252a** | *Signatory: A. S. J. O'Neill (Manager)* | | |
| | Prefix A........................................................................................ | £350 | £450 |
| **NI.252b** | *Signatory: D. J. Harrison (Manager)* | | |
| | Prefix A........................................................................................ | £250 | £340 |

Size 164 mm x 90 mm approximately

*Obverse—red and brown on a multicoloured underprint. Hibernia seated in a roundel to the left*
*Reverse—mainly red on a multicoloured underprint. Illustration of the Queen's University of Belfast*

| | | | |
|---|---|---|---|
| **NI.253** | *Signatory: D. J. Harrison (Manager)* | | |
| | Prefix A dated 28.8.1992................................................. | £220 | £300 |

*Obverse—red, mauve, brown and blue on a multicoloured underprint. Hibernia seated in a roundel to the left.*
*Reverse—mainly mauve on a multicoloured underprint. Illustration of the Queen's University of Belfast.*

|  |  | EF | UNC |
|---|---|---|---|
| **NI.254a** | *Signatory: G. McGinn (Chief Executive N. I.)* | | |
| | Prefix A dated 1.7.1995 | £170 | £280 |
| | Prefix Z—replacement note | £300 | £450 |
| **NI.254b** | *Signatory: G. McGowan (Chief Executive N. I.)* | | |
| | Prefix A dated 1.3.2005 | --- | £190 |
| | Prefix Z—replacement note | £250 | £360 |

# BELFAST BANKING COMPANY LIMITED

The Belfast Banking Company was formed in Belfast in 1827, taking over the business of two local private banking partnerships which dated back to 1808 and 1809. In 1917 it was acquired by the London City and Midland Bank, and six years later all of its branches in what was then the Irish Free State were sold off to the Royal Bank of Ireland. This made the Belfast Bank the only Irish note-issuing bank which had no branches outside Northern Ireland.

The Midland Bank made a successful takeover bid for the Northern Bank in 1965, and in July 1970 the Belfast Bank's separate existence ended when the Midland's two Irish subsidiaries were merged in the name of the Northern Bank Limited.

## ONE POUND

Size 152 mm x 84 mm approximately

*Obverse—black with a blue value panel at the centre*
*Reverse—blue panel with the name of the bank and value*

|  |  | F | VF |
|---|---|---|---|
| **NI.301a** | *Handsigned, with black serial numbers*<br>Prefix A dated 2.1.1922 to prefix E/E dated 8.11.1928 ............. | £110 | £180 |

|  |  | EF | UNC |
|---|---|---|---|
| **NI.301b** | *Handsigned, with blue serial numbers*<br>Prefix E/F dated 9.11.1939 to prefix F/G dated 10.8.1940 ...... | £45 | £65 |

# FIVE POUNDS

Size 185 mm x 90 mm approximately

*Obverse—black with the value in red at the centre*
*Reverse—red panel with the name of the bank and value*

| | | F | VF |
|---|---|---|---|
| **NI.302a** | *Handsigned, with black serial numbers* | F | VF |
| | Prefix B/G dated 3.1.1923 to prefix B/U dated 7.9.1927 ......... | | Rare |
| **NI.302b** | *Handsigned, with red serial numbers* | VF | EF |
| | Prefix B/U dated 8.3.1928 to prefix D/X dated 2.10.1942 ....... | £70 | £120 |
| **NI.302c** | *Handsigned, with red serial numbers* | EF | UNC |
| | Prefix D/X to prefix E/D dated 6.1.1966 ................................. | £70 | £120 |

# TEN POUNDS

Size 213 mm x 108 mm approximately

*Obverse—black with the value in green at the centre*
*Reverse—green panel with the name of the bank and value*

| | | F | VF |
|---|---|---|---|
| **NI.303a** | *Handsigned, with black serial numbers* | F | VF |
| | Prefix X to prefix Y dated 3.1.1923 .............................................. | | Rare |

| **NI.303b** | *Handsigned, with green serial numbers* | *VF* | *EF* |
| | Prefix Y dated 9.1.1929 to prefix A/N dated 1.1.1943.............. | £100 | £180 |
| **NI.303c** | *Handsigned, with green serial numbers* | *EF* | *UNC* |
| | Prefix A/N dated 3.12.1963 to prefix A/O dated 5.6.1965...... | £90 | £140 |

# TWENTY POUNDS

Size 210 mm x 110 mm approximately

*Obverse—black with the value in purple at the centre*
*Reverse—purple panel with the name of the bank and value*

| | | *F* | *VF* |
| --- | --- | --- | --- |
| **NI.304a** | *Handsigned, with black serial numbers* | | |
| | Prefix D dated 3.1.1923................................................. | £280 | £500 |
| **NI.304b** | *Handsigned, with purple serial numbers* | | |
| | Prefix D dated 9.11.1939 to prefix E dated 10.8.1940................ | £200 | £380 |
| **NI.304c** | *Handsigned, with black serial numbers* | | |
| | Prefix E dated 3.2.1943 and 5.6.1965........................................ | £180 | £320 |

# FIFTY POUNDS

Size 210 mm x 110 mm approximately

*Obverse—black with the value in orange at the centre*
*Reverse—orange panel with the name of the bank and value*

|  | | F | VF |
|---|---|---|---|
| **NI.305a** | *Handsigned, with black serial numbers* | | |
| | Prefix B dated 3.1.1923 and 3.5.1923............................................. | £400 | £650 |
| | | | |
| **NI.305b** | *Handsigned, with orange serial numbers* | | |
| | Prefix B dated 9.11.1939 and 10.8.1940..................................... | £320 | £480 |
| | | VF | EF |
| **NI.305c** | *Handsigned, with black serial numbers* | | |
| | Prefix B dated 3.2.1943 and 3.12.1963......................................... | £350 | £650 |

# ONE HUNDRED POUNDS

Size 210 mm x 110 mm approximately

*Obverse—black with the value in red at the centre*
*Reverse—red panel with the name of the bank and value*

|  |  | F | VF |
|---|---|---|---|
| **NI.306a** | *Handsigned, with black serial numbers* | | |
| | Prefix A dated 3.1.1923 and 3.5.1923 ......................................... | £400 | £650 |
| **NI.306b** | *Handsigned, with red serial numbers* | | |
| | Prefix A dated 9.11.1939 ............................................... | £400 | £650 |
| **NI.306c** | *Handsigned, with black serial numbers* | | |
| | Prefix A dated 3.2.1943 ............................................... | £350 | £600 |

|  |  | VF | EF |
|---|---|---|---|
| **NI306d** | *Handsigned, with red serial numbers* | | |
| | Prefix A dated 3.12.1963 ............................................. | £400 | £650 |
| **NI306e** | *Printed signature G. B. Smyth, red serial numbers* | | |
| | Prefix B dated 8.5.1968................................................ | £450 | £750 |

# FIRST TRUST BANK

The First Trust Bank was established in the early 1990's as a result of a merger between Allied Irish Banks plc and the Trustee Savings Bank. The new bank did not issue any five Pound notes.

## TEN POUNDS

Size 142 mm x 75 mm approximately

*Obverse—brown and purple on a multicoloured underprint. Portrait of a young man to the right.*
*Reverse—brown and multicoloured. Illustration of the Spanish galleass "The Girona" at the centre*

|  |  | EF | UNC |
|---|---|---|---|
| **NI.411a** | *Signatory: E. F. McElroy (Group Managing Director)* | | |
| | Prefix AB to prefix HB dated 10.1.1994 ..................................... | £30 | £40 |
| | Prefix ZB – replacement note. ...................................................... | | Rare |
| | | | |
| **NI.411b** | *Signatory: D. E. Harvey (Managing Director)* | | |
| | Prefix JB to prefix NB dated 1.3.1996 ......................................... | £45 | £60 |
| | Prefix ZB – replacement note. ...................................................... | | Rare |

*Obverse—brown and purple on a multicoloured underprint. Portrait of a young man to the right. Additional gold security feature at top right.*

*Reverse—brown and multicoloured. Illustration of the Spanish galleass "The Girona" at the centre*

|  | EF | UNC |
|---|---|---|
| **NI.412** *Signatory: D. J. Licence (Managing Director, First Trust Bank)* | | |
| Prefix AA to prefix LA dated 1.1.1998, and ongoing................ | — | £25 |
| Prefix ZA – replacement note. ..................................................... | £80 | £120 |

# TWENTY POUNDS

Size 150 mm x 80 mm approximately

*Obverse—mauve and brown on a multicoloured underprint; portrait of a mature lady to the right.*

*Reverse—mauve on a multicoloured underprint. Illustration of rock chimney at Lacada Point, Giant's Causeway*

| | | |
|---|---|---|
| **NI.421a** *Signatory: E. F. McElroy (Group Managing Director)* | | |
| Prefix AC to prefix HC dated 10.1.1994..................................... | £40 | £60 |
| Prefix ZC—replacement note....................................................... | Rare | |
| | | |
| **NI.421b** *Signatory: D. E. Harvey (Managing Director)* | | |
| Prefix JC to prefix NC dated 1.1.1996, and ................................ | £65 | £100 |
| Prefix PC to prefix RC dated 1.3.1996......................................... | £65 | £100 |
| Prefix ZC—replacement note....................................................... | Rare | |

*Obverse—mauve and brown on a multicoloured underprint; portrait of a mature lady to the right. Additional gold security feature at top right*
*Reverse—mauve on a multicoloured underprint. Illustration of rock chimney at Lacada Point, Giant's Causeway*

**NI.422**  *Signatory: D. J. Licence (Managing Director, First Trust Bank)*

| | EF | UNC |
|---|---|---|
| Prefix AA to prefix XA dated 1.1.1998, and ongoing............... | — | £40 |
| Prefix ZA—replacement note. .................................................... | £100 | £140 |

# FIFTY POUNDS

Size 155 mm x 85 mm approximately

*Obverse—blue and green on a multicoloured underprint. Portrait of a mature man to the right*
*Reverse—blue, green and multicoloured. Picture of two cherubs holding a commemorative medal of 1588 depicting the defeat of the Spanish Armada*

**NI.431**  *Signatory: E. F. McElroy (Group Managing Director)*

| | | |
|---|---|---|
| Prefix AD dated 10.1.1994 ........................................................... | £100 | £150 |
| Prefix ZD—replacement note. .................................................... | | Rare |

*Obverse—blue and green on a multicoloured underprint. Portrait of a mature man to the right. Additional silver security feature over value at top right*

*Reverse—blue, green and multicoloured. Picture of two cherubs holding a commemorative medal of 1588 depicting the defeat of the Spanish Armada*

|  | *EF* | *UNC* |
|---|---|---|
| **NI.432**    *Signatory: D. J. Licence (Managing Director, First Trust Bank)* | | |
| Prefix AA dated 1.1.1998.............................................................. | — | £100 |
| Prefix ZA—replacement note. ..................................................... | | Rare |

# ONE HUNDRED POUNDS

Size 160 mm x 90 mm approximately

*Obverse—green, brown and black on a multicoloured underprint. Portraits of a mature man and woman to the right*
*Reverse—green, brown and black on a multicoloured underprint. Illustration of the Spanish Armada at the centre*

|  |  | EF | UNC |
|---|---|---|---|
| **NI.441a** | *Signatory: E. F. McElroy (Group Managing Director)* | | |
| | Prefix AE dated 10.1.1994.............................................................. | £180 | £250 |
| | Prefix ZE—replacement note. ....................................................... | | Rare |
| **NI.441b** | *Signatory: D. E. Harvey (Managing Director)* | | |
| | Prefix AE dated 1.3.1996................................................................ | £260 | £400 |
| | Prefix ZE—replacement note. ....................................................... | | Rare |

*Obverse—green, brown and black on a multicoloured underprint. Portraits of a mature man and woman to the right. Additional silver security feature over value at top right*
*Reverse—green, brown and black on a multicoloured underprint. Illustration of the Spanish Armada at the centre*

|  |  | EF | UNC |
|---|---|---|---|
| **NI.442** | *Signatory: D. J. Licence (Managing Director, First Trust Bank)* | | |
| | Prefix AA dated 1.1.1998................................................................ | — | £200 |
| | Prefix ZA—replacement note. ....................................................... | | Rare |

# NATIONAL BANK LIMITED

The Bank was founded in 1835 by Daniel O'Connell. Its Irish branches were acquired by the Bank of Ireland in December 1965, and for a short time thereafter it carried on business as the National Bank of Ireland Limited. A few years later its separate identity disappeared when it was merged into the Bank of Ireland.

Examples of early National Bank notes.

# ONE POUND

Size 149 mm x 80 mm approximately

*Obverse — black — green panel at centre with "£1"*
*Reverse — green — Hibernia with harp and wolfhound at the  centre flanked by £1 value*

|  | | F | VF |
|---|---|---|---|
| **NI.501** | Signatory: F. H. Green | | |
| | No prefix letters; dated 6.5.1929, 1.11.1931, 1.1.1932 ................ | £100 | £200 |
| | 15.8.1932 and 1.8.1933. | | |

Size 152 mm x 84 mm approximately

*Obverse — black on a green and yellow underprint. Hibernia with harp and wolfhound at the centre*
*Reverse — green and lilac. Bank's Coat of Arms flanked by £1 value panels*

|  | | VF | EF |
|---|---|---|---|
| **NI.502** | Signatory: F. H. Green | | |
| | Prefix A dated 1.2.1937, 1.9.1937 and 2.10.1939 ........................ | £80 | £160 |

# FIVE POUNDS

Size 149 mm x 80 mm approximately
*Obverse—dark blue—brown panel at centre with "£5"*
*Reverse—brown—Hibernia with harp and wolfhound at centre flanked by £5 value*

|  |  | F | VF |
|---|---|---|---|
| **NI.503** | *Signatory: F. H. Green*<br>No prefix letters; dated 6.5.1929, 1.8.1933 and 1.10.1934 ......... |  | Rare |

Size 155 mm x 91 mm approximately

*Obverse—blue on a blue and tan underprint. Hibernia at lower left with harp and wolfhound*
*Reverse—black on a green and tan underprint. Bank's Coat of Arms at centre*

|  |  | VF | EF |
|---|---|---|---|
| **NI.504a** | *Signatory: F. H. Green*<br>Prefix A dated 1.2.1937; 9.1.1937 and 2.10.1939 ........................ | £120 | £220 |
| **NI.504b** | *Signatory: J. J. O'Donnell*<br>Prefix A dated 1.8.1942; 1.1.1949 and 2.5.1949 .......................... | £120 | £220 |
| **NI.504c** | *Signatory: R. W. Maguire.*<br>Prefix A dated 1.5.1964 – specimens only ................................. |  | Rare |

# TEN POUNDS

Size 149 mm x 80 mm approximately

*Obverse—green – red/brown panel at centre with "£10"*
*Reverse—brown – Hibernia with harp and wolfhound at centre flanked by £10 value*

|  | | F | VF |
|---|---|---|---|
| **NI.505** | Signatory: F. H. Green.<br>No prefix letters; dated 6.5.1929; 2.10.1931 and 1.8.1933 ........ | | Rare |

Size 152 mm x 84 mm approximately

*Obverse—green on a pink and yellow underprint. Hibernia seated with harp and wolfhound at the centre*
*Reverse—brown on a green and yellow underprint. Bank's Coat of Arms at left centre flanked by £10 value panels*

|  | | VF | EF |
|---|---|---|---|
| **NI.506a** | Signatory: F. H. Green<br>Prefix A dated 1.2.1937, 1.9.1937 and 2.10.1939 ........................ | £180 | £300 |
| **NI.506b** | Signatory: J. J. O'Donnell<br>Prefix A dated 1.8.1942 and 2.5.1949 .......................................... | £160 | £280 |
| **NI.506c** | Signatory: R.H.R. Fry<br>Prefix A dated 1.7.1959 ................................................................ | £150 | £260 |

# TWENTY POUNDS

Size 149 mm x 80 mm approximately

*Obverse—brown—blue panel at centre with "£20"*
*Reverse—blue—Hibernia with harp and wolfhound at centre flanked by £20 value panels*

|  |  | F | VF |
|---|---|---|---|
| **NI.507** | Signatory: F. H. Green | | |
| | No prefix letters; dated 6.5.1929 ................................................... | | Rare |

Size 160 mm x 90 mm approximately

*Obverse—brown on a grey and yellow underprint. Hibernia at lower left with harp and wolfhound*
*Reverse—blue, green and yellow. Bank's Coat of Arms at the centre*

|  |  | VF | EF |
|---|---|---|---|
| **NI.508a** | Signatory: F. H. Green | | |
| | Prefix A dated 1.2.1937 and 2.10.1939......................................... | £350 | £600 |
| **NI.508b** | Signatory: J. J. O'Donnell | | |
| | Prefix A dated 1.8.1942 and 1.1.1949.......................................... | £330 | £550 |
| **NI.508c** | Signatory: R.H.R. Fry | | |
| | Prefix A dated 1.7.1959................................................................ | £320 | £550 |

# NORTHERN BANK LIMITED

The Northern Bank began life as a private partnership in Belfast in 1809, and became the joint stock Northern Banking Company in 1824, at which time it was the only joint stock banking company anywhere in the British Isles apart from Scotland.

Branches outside Belfast were established from 1835 onwards, and in 1888 the bank opened its first office in Dublin by acquiring the business of the private bankers Ball & Co. Five years earlier the Northern had adopted limited liability, thereby becoming the Northern Banking Company Limited, and in 1929 it shortened its name to Northern Bank Limited.

The Midland Bank (which already owned the Belfast Banking Company) acquired the share capital of the Northern Bank in 1965, and in 1970 merged its two Irish banks in the name of the Northern. In order to raise capital following a disastrous investment in the USA, the Midland sold the Northern Bank in 1987 to National Banks Australia Limited, who in turn are now in the process of selling it to Danske Bank, Copenhagen.

Some examples of early notes

# ONE POUND

Size 151 mm x 84 mm approximately

*Obverse—black with "ONE" in a blue panel at the centre; vignette with sailing ship above*
*Reverse—blue. "NBL" in round design at centre with value "1" at either side*

|  |  | F | VF |
|---|---|---|---|
| **NI.601a** | *Signatory: S.W.Knox (on prefix N-I/A and N-I/E)* | | |
| **NI.601b** | *Signatory: H.H.Stewart (on prefix N-I/B and N-I/F)* | | |
| **NI.601c** | *Signatory: W.F.Scott (on prefix N-I/C)* | | |
| **NI.601d** | *Signatory: A.P.Tibbey (on prefix N-I/D)* | | |

Red serial numbers
Prefix <u>N-I</u> dated 6.5.1929 to prefix <u>N-I</u> dated 1.8.1929 ............. £50 £85
     A                            F

|  |  | EF | UNC |
|---|---|---|---|
| **NI.601e** | *Signatory: F. W. White* | | |
| | Black serial numbers | | |
| | Prefix N-I dated 1.1.1940 ........................................................... | £45 | £60 |
| |    H | | |

Size 135 mm x 67 mm approximately

*Obverse—green on a multicoloured background; illustrations of agriculture, shipbuilding and weaving*
*Reverse green on a multicoloured background; Griffin emblem at the centre*

|  | | *EF* | *UNC* |
|---|---|---|---|
| **NI.602a** | *Signatory: W. S. Wilson* | | |
| | Prefix C dated 1.7.1970...................................................... | £17 | £24 |
| **NI.602b** | *Signatory: H. M. Gabbey* | | |
| | Prefix C dated 1.10.1971.................................................... | £17 | £24 |
| **NI.602c** | *Signatory: W. Ervin* | | |
| | Prefix C dated 1.8.1978...................................................... | £10 | £16 |

# FIVE POUNDS

Size 150 mm x 86 mm approximately

Heading: Northern Bank Ltd. on earlier notes of the Northern Banking Company Limited.
*Obverse – black with "FIVE" in a blue panel at the centre. Vignette with sailing ship above*
*Reverse – blue; "NBC" in a round panel at the centre with "5" in small round panels at either side*

|  | | *F* | *VF* |
|---|---|---|---|
| **NI.611** | *Signatories: Handsigned.* | | |
| | Prefix B dated 1.9.1927 (but issued on or after 6th May 1929) | | Rare |

Heading: Northern Bank Limited

*Obverse—black with "FIVE" in a blue panel at the centre. Vignette with sailing ship above*
*Reverse—blue; "NBL" in a round panel at the centre with "5" in small round panels at either side*

|  |  |  | F | VF |
|---|---|---|---|---|
| **NI.612a** | *Signatory: S.W.Knox.* | | | |
| | Prefix <u>N-I</u> dated 6.5.1929 .......................................................... | | £80 | £150 |
| | A | | | |
| | | | | |
| **NI.612b** | Signatory: H. H. Stewart. | | | |
| | Prefix <u>N-I</u> dated 6.5.1929 .......................................................... | | £80 | £150 |
| | B | | | |

Size 170 mm x 95 mm approximately

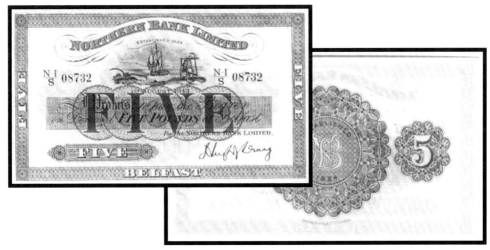

*Obverse—black with "FIVE" in a green panel at the centre. Vignette with sailing ship above*
*Reverse—blue; "NBL" in a round panel at the centre with "5" in small round panels at either side*

| | | VF | FF |
|---|---|---|---|
| **NI.613a** | *Signatory: F.W.White (on prefix N-I/D, N-I/H, N-I/L, N-I/P)* | | |
| **NI.613b** | *Signatory: H.J.Craig (on prefix N-I/E, N-I/I, N-I/M, N-I/S)* | | |
| **NI.613c** | *Signatory: W.F.Scott (on prefix N-I/B, N-I/F, N-I/J, N-I/N, N-I/T)* | | |
| **NI.613d** | *Signatory: A.P.Tibbey (on prefix N-I/C, N-I/G, N-I/K, N-I/O)* | | |
| **NI.613e** | *Signatory: J. E. Forde (on prefix N-I/R)* | | |

|  |  | VF | FF |
|---|---|---|---|
| Prefix <u>N-I</u> dated 1.9.1937 to prefix <u>N-I</u> dated 1.11.1943............ | | £70 | £120 |
| B | T | | |

Size 150 mm x 86 mm approximately

*Obverse—black with "FIVE" in a green panel at the centre. Vignette with sailing ship above*
*Reverse—blue; "NBL" in a round panel at the centre with "5" in small round panels at either side*

|  | | EF | UNC |
|---|---|---|---|
| **NI.614** | *Signatory: E.D.Hill.* | | |
| | Prefix <u>N-I</u> dated 1.10.1968 ............................................................ U | £50 | £80 |

Size 150 mm x 84 mm approximately

*Obverse—blue on a multicoloured background; illustrations of agriculture, shipbuilding and weaving*
*Reverse—blue on a multicoloured background; Griffin emblem at the centre*

| **NI.615a** | *Signatory: W. S. Wilson* | | |
|---|---|---|---|
| | Prefix D dated 1.7.1970 ................................................... | £65 | £90 |
| **NI.615b** | *Signatory: H. M. Gabbey* | | |
| | Prefix D dated 1.10.1971 ................................................. | £65 | £90 |
| **NI.615c** | *Signatory: J. B. Newland* | | |
| | Prefix D dated 1.7.1974 and 1.1.1976........................... | £30 | £45 |
| **NI.615d** | *Signatory: W. Ervin* | | |
| | Prefix D dated 1.4.1982 .................................................. | £28 | £40 |
| **NI.615e** | *Signatory: J. Roberts* | | |
| | Prefix D dated 3.2.1986 .................................................. | £28 | £40 |

Size 136 mm x 70 mm approximately

*Obverse—blue on a multicoloured background; portrait of W.A.Trail 1844-1933*
*Reverse—blue on a multicoloured background; images of satellite dish and computer systems*

|  |  | EF | UNC |
|---|---|---|---|
| **NI.616** | *Signatory: S.H.Torrens (Chief Executive).* | | |
| | Prefix A dated 24.8.1988 to 24.8.1990. ........................................ | £15 | £25 |
| | Prefix Z—replacement note ....................................................... | £50 | £75 |

Size 70 mm x 136 mm approximately

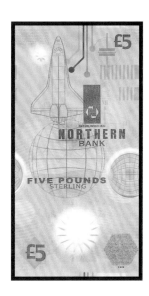

*Polymer note—vertical format*
*Obverse—blue with a coloured globe to left and right of centre and a transparent star shape at the bottom*
*Reverse - blue with a line drawing of a globe and the space shuttle*

|  |  | EF | UNC |
|---|---|---|---|
| **NI.617** | *Signatory: D.Price (Chief Executive).* | | |
| | Prefix MM dated 8.10.1999............................................. | --- | £15 |
| | Prefix Y2K dated 1.1.2000, issued in a presentation pack........ | --- | £20 |
| | Prefix N (replacement notes). ....................................... | £35 | £50 |

# TEN POUNDS

Size 200 mm x 112 mm approximately

Heading: Northern Bank Ltd. on earlier notes of the Northern Banking Company Limited.
*Obverse—black with "TEN" in a blue panel at the centre. Vignette with sailing ship above. Listing of the various branches of the Bank printed across the lower centre*
*Reverse—blue; "NBC" in a round panel at the centre with "10" in small round panels at either side*

F     VF

**NI.621**     *Signatory: handsigned*
          Prefix A dated 1.3.1920 (but issued on or after 6th May 1929)       Rare

Heading: Northern Bank Ltd. on earlier notes of the Northern Banking Company Limited.
*Obverse—black with "TEN" in a blue panel at the centre. Vignette with sailing ship above. Without the listing of the Bank's branches..*
*Reverse—blue; "NBC" in a round panel at the centre with "10" in small round panels at either side.*

**NI.622**     *Signatory: handsigned*
          Prefix B dated 10.10.1921 (but issued on or after 6th May 1929)       Rare

Size 168 mm x 95 mm approximately

*Obverse—black with "TEN" in a red panel at the centre. Vignette with sailing ship above*
*Reverse—blue; "NBL" in a round panel at the centre with "10" in small round panels at either side*

|  | F | VF |
|---|---|---|

**NI.623a**   *Signatory: handsigned*

| | F | VF |
|---|---|---|
| Prefix <u>N-I</u> dated 1.1.1930 to prefix <u>N-I</u> dated 1.1.1940 ............. <br> A                                                  E | £60 | £100 |

|  | VF | EF |
|---|---|---|

**NI.623b**   *Signatory: W. F. Scott (on prefix N-I/F, N-I/J)*
**NI.623c**   *Signatory: A. P. Tibbey (on prefix N-I/G, N-I/K)*
**NI.623d**   *Signatory: F. W. White (on prefix N-I/H, N-I/L)*
**NI.623e**   *Signatory: H. J. Craig (on prefix N-I/I, N-I/N)*
**NI.623f**   *Signatory: J. E. Forde (on prefix N-I/M)*

| Prefix <u>N-I</u> dated 1.8.1940 to prefix <u>N-I</u> dated 1.11.1943............ <br> F                                                  N | £85 | £150 |
|---|---|---|

**NI.623g**   *Signatory: E. D. Hill*

.

| Prefix <u>N-I</u> dated 1.10.1968 ......................................................... <br> OO | £85 | £150 |
|---|---|---|

Size 151 mm x 85 mm approximately

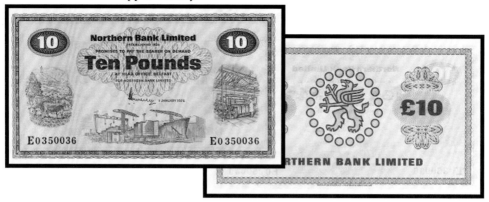

*Obverse—brown on a multicoloured background; illustrations of agriculture, shipbuilding and weaving*
*Reverse—brown on a multicoloured background; Griffin emblem at the centre*

|  |  | EF | UNC |
|---|---|---|---|
| **NI.624a** | *Signatory: W. S. Wilson*<br>Prefix E dated 1.7.1970 | £90 | £150 |
| **NI.624b** | *Signatory: H. M. Gabbey*<br>Prefix E dated 1.10.1971 | £90 | £150 |
| **NI.624c** | *Signatory: J. B. Newland*<br>Prefix E dated 1.7.1975 to 1.1.1978 | £80 | £120 |
| **NI.624d** | *Signatory: W. Ervin*<br>Prefix E dated 1.3.1981 and 1.4.1982 | £55 | £80 |
| **NI.624e** | *Signatory: J. Roberts*<br>Prefix E dated 2.1.1985 to 2.3.1987 | £55 | £80 |
| **NI.624f** | *Signatory: S. H. Torrens*<br>Prefix E dated 15.6.1988 | £50 | £75 |

Size 142 mm x 75 mm approximately

*Obverse—brown and red on a multicoloured background; portrait of J.B.Dunlop 1840-1921*
*Reverse—brown on a multicoloured background; images of satellite dish and computer systems*

| **NI.625a** | *Signatory: S.H.Torrens (Chief Executive).*<br>Prefix B dated 24.8.1988 to 24.8.1993.<br>Prefix Z – replacement note. | £35<br>£70 | £50<br>£100 |
|---|---|---|---|
| **NI.625b** | *Signatory: J.R.Wright (Chief Executive).*<br>Prefix B dated 30.8.1996.<br>Prefix Z – replacement note. | £30<br>£65 | £45<br>£95s |

*Obverse—brown and red on a multicoloured background; portrait of J.B.Dunlop 1840-1921*
*Reverse—brown on a multicoloured background; picture of façade of City Hall, Belfast*

|  |  | EF | UNC |
|---|---|---|---|
| **NI.626a** | *Signatory: G. Savage (Chief Executive).* | | |
| | Prefix BA and BB dated 24.2.1997. ............................................... | £20 | £28 |
| | Prefix ZZ – replacement note........................................................ | £50 | £70 |
| | | | |
| **NI.626b** | *Signatory: D. Price (Chief Executive).* | | |
| | Prefix BC dated 8.10.1999. ............................................................ | £18 | £25 |
| | Prefix ZZ – replacement note........................................................ | £40 | £60 |

Similar to previous issue but change of colours to "Northern Bank" typeface and logo.
*Obverse—brown and red on a multicoloured background; portrait of J.B.Dunlop 1840-1921*
*Reverse—brown on a multicoloured background; picture of façade of City Hall, Belfast*

| **NI.627** | *Signatory: D. Price (Chief Executive).* | | |
|---|---|---|---|
| | Prefix BD dated 29.4.2004............................................................. | £40 | £55 |
| | Prefix ZZ—replacement note........................................................ | — | Rare |

Similar to previous issue but change of colour
*Obverse—mainly green on a multicoloured background; portrait of J.B.Dunlop 1840-1921*
*Reverse—green on a multicoloured background; picture of façade of City Hall, Belfast*

**NI.628** *Signatory: D. Price (Chief Executive).*
Prefix GE and GF dated 19.1.2005.............................................. — £20
Prefix ZZ—replacement note..................................................... — £50

# TWENTY POUNDS

Size 203 mm x 117 mm approximately

Heading: Northern Bank Ltd. on earlier notes of the Northern Banking Company Limited.
*Obverse—black with "TWENTY" in a blue panel at the centre. Vignette with sailing ship above*
*Reverse—blue; "NBC" in a round panel at the centre with "20" in small round panels at either side*

|  |  | F | VF |
|---|---|---|---|
| **NI.631** | *Signatory: Handsigned* | | |
| | Prefix A dated 20.10.1921 (but issued on or after 6th May 1929) | £400 | £750 |

Size 159 mm x 90 mm approximately

*Obverse—purple on a multicoloured background; illustrations of agriculture, shipbuilding and weaving*
*Reverse—purple on a multicoloured background; Griffin emblem at the centre*

|  |  | EF | UNC |
|---|---|---|---|
| **NI.632a** | *Signatory: W. S. Wilson* | | |
| | Prefix F dated 1.7.1970 ................................................................ | £180 | — |
| **NI.632b** | *Signatory: W. Ervin* | | |
| | Prefix F dated 1.3.1981 and 1.12.1984 ........................................ | £90 | £140 |
| **NI.632c** | *Signatory: J. Roberts* | | |
| | Prefix F dated 2.3.1987 ................................................................ | £90 | £130 |
| **NI632d** | *Signatory: S. H. Torrens* | | |
| | Prefix F dated 15.6.1988 .............................................................. | £80 | £110 |

Size 150 mm x 80 mm approximately

*Obverse — mauve and brown on a multicoloured background; portrait of H. Ferguson 1884–1960*
*Reverse — mauve on a multicoloured background; images of satellite dish and computer systems*

|  |  | EF | UNC |
|---|---|---|---|
| **NI.633a** | *Signatory: S.H.Torrens (Chief Executive).* | | |
| | Prefix C dated 24.8.1988 to 24.8.1993. | £65 | £90 |
| | Prefix Z – replacement note. | £110 | — |
| **NI.633b** | *Signatory: J.R.Wright (Chief Executive).* | | |
| | Prefix C dated 30.8.1996. | £50 | £70 |
| | Prefix Z – replacement note. | £90 | £140 |

*Obverse — mauve on a multicoloured background; portrait of H. Ferguson 1884–1960*
*Reverse — mauve on a multicoloured background; picture of façade of City Hall, Belfast*

|  |  | EF | UNC |
|---|---|---|---|
| **NI.634a** | *Signatory: G.Savage (Chief Executive).* | | |
| | Prefix CA and CB dated 24.2.1997. | £40 | £50 |
| | Prefix ZZ – replacement note. | £70 | — |
| **NI.634b** | *Signatory: D.Price (Chief Executive).* | | |
| | Prefix CB to CD dated 8.10.1999. | £32 | £45 |
| | Prefix ZZ – replacement note. | £65 | — |

Commemorative issue "175 Years of Banking 1824 – 1999".
*Obverse — mauve on a multicoloured background; portrait of H.Ferguson 1884-1960*
*Reverse — mauve on a multicoloured background; picture of façade of City Hall, Belfast*

|  | EF | UNC |
|---|---|---|
| **NI.635**    *Signatory: D.Price (Chief Executive).* | | |
| Prefix NB dated 1.9.1999.............................................................. | £35 | £48 |

*Obverse–blue on a multicoloured background; portrait of H.Ferguson 1884-1960.*
*Reverse–blue on a multicoloured background; picture of façade of City Hall, Belfast.*

| **NI.636**    *Signatory: D.Price (Chief Executive).* | | |
|---|---|---|
| Prefix HE to HF dated 19.1.2005................................................. | — | £40 |
| Prefix ZZ – replacement note...................................................... | £65 | £85 |

# FIFTY POUNDS

Size 195 mm x 108 mm approximately

Heading: Northern Bank Ltd. on earlier notes of the Northern Banking Company Limited.
*Obverse—black with "FIFTY" in a blue panel at the centre. Vignette with sailing ship above.*
*Reverse—blue; "NBC" in a round panel at the centre with "50" in small round panels at either side.*
*These notes were issued on or after 6th May 1929*

|  | F | VF |
|---|---|---|
| **NI.641a** *Signatory: Handsigned (usually S. W. Knox)* <br> No prefix letter, red serial numbers—dated 5.8.1914 | | from £550 |
| **NI.641b** *Signatory: Handsigned (usually H. J. Craig)* <br> No prefix letter, black serial numbers – dated 25.4.1918 | | from £550 |

Size 185 mm x 110 mm approximately

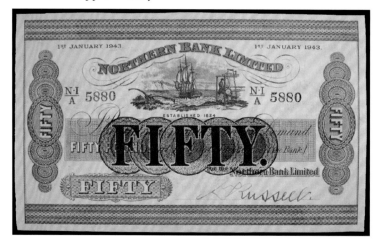

*Obverse—black with "FIFTY" in a blue panel at the centre. Vignette with sailing ship above*
*Reverse—blue; "NBC" in a round panel at the centre with "50" in small round panels at either side*

|  | VF | EF |
|---|---|---|
| **NI.642a** *Signatory: Handsigned* <br> Prefix <u>N-I</u> dated 1.1.1943 <br> A | £350 | £600 |

Letters in central panel on the reverse changed to "NBL"

**NI.642b**    *Signatory: Handsigned*
Prefix N-I dated 1.10.1968 ..............................................    £350     £600
B

Size 170 mm x 95 mm approximately

*Obverse—orange/brown on a multicoloured background; illustrations of agriculture, shipbuilding and weaving*
*Reverse—reddish brown; Griffin emblem at the centre*

                                                              *EF*     *UNC*

**NI.643a**    *Signatory: W. S. Wilson*
Prefix G dated 1.7.1970 ................................................    £400     —

**NI.643b**    *Signatory: J. B. Newland*
Prefix G dated 1.1.1975 ................................................    £240     £320

**NI.643c**    *Signatory: W. Ervin*
Prefix G dated 1.3.1981 ................................................    £180     £260

Size 156 mm x 85 mm approximately

*Obverse—green and multicoloured; portrait of Sir F. C. Davidson 1846-1921*
*Reverse—green and multicoloured; images of satellite dish and computer systems*

**NI.644**    *Signatory: S. H. Torrens (Chief Executive).*
Prefix D dated 1.11.1990..............................................    £110     £140

*Obverse—green, blue and multicolored; portrait of Sir F. C. Davidson 1846–1921*
*Reverse—green, blue and multicolored; picture of façade of City Hall, Belfast*

|  | EF | UNC |
|---|---|---|
| **NI.645** *Signatory: D.Price (Chief Executive).* | | |
| Prefix DA dated 8.10.1999. | £85 | £120 |
| Prefix ZZ – replacement note | £200 | — |

*Obverse—violet and multicoloured; portrait of Sir F. C. Davidson 1846–1921*
*Reverse—violet and multicolored; picture of façade of City Hall, Belfast*

| **NI.646** *Signatory: D.Price (Chief Executive).* | | |
|---|---|---|
| Prefix JB dated 8.10.1999 | — | £95 |
| Prefix ZZ – replacement note | £150 | £220 |

# ONE HUNDRED POUNDS

Size 210 mm x 110 mm approximately

Heading: Northern Bank Ltd. on earlier notes of the Northern Banking Company Limited.
*Obverse—black with "£100" in a blue panel at the centre. Vignette with sailing ship above*
*Reverse—blue; "NBC" in a round panel at the centre with "100" in small round panels at either side*

|  |  | F | VF |
|---|---|---|---|
| **NI.651** | *Signatory: handsigned.* | | |
| | No prefix letter – dated 2.6.1919................................................. | £650 | £950 |

Size 190 mm x 115 mm approximately

*Obverse—black with "£100" in a blue panel at the centre. Vignette with sailing ship above*
*Reverse—blue; "NBC" in a round panel at the centre with "100" in small round panels at either side*

|  |  | VF | EF |
|---|---|---|---|
| **NI.652a** | *Signatory: handsigned.* | | |
| | Prefix N-I dated 1.1.1943 ........................................... <br> A | £650 | £950 |

Letters in central panel on the reverse changed to "NBL"
|  |  | | |
|---|---|---|---|
| **NI.652b** | *Signatory: handsigned.* | | |
| | Prefix N-I dated 1.10.1968 ......................................... <br> BB | £550 | £850 |

Size 170 mm x 95 mm approximately

*Obverse—red on a multicoloured background; illustrations of agriculture, shipbuilding and weaving*
*Reverse—red; Griffin emblem at the centre*

|  |  | EF | UNC |
|---|---|---|---|
| **NI.653a** | *Signatory: W. S. Wilson* | | |
| | Prefix H dated 1.7.1970 ................................................... | £450 | — |
| **NI.653b** | *Signatory: H. M. Gabbey* | | |
| | Prefix H dated 1.10.1971 ................................................ | £450 | — |
| **NI.653c** | *Signatory: J. B. Newland* | | |
| | Prefix H dated 1.1.1975 to 1.2.1977............................. | £280 | £400 |
| **NI.653d** | *Signatory: W. Ervin* | | |
| | Prefix H dated 1.10.1978 and 1.1.1980 ........................ | £260 | £350 |

Size 164 mm x 90 mm approximately

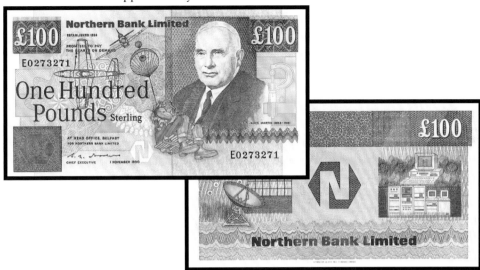

*Obverse—red, brown and multicoloured; portrait of Sir James Martin 1893–1981*
*Reverse—red, brown and multicoloured; images of satellite dish and computer systems*

|  | EF | UNC |
|---|---|---|
| **NI.654** Signatory: S. H. Torrens (Chief Executive). Prefix E dated 1.11.1990. | £220 | £300 |

*Obverse—brown and multicoloured; portrait of Sir James Martin 1893-1981*
*Reverse—mauve and multicoloured; picture of façade of City Hall, Belfast*

| **NI.655** Signatory: D. Price (Chief Executive) Prefix EA dated 8.10.1999 | — | £220 |

*Obverse—red, mauve and multicoloured; portrait of Sir James Martin 1893-1981*
*Reverse—red and multicoloured; picture of façade of City Hall, Belfast*

|  |  | EF | UNC |
|---|---|---|---|
| **NI.655** | *Signatory: D. Price (Chief Executive)* | | |
| | Prefix KB dated 19.1.2005 | — | £190 |
| | Prefix YY — replacement note | £300 | £400 |

# PROVINCIAL
# BANK OF IRELAND LIMITED

The Provincial Bank of Ireland was formed in 1825 with its head office in London, and the majority of its initial shareholders were resident in England. It gradually took on a more Irish character, and in 1953 the Head Office was moved from London to Dublin. In 1966 the Provincial Bank merged with the Munster & Leinster Bank and the Royal Bank of Ireland to form Allied Irish Banks Limited, and the operations of the three banks were integrated under the Allied Irish name in 1969. Because of legal problems, however, the Provincial Bank retained an office in Royal Avenue, Belfast and continued to issue notes in its own name until 1981. By then the legal difficulties had been overcome and later note issues were in the name of Allied Irish Banks.

## SOME EXAMPLES OF EARLY BANKNOTES

# ONE POUND

Size 148mm x 85 mm approximately

*Obverse—black with "£1" in a green panel at the centre; vignette with Bank building above*
*Reverse—blue panel with Britannia and Hibernia seated at the centre*

|  |  | F | VF |
|---|---|---|---|
| **NI.701a** | *Signatory: Hume Robertson.* | | |
| | Prefix N dated 6.5.1929 and prefix N/A dated 1.8.1930 ......... | £80 | £160 |
| **NI.701b** | *Signatory: F. S. Forde.* | | |
| | Prefix N/A dated 1.2.1932 to prefix N/B dated 1.6.1934......... | £75 | £160 |

*Obverse—black with "£1" in a green panel at the centre; vignette with Bank building above*
*Reverse—green panel with Britannia and Hibernia seated at the centre*

|  |  | VF | EF |
|---|---|---|---|
| **NI.702a** | *Signatory: F. S. Forde.* |  |  |
|  | Prefix N/C dated 1.8.1935 and 2.11.1936 .................................. | £90 | £160 |
| **NI.702b** | *Signatory: G. A. Kennedy* |  |  |
|  | Prefix N/D dated 1.9.1937 to prefix N/J dated 1.5.1946.......... | £75 | £135 |

Size 150 mm x 85 mm approximately

*Obverse—black with a mesh background and with "£1" in a green panel at the centre; vignette with Bank building above*
*Reverse—green panel with Britannia and Hibernia seated at the centre*

| **NI.703a** | *Signatory: G. A. Kennedy* |  |
|---|---|---|
|  | Prefix N/J dated 1.5.1946 ............................................................ | Rare |
|  | These notes were not issued. A few un-numbered specimen notes are known. | |
| **NI.703b** | *Signatory: H. W. M. Clarke.* |  |
|  | Prefix NJ and NK dated 1.9.1951................................................. | Rare |
|  | These notes were not issued. A few un-numbered specimen notes are known, as well as a few numbered notes with prefix NJ. | |

*Obverse—Olive green on a pale green underprint with a cameo at the centre*
*Reverse—green panel with the Bank's office building in Belfast at the centre*

| | | VF | EF |
|---|---|---|---|
| | *Signatory: N. J. Shaw* | | |
| **NI.704a** | Prefix KN dated 1.3.1954 to prefix LN dated 1.10.1954 ........... | £90 | £160 |
| | (printed by Waterlow & Sons Limited) | | |
| **NI.704b** | Prefix LN dated 1.12.1965............................................................ | £90 | £160 |
| | (printed by Thomas de la Rue & Co. Ltd.) | | |

Size 150 mm x 72 mm approximately

*Obverse—Olive green on a pale green underprint with a cameo at the centre*
*Reverse—green panel with the Bank's office building in Belfast at the centre*

| | | EF | UNC |
|---|---|---|---|
| **NI.705** | *Signatory: J. G. McClay* | | |
| | Prefix LN dated 1.1.1968 to prefix UN dated 1.1.1972 ............. | £35 | £50 |
| | Prefix ZZ – replacement note..................................................... | £100 | ---- |

Size 135 mm x 67 mm approximately

*Obverse—green and brown on a multicoloured underprint. Portrait of a boy to the right*
*Reverse—mainly green. Illustration of the Spanish galleass "The Girona" at the centre*

|  |  | EF | UNC |
|---|---|---|---|
| **NI.706a** | *Signatory: J. G. McClay (Manager).* | | |
| | Prefix PN dated 1.1.1977................................................ | £16 | £25 |
| | Prefix ZY – replacement note.................................... | £70 | --- |
| | | | |
| **NI.706b** | *Signatory: F.H. Hollway (Manager).* | | |
| | Prefix PN dated 1.1.1979................................................ | £15 | £23 |
| | Prefix ZY – replacement note.................................... | £70 | --- |

# FIVE POUNDS

Size 148 mm x 86 mm approximately

*Obverse—black with "£5" in a blue panel at the centre; vignette with Bank building above*
*Reverse—green panel with Britannia and Hibernia seated at the centre*

|  |  | F | VF |
|---|---|---|---|
| **NI.711a** | *Signatory: Hume Robertson.* | | |
| | Prefix N dated 6.5.1929. ............................................... | £200 | £360 |
| | | | |
| **NI.711b** | *Signatory: F. S. Forde.* | | |
| | Prefix N dated 5.10.1933 ............................................... | £180 | £340 |

Size 150 mm x 88 mm approximately

*Obverse—blue/grey with "£5" in a brown panel at the centre; vignette with Bank building above*
*Reverse—brown panel with Britannia and Hibernia seated at the centre*

|  |  | VF | EF |
|---|---|---|---|
| **NI.712a** | *Signatory: F. S. Forde.* |  |  |
|  | Prefix N dated 5. 8.1935 and 5.5.1936 ........................................ | £170 | £320 |
| **NI.712b** | *Signatory: G. A. Kennedy* |  |  |
|  | Prefix N/A dated 5.5.1938 to prefix N/B dated 5.4.1946......... | £140 | £280 |

*Obverse—grey with a mesh background and with "£5" in a brown panel at the centre; vignette with Bank building above*
*Reverse—brown panel with Britannia and Hibernia seated at the centre*

|  |  | VF | EF |
|---|---|---|---|
| **NI.713** | *Signatory: H. W. M. Clarke* |  |  |
|  | Prefix N/B dated 5.1.1948 ............................................................ |  | Rare |
|  | Prefix NB dated 5.12.1949 to 5.4.1952 ........................................ | £75 | £120 |

Size 166 mm x 93 mm approximately

*Obverse—Brown on a pale brown underprint with a cameo at the centre*
*Reverse—brown panel with the Bank's office building in Belfast at the centre*

|  |  | VF | EF |
|---|---|---|---|
| | *Signatory: N. J. Shaw* | | |
| **NI.714a** | Prefix CN dated from 5.10.1954 to 5.5.1959 .............................. | £70 | £120 |
| | (printed by Waterlow & Sons Limited) | | |
| **NI.714b** | Prefix DN dated from 5.7.1961 to 6.12.1965............................. | £70 | £120 |
| | (printed by Thomas de la Rue & Co. Ltd.) | | |

Size 140 mm x 85 mm approximately
*Obverse—Brown on a pale brown underprint with a cameo at the centre*
*Reverse—brown panel with the Bank's head office building at the centre*

|  |  | EF | UNC |
|---|---|---|---|
| **NI.715** | *Signatory: J. G. McClay* | | |
| | Prefix DN dated 5.1.1968 to prefix ON dated 5.1.1972............. | £35 | £50 |
| | Prefix ZZ—replacement note....................................... | £100 | — |

Size 140 mm x 85 mm approximately

*Obverse—blue and purple on a multicoloured underprint. Portrait of a girl to the right*
*Reverse—mainly blue. Illustration of Dunluce Castle at the centre*

|  |  | EF | UNC |
|---|---|---|---|
| **NI.716a** | *Signatory: J. G. McClay (Manager)* |  |  |
|  | Prefix QN dated 1.1.1977 | £40 | £55 |
|  | Prefix ZY—replacement note | £120 | — |
| **NI.716b** | *Signatory: F.H.Hollway (Manager)* |  |  |
|  | Prefix QN dated 1.1.1979. | £35 | £50 |
|  | Prefix ZY—replacement note | £120 | — |

# TEN POUNDS

Size 150 mm x 87 mm approximately

*Obverse—black with "£10" in a violet panel at the centre; vignette with Bank building above*
*Reverse—purple panel with Britannia and Hibernia seated at the centre*

| | | F | VF |
|---|---|---|---|
| **NI.721a** | *Signatory: Hume Robertson.* | | |
| | Prefix N dated 6.5.1929. ................................................................ | | Rare |
| **NI.721b** | *Signatory: F. S. Forde.* | | |
| | Prefix N dated 10.12.1934 .......................................................... | | Rare |

*Obverse—green with "£10" in a red panel at the centre; vignette with Bank building above*
*Reverse—red panel with Britannia and Hibernia seated at the centre*

| | | VF | EF |
|---|---|---|---|
| **NI.722** | *Signatory: G. A. Kennedy* | | |
| | Prefix N dated from 10.10.1938 to 10.4.1946 .............................. | £260 | £400 |

*Obverse—green with a mesh background and with "£10" in a red panel at the centre; vignette with Bank building above*
*Reverse—red panel with Britannia and Hibernia seated at the centre*

|  |  | VF | EF |
|---|---|---|---|
| **NI.723** | *Signatory: H. W. M. Clarke* | | |
| | Prefix N dated 10.1.1948 ................................................................ | £190 | £350 |

Size 152 mm x 85 mm approximately

*Obverse—brown on a multicoloured underprint. Portrait of a young man to the right*
*Reverse—mainly brown. Illustration of the sinking of the "Girona"*

|  |  | EF | UNC |
|---|---|---|---|
| **NI.724a** | *Signatory: J. G. McClay (Manager)* | | |
| | Prefix RN dated 1.1.1977 ............................................................. | £65 | £90 |
| | Prefix ZY—replacement note....................................................... | | Rare |
| **NI.724b** | *Signatory: F.H.Hollway (Manager)* | | |
| | Prefix RN dated 1.1.1979 and 1.1.1981....................................... | £60 | £90 |
| | Prefix ZY—replacement note....................................................... | | Rare |

# TWENTY POUNDS

Size 148 mm x 85 mm approximately

*Obverse—black with "£20" in a brown panel at the centre; vignette with Bank building above*
*Reverse—rose-red panel with Britannia and Hibernia seated at the centre*

|  | | F | VF |
|---|---|---|---|
| **NI.731a** | *Signatory: Hume Robertson.* | | |
|  | Prefix N dated 6.5.1929. ................................................................ | | Rare |
| **NI.731b** | *Signatory: G. A. Kennedy* | | |
|  | Prefix N dated 20.4.1943 and 20.11.1944.................................... | £260 | £400 |

Size 160 mm x 90 mm approximately

*Obverse—mauve on a multicoloured underprint; portrait of a mature lady to the right*
*Reverse—mauve on a multicoloured underprint. Illustration of rock chimney at Lacada Point, Giant's Causeway*

|  | | EF | UNC |
|---|---|---|---|
| **NI.732** | *Signatory: F. H. Hollway (Manager).* | | |
|  | Prefix SN dated 1.3.1981 ............................................................... | £170 | £250 |
|  | Prefix ZY—replacement note....................................................... | | probably exists |

# ONE HUNDRED POUNDS

Size 160 mm x 90 mm approximately

*Obverse—green on a multicoloured underprint. Portrait of a mature man to the right*
*Reverse—green on a multicoloured underprint. Illustration of the Spanish Armada at the centre*

|  | EF | UNC |
|---|---|---|
| **NI.741**    *Signatory: F. H. Hollway (Manager)* | | |
| Prefix TN dated 1.3.1981.............................................................. | £550 | — |
| Prefix ZY—replacement note...................................................... | | probably exists |

# ULSTER BANK LIMITED

The bank was formed in 1836 by investors who had intended to participate in the establishment of a branch of the National Bank of Ireland in Belfast, but who found the terms offered to them insufficiently inviting. They formed their own bank instead.

The Ulster Bank was acquired by the London County and Westminster Bank Ltd. in 1917, and is now part of the Royal Bank of Scotland group.

## EXAMPLES OF EARLY BANKNOTES

# ONE POUND

Size 153 mm x 85 mm approximately

*Obverse—black with "ONE" in a blue panel at the centre; vignette with sailing ship above Uniface. Multiple rubber stamp overprints reading "ISSUED IN NORTHERN IRELAND AFTER 6TH MAY 1929"*

|  | | F | VF |
|---|---|---|---|
| **NI.801** | *Handsigned.* No prefix letters—dated 1.3.1926, 1.6.1927, 1.12.1927 ............. (and possibly others). | Rare | |

*Obverse—black with "ONE" in a blue panel at the centre; vignette with sailing ship above. Uniface.*

| **NI.802** | *Handsigned.* No prefix letters – dated from 6.5.1929 to 1.1.1934 ................... | £80 | £130 |
|---|---|---|---|

*Obverse—black with "ONE" in a blue panel at the centre; vignette with sailing ship above*
*Reverse—blue; unframed illustration of the Bank's head office building in Belfast*

|  | F | VF |
|---|---|---|

**NI.803** *Handsigned.*
No prefix letters—dated from 1.1.1935 to 1.2.1938 .................. £65 £110

*Obverse—black with "ONE" in a blue panel at the centre; vignette with sailing ship above*
*Reverse—blue; illustration of the Bank's head office building framed in a sunburst pattern*

|  | VF | EF |
|---|---|---|

**NI.804a** *Handsigned.*
No prefix letters—dated 1.9.1939, and ...................................... £85 £140
Prefix A dated 1.9.1939 and 1.1.1940

**NI.804b** *Signatory: J. R. Williams.*
No serial number dated 1.1.1948—specimen only.................... Rare
Prefix A dated 1.5.1956................................................................. £75 £110

Size 152 mm x 72 mm approximately

*Obverse—blue/grey on a multicoloured underprint*
*Reverse—blue/grey on a red and purple underprint; Coat of Arms at the centre*

|  |  | EF | UNC |
|---|---|---|---|
| **NI.805** | *Signatory: J. J. A. Leitch.* | | |
| | No prefix letters—dated 4.10.1966............................................ | £25 | £35 |

Size 135 mm x 67 mm approximately

*Obverse—blue/grey on a multicoloured underprint*
*Reverse—blue/grey on a red and purple underprint; Coat of Arms at the centre*

| **NI.806a** | *Signatory: A. E. G. Brain (Chief Executive).* | | |
|---|---|---|---|
| | Prefix A dated 15.2.1971.................................................. | £20 | £30 |
| **NI.806b** | *Signatory: R. W. Hamilton (Chief Executive).* | | |
| | Prefix A dated 1.3.1973 and 1.3.1976.......................................... | £9 | £15 |

# FIVE POUNDS

Size 205 mm x 115 mm approximately

*Obverse—black with "FIVE" in a green panel at the centre; vignette with sailing ship above. Uniface*

| | | F | VF |
|---|---|---|---|
| **NI.811** | *Handsigned.* | | |
| | No prefix letters – dated 6.5.1929 to 1.1.1934............................. | £100 | £170 |

*Obverse—black with "FIVE" in a green panel at the centre; vignette with sailing ship above*
*Reverse—green; unframed illustration of the Bank's head office building in Belfast*

| | | | |
|---|---|---|---|
| **NI.812** | *Handsigned.* | | |
| | No prefix letters—dated 1.1.1935 to 1.10.1937......................... | £100 | £170 |

*Obverse—black with "FIVE" in a green panel at the centre; vignette with sailing ship above.*
*Reverse—green; illustration of the Bank's head office building framed in a sunburst pattern.*

|  | VF | EF |
|---|---|---|

**NI.813a** *Handsigned.*
No prefix letters—dated from 1.2.1939 to 1.1.1943 ................... £85 £135

**NI.813b** *Signatory: J. R. Williams.*
No prefix letters—dated 1.5.1956 ............................................... £80 £130

Size 141 mm x 85 mm approximately

*Obverse—brown on a light multicoloured underprint*
*Reverse—brown on a multicoloured underprint; Coat of Arms at the centre*

**NI.814** *Signatory: J. J. A. Leitch.*
No prefix letters—dated 4.10.1966. ............................................. £90 £160

Size 145 mm x 78 mm approximately

*Obverse—brown on a light multicoloured underprint*
*Reverse—brown on a multicoloured underprint; Coat of Arms at the centre*

|  |  | EF | UNC |
|---|---|---|---|
| **NI.815a** | Signatory: A. E. G. Brain (Chief Executive) |  |  |
|  | Prefix B dated 15.2.1971. | £75 | £110 |
| **NI.815b** | Signatory: R. W. Hamilton (Chief Executive) |  |  |
|  | Prefix B dated 1.3.1973 to 1.3.1977. | £35 | £50 |
| **NI.815c** | Signatory: V. Chambers (Chief Executive) |  |  |
|  | Prefix B dated 1.10.1982 to prefix C dated 1.2.1988 | £30 | £45 |

Size 135 mm x 70 mm approximately

*Obverse—brown on a multicoloured underprint.*
*Reverse—brown on a multicoloured underprint; Coat of Arms at the centre*

|  |  | EF | UNC |
|---|---|---|---|
| **NI.816** | Signatory: D. Went (Chief Executive) |  |  |
|  | Prefix D dated 1.12.1989 to prefix G dated 1.1.1993 | £17 | £25 |
|  | Prefix Z—replacement note | probably exists |  |

*Obverse—brown on a multicoloured underprint.*
*Reverse—brown on a multicoloured underprint; Coat of Arms at the centre*

|  |  | EF | UNC |
|---|---|---|---|
| **NI.817** | *Signatory: M. J. Wilson (Group Chief Executive)* | | |
| | Prefix A dated 1.7.1998 to prefix C dated 1.1.2001 ................... | — | £10 |
| | Prefix Z—replacement note ........................................................ | — | £25 |

1,000,000 notes issued December 2006 to commemorate the footballer George Best 1946—2006.
*Obverse—brown on a multicoloured underprint.*
*Reverse—multicoloured with three picture of George Best*

|  |  | | |
|---|---|---|---|
| **NI.818** | *Signatory: C. McCarthy (Group Executive)* | | |
| | Prefix GB dated 25.11.2006 ........................................................ | — | £15 |

# TEN POUNDS

Size 205 mm x 120 mm approximately

*Obverse—black with "TEN" in a red panel at the centre; vignette with sailing ship above*
*Uniface*

|  | F | VF |
|---|---|---|
| **NI.821** Handsigned. No prefix letters—dated 1.6.1929 to 1.5.1933............................ £110 | | £220 |

*Obverse—black with "TEN" in a red panel at the centre; vignette with sailing ship above*
*Reverse—red; unframed illustration of the Bank's head office building*

| | F | VF |
|---|---|---|
| **NI.822** Handsigned. No prefix letters—dated 1.5.1936. ................................................ £110 | | £220 |

*Obverse—black with "TEN" in a red panel at the centre; vignette with sailing ship above*
*Reverse—red; illustration of the Bank's head office building framed in a sunburst pattern*

|  | | VF | EF |
|---|---|---|---|
| **NI.823** | *Handsigned.* | | |
| | No prefix letters—dated from 1.2.1939 to 1.1.1948 ................... | £120 | £240 |

Size 152 mm x 93 mm approximately

*Obverse—green on a light multicoloured underprint*
*Reverse—green on a multicoloured underprint; Coat of Arms at the centre*

| **NI.824** | *Signatory: J. J. A. Leitch.* | |
|---|---|---|
| | No prefix letters—dated 4.10.1966. ........................................... | Rare |

Size 151 mm x 85 mm approximately

*Obverse—green on a light multicoloured underprint.*
*Reverse—green on a multicoloured underprint; Coat of Arms at the centre*

|  |  | EF | UNC |
|---|---|---|---|
| **NI.825a** | Signatory: A. E. G. Brain (Chief Executive).<br>Prefix C dated 15. 2.1971.............................................................. | £140 | £250 |
| **NI.825b** | Signatory: R. W. Hamilton (Chief Executive)<br>Prefix C dated 12.11.1972 to 2.6.1980. ......................................... | £55 | £85 |
| **NI.825c** | Signatory: V. Chambers (Chief Executive)<br>Prefix C dated 1.10.1982 to prefix D dated 1.2.1988.................. | £40 | £55 |
| **NI.825d** | Signatory:  D. Went (Chief Executive)<br>Prefix D and prefix E dated 1.12.1989......................................... | £35 | £50 |

Size 142 mm x 75 mm approximately

*Obverse—green on a mullicoloured underprint*
*Reverse—green on a multicoloured underprint; Coat of Arms at the centre*

|  |  |  |  |
|---|---|---|---|
| **NI.826** | Signatory: D. Went (Chief Executive)<br>Prefix F to prefix H dated 1.12.1990. ........................................... | £32 | £45 |
|  | Replacement note—prefix Z ......................................................... | £60 | £80 |

*Obverse—green on a multicoloured underprint.*
*Reverse—green on a multicoloured underprint; Coat of Arms at the centre*

|  |  | EF | UNC |
|---|---|---|---|
| **NI.827a** | *Signatory: R. D. Kells (Group Chief Executive).* | | |
|  | Prefix A and Prefix B dated 1.1.1997 .......................................... | £20 | £30 |
|  | Prefix Z—replacement note ........................................................ | £45 | £65 |
| **NI.827b** | *Signatory: M. J. Wilson (Group Chief Executive)* | | |
|  | Prefix B and prefix C dated 1.7.1999 ......................................... | --- | £25 |
|  | Prefix Z—replacement note. ....................................................... | £40 | £60 |
| **NI.827c** | *Signatory: L. McCarthy (Group Chief Executive)* | | |
|  | Prefix C dated 6.1.2004................................................................ | --- | £20 |
|  | Prefix Z—replacement note. ....................................................... | £25 | £40 |

# TWENTY POUNDS

Size 205 mm x 118 mm approximately

*Obverse – black with "TWENTY" in a blue panel at the centre; vignette with sailing ship above*
*Uniface*

|          |                                                      | VF    | EF    |
|----------|------------------------------------------------------|-------|-------|
| **NI.831** | *Handsigned.* | | |
|          | No prefix letters—dated 1.6.1929 ............................................... | £150  | £250  |

*Obverse—black with "TWENTY" in a blue panel at the centre; vignette with sailing ship above*
*Reverse—blue; illustration of the Bank's head office building framed in a sunburst pattern*

|          |                                                      | VF    | EF    |
|----------|------------------------------------------------------|-------|-------|
| **NI.832** | *Handsigned.* | | |
|          | No prefix letters—dated from 1.3.1941 to 1.1.1948 .................. | £180  | £250  |

Size 161 mm x 90 mm approximately

*Obverse—purple on a light multicoloured underprint*
*Reverse—purple on a multicoloured underprint; Coat of Arms at the centre*

|  |  | EF | UNC |
|---|---|---|---|
| **NI.833a** | *Signatory: J. J. A. Leitch.* |  |  |
|  | No prefix letter – dated 1.7.1970................................................ |  | Rare |
| **NI.833b** | *Signatory: A. E. G. Brain (Chief Executive).* |  |  |
|  | Prefix D dated 15.2.1971 ................................................ |  | Rare |
| **NI.833c** | *Signatory: R. W. Hamilton (Chief Executive)* |  |  |
|  | Prefix D dated 1.3.1976 and 2.6.1980.......................................... | £80 | £105 |
| **NI.833d** | *Signatory: V. Chambers (Chief Executive)* |  |  |
|  | Prefix D dated 1.10.1982 to 1.2.1988........................................... | £60 | £85 |

Size 148 mm x 80 mm approximately

*Obverse—purple and blue on a light multicoloured underprint*
*Reverse—purple on a multicoloured underprint; Coat of Arms at the centre*

| **NI.834** | *Signatory: D. Went (Chief Executive).* |  |  |
|---|---|---|---|
|  | Prefix E and prefix F dated 1.11.1990.......................................... | £50 | £65 |

*Obverse—purple and mauve on a multicoloured underprint*
*Reverse—purple on a multicoloured underprint; Coat of Arms at the centre*

|  |  | EF | UNC |
|---|---|---|---|
| **NI.835a** | *Signatory: R. D. Kells (Group Chief Executive).* | | |
| | Prefix A and prefix B dated 1.1.1996 .......................................... | £38 | £55 |
| | | | |
| **NI.835b** | *Signatory: M. J. Wilson (Group Chief Executive).* | | |
| | Prefix B dated 1.7.1999 to prefix D dated 1.7.2002 ................... | --- | £40 |
| | Prefix Z—replacement note. ....................................................... | £55 | £75 |
| | | | |
| **NI.835b** | *Signatory: C. McCarthy (Group Chief Executive).* | | |
| | Prefix D dated 6.1.2004 and ongoing......................................... | --- | £40 |
| | Prefix Z—replacement note. ....................................................... | £45 | £65 |

# FIFTY POUNDS

Size 200 mm x 115 mm approximately

*Obverse—black with "FIFTY" in a blue panel at the centre; vignette with sailing ship above*
*Uniface*

|  | | VF | EF |
|---|---|---|---|
| **NI.841** | *Handsigned.* | | |
| | No prefix letters—dated 1.6.1929 .................................................. | £350 | £550 |

*Obverse—black with "FIFTY" in a blue panel at the centre; vignette with sailing ship above*
*Reverse—blue; illustration of the Bank's head office building framed in a sunburst pattern*

|  | | VF | EF |
|---|---|---|---|
| **NI.842** | *Handsigned.* | | |
| | No prefix letters—dated 1.3.1941 and 1.1.1943 ........................ | £220 | £300 |

Size 168 mm x 95 mm approximately

*Obverse—green and brown on a light multicoloured underprint*
*Reverse—green and brown on a multicoloured underprint; Coat of Arms at the centre*

|  |  | EF | UNC |
|---|---|---|---|
| **NI.843** | *Signatory: V. Chambers (Chief Executive)* |  |  |
|  | Prefix E dated 1.10.1982. ............................................................ | £150 | £220 |

Size 157 mm x 85 mm approximately

*Obverse—green, brown and multicoloured on a light multicoloured underprint*
*Reverse—mainly green and brown on a multicoloured underprint; Coat of Arms at the centre*

|  |  | EF | UNC |
|---|---|---|---|
| **NI.844** | *Signatory: R. D. Kells (Chief Executive).* |  |  |
|  | Prefix D dated 1.1.1997 ................................................... | £95 | £120 |
|  | Prefix Z—replacement note ......................................... | £140 | £200 |

# ONE HUNDRED POUNDS

Size 203 mm x 120 mm approximately

*Obverse—black with "£100" in a blue panel at the centre; vignette with sailing ship above*
*Uniface*

|  |  | VF | EF |
|---|---|---|---|
| **NI.851** | *Handsigned.* |  |  |
|  | No prefix letters—dated 1.6.1929 ................................................ | £450 | £750 |

*Obverse—black with "£100" in a blue panel at the centre; vignette with sailing ship above*
*Reverse—blue; illustration of the Bank's head office building framed in a sunburst pattern*

|  |  | VF | EF |
|---|---|---|---|
| **NI.852** | *Handsigned.* |  |  |
|  | No prefix letters—dated 1.3.1941 and 1.1.1943 ......................... | £250 | £400 |

Size 157 mm x 100 mm approximately

*Obverse—red on a light multicoloured underprint*
*Reverse—red on a light red and blue underprint; Coat of Arms at the centre*

|  |  | EF | UNC |
|---|---|---|---|
| **NI.853a** | *Signatory: R. W. Hamilton (Chief Executive)* |  |  |
|  | Prefix F dated 1.3.1973 and 1.3.1977. | £450 | £600 |
| **NI.853b** | *Signatory: V. Chambers (Chief Executive)* |  |  |
|  | Prefix E dated 1.10.1982. | £400 | £550 |

Size 162 mm x 90 mm approximately
*Obverse—purple on a light multicoloured underprint.*
*Reverse—purple on a light multicoloured underprint; Coat of Arms at the centre*

| **NI.854** | *Signatory: D. Went (Chief Executive).* |  |  |
|---|---|---|---|
|  | Prefix G dated 1.12.1990 | £350 | £450 |

# Britain's Biggest Selling Coin Magazine

Save money when you take out a subscription to *Coin News* for either yourself or a friend. Pay just £34 for 12 issues (save £5.00 on the cover price) or £17 for 6 issues (UK only) and enjoy having Britain's Biggest Selling Coin Magazine delivered straight to your door each month.

## Subscriber Benefits

- **FREE** delivery before the magazine goes on sale in the newsagents

- **FREE** classified advertising for all subscribers

- **SAVE** £5.00 per year on the cover price

- Never miss an issue!

*"Subscribe today and keep up to date with the UK's biggest-selling coin magazine"*

John Mussell, Group Managing Editor

## Subscribing is easy.

☎ Call 01404 44166

🖅 Complete the order form below and send it to Token Publishing Ltd.

🖶 Complete the order form and fax it to 01404 44788

🖱 log on to www.tokenpublishing.com

---

**COIN NEWS SUBSCRIBERS ORDER FORM.**

Your subscription will start from the next available issue.

Three easy ways to pay: *(Please tick as appropriate)*

☐ By Direct Debit (UK Only) £34 every 12 issues

☐ By Direct Debit (UK Only) £17 every 6 issues

By Credit or Debit card or Cheque: ☐ £34 for 12 issues

☐ Europe/World Surface £42 ☐ Worldwide Airmail £52

**YOUR DETAILS**

Title ___ Initial ___ Surname ___

Address ___

Postcode ___ Telephone ___

E-mail ___

**CREDIT OR DEBIT CARD PAYMENT**

☐ Visa ☐ Mastercard ☐ JCB ☐ Switch

Card Number

Issue no. ___ Authorisation code * ___

Valid from ___ Expiry date ___

Signature ___

\* The last 3 digits from the back of the card

We will not pass your details on to any other organisation, however we may send you information we feel is of interest to you. If you DO NOT want to receive this information please tick this box. ☐

**INSTRUCTION TO BANK OR BUILDING SOCIETY TO PAY BY DIRECT DEBIT.**

**Instructions to your Bank or Building Society.** Please pay Token Publishing Ltd. Direct Debit from the account detailed in this instruction subject to the safeguards assured by The Direct Debit Guarantee. I understand that this instruction may remain with Token Publishing Ltd. and, if so, details may be passed electronically to my Bank/Building Society.

**DIRECT Debit**

Originators reference

| 6 | 8 | 4 | 6 | 0 | 7 |
|---|---|---|---|---|---|

Signature ___ Date ___

Ref no. to be completed by Token Publishing Ltd for official use only.

Name of Bank ___

Bank Address ___

Bank Postcode ___

Account Holder ___

Sort Code

Account Number

*Please note Banks & Building Societies may not accept Direct Debit Instructions for some type of accounts.*

Please send to: Token Publishing Ltd, Orchard House, Duchy Road, Heathpark, Honiton, Devon EX14 1YD

Photocopies are accepted

# The banknotes of Scotland

The first Scottish notes appeared in 1695 in the year of the foundation of the Bank of Scotland and contemporary with the earliest notes of the Bank of England. They were released in values from £5 to £100 sterling; when pound notes appeared in 1704 they were denominated £12 Scots, reflecting the prevailing exchange rate. The Bank's monopoly expired in 1721 and within six years it was faced with a rival with the title of the Royal Bank of Scotland, although the general public referred to them simply as the Old and New Banks.

Both banks originated from a need to put banking on a proper footing and supply paper money for the convenience of the mercantile classes. The third bank, however, appeared in 1746 with the primary objective of stimulating the linen industry, and this was reflected in its name, the British Linen Company which did not change its title to the British Linen Bank until 1906. In the second half of the 18th century smaller banks appeared in various parts of the country, usually confined to a specific locality. Although these banks did much to foster trade and industry in their own areas, the spectacular crash of Douglas Heron & Company in 1772 bankrupted many of the leading families in the south-west of Scotland. Many of the smaller banks, confined to a single town, were fairly ephemeral, remembered by their elusive notes which are now much sought after by collectors of local history as well as notaphilists.

Early in the 19th century, however, there emerged a number of joint-stock banks which were destined to play a major role in the economic development of Scotland. These included the Caledonian Banking Company (1838–1907), the Central Bank (1834–68), the City of Glasgow Bank (1839–79), the Clydesdale Bank (1838), the Commercial Bank (1810–1959), the Eastern Bank (1838–63), the National Bank (1825–1959), the North of Scotland Bank (1836–1950), the Town & County Bank (1825–1908), the Union Bank (1843–1955) and the Western Bank (1832–57). Although the Bank Charter Act of 1844 severely restricted the note-issuing activities of the English provincial banks, the comparable legislation for Scotland a year later enabled the Scottish banks to continue to issue their own notes, although the act banned the foundation of any new note-issuing banks after that date.

Although banking in Scotland was on a sounder footing than in England, the failure of the West of Scotland Bank in 1857 and the City of Glasgow Bank in 1878 both had severe repercussions on the economy of the west of Scotland. The worst effects, so far as the general public possessing notes of these banks was concerned, were mitigated by the undertaking of the National Bank to redeem the notes of the West of Scotland, and by all the other banks acting in concert to redeem the City of Glasgow notes.

As a result of mergers and amalgamations the number of note-issuing banks gradually fell, although by the beginning of the 20th century there were still ten in existence. The Caledonian was absorbed by the Bank of Scotland in 1907 and the Town & County merged with the North of Scotland Bank the following year. In the period after World War II there were further amalgamations. For example, in 1959 the Commercial Bank joined forces with the National Bank to form the National Commercial Bank of Scotland which, in turn, combined with the Royal Bank of Scotland which now acquired the suffix "Limited" inscribed on notes since that date. In the same year the British Linen Bank (acquired by Barclays in 1919) was sold to the Bank of Scotland and the merger was completed the following year.

Of the 19th century joint-stock banks, only the Clydesdale has survived, although it, too, has undergone enormous changes. It was formed in 1838 by the union of the Greenock Union Bank, the Edinburgh & Glasgow Bank, the Eastern Bank and the Dundee Commercial Bank. In 1919 it was acquired by the Midland Bank which four years later also took over the North of Scotland Bank. These banks continued to operate separately until 1950 when they merged to form the Clydesdale & North of Scotland Bank which reverted to the shorter title of the Clydesdale Bank in 1963.

Today, therefore, Scotland enjoys the colourful variety of notes produced by three banks, a far cry from the relatively plain black and white notes of the 18th and early 19th centuries. Although many of the earlier notes were engraved and printed by local firms such as Kirkwood, Lizars and Johnston, later notes were produced by the great English security printers, from Perkins Bacon to De La Rue. Prior to the late 1960s there was no uniformity regarding size or colours but since then both have been brought into line with the notes of the Bank of England. In 1975 James Douglas estimated the total circulation of the three Scottish banks in excess of £250 million, or about 7 per cent of the total for the British Isles. The Royal Bank is now the only Scottish bank to continue issuing pound notes and all three have notes up to £100. Moreover, they have shown a penchant for commemorative notes in recent years, notably the Royal Bank's pounds honouring Alexander Graham Bell, Robert Louis Stevenson and the advent of the Scottish Parliament, and the Clydesdale's £20 notes for the Commonwealth Heads of Government Meeting (1997) and Glasgow and UK City of Architecture and Design (1999), not to mention the series of four £5 notes of 1996 marking the bicentenary of Robert Burns by including verses from his poems.

# BANK OF SCOTLAND

Scotland's oldest bank, the Bank of Scotland was founded in 1695 and is thus just a year younger than the Bank of England. During its long history the Bank of Scotland has absorbed the Central Bank of Scotland (1866), the Caledonian Banking Co. Ltd. (1907), and more recently The Union Bank of Scotland Ltd (1955), and the British Linen Bank (1971). Elements of the designs of the banknotes of these two latter Banks can be seen in the contemporary notes of the Bank of Scotland.

## ONE POUND

**"A" size square notes**   (175 mm x 128 mm approximately)

*Obverse—brown with a yellow/brown underprint. Royal Arms in a Panel to the left, with the Bank's Coat of Arms towards the top of the note above a grey medallion. Uniface.*

|  |  | F | VF |
|---|---|---|---|
| **SC101a** *Signatory: Duncan McNeill (Secretary)* | | | |
| Prefix 70/H dated 18.2.1894 to prefix 59/X dated 19.12.1910 .... | | £450 | £850 |
| **SC101b** *Signatory: P. Macdonald (Secretary)* | | | |
| Prefix 60/X dated 3.1.1911 to prefix 59/AL dated 24.11.1920..... | | £220 | £480 |
| **SC101c** *Signatory: A. J. Rose (Secretary)* | | | |
| Prefix 60/AL dated 8.12.1920 to prefix 9/AU dated 16.11.1927. | | £180 | £380 |

**"B" size notes**   (152mm x 84mm approximately)

*Obverse—brown and grey with the Royal Coat of Arms in panel at the left; grey and brown medallion at centre.*
*Reverse—grey; unframed illustration of Head Office building.*

| | | VF | EF |
|---|---|---|---|
| **SC102** | Signatories: (Lord) Elphinstone (Governor); G. J. Scott (Treasurer) | | |
| | Prefix A dated 1.1.1927 to prefix J dated 17.7.1933 ...................... | £90 | £160 |

*Obverse—brown and grey with the Bank's Coat of Arms in panel at the left; grey medallion at centre.*
*Reverse—grey; framed illustration of Head Office building*

| | | VF | EF |
|---|---|---|---|
| **SC103a** | Signatories: (Lord) Elphinstone (Governor); A. W. M.Beveridge (Treasurer) | | |
| | Prefix K dated 15.1.1935 to prefix Q dated 15.9.1937 ................... | £45 | £85 |
| **SC103b** | Signatories: (Lord) Elphinstone (Governor); J. Macfarlane (Treasurer) | | |
| | Prefix R dated 5.1.1939 to prefix Y dated 7.5.1941 ........................ | £35 | £70 |
| **SC103c** | Signatories: (Lord) Elphinstone (Governor); J. B. Crawford (Treasurer) | | |
| | Prefix Z dated 2.6.1942 to prefix AA dated 16.10.1943................ | £35 | £70 |

*Obverse—brown and grey; no panel at left; larger grey medallion at centre.*
*Reverse—dark chocolate brown; Bank's Arms at centre.*

**SC104**  *Signatories: (Lord) Elphinstone* (Governor); *J.B.Crawford* (Treasurer)   *VF*   *EF*
Prefix A dated 4.1.1945 to prefix B dated 6.2.1945 ...................... £55   £100

*Obverse—brown and grey; no panel at left; larger grey medallion at centre.*
*Reverse—light brown; Bank's Arms at centre.*

**SC105a**  *Signatories: (Lord) Elphinstone* (Governor); *J.B.Crawford* (Treasurer)   *EF*   *UNC*
Prefix B dated 6.2.1945 to prefix R dated 19.11.1952 ................... £30   £50

**SC105b**  *Signatories: (Lord) Elphinstone* (Governor); *Sir William Watson* (Treasurer)
Prefix R dated 4.9.1953 to prefix T dated 9.11.1953 ...................... £35   £55

*Obverse—brown with slate blue medallion at centre*
*Reverse—grey; sailing ship at centre surrounded by thistles.*

**SC106a**  *Signatories: (Lord) Elphinstone* (Governor); *Sir William Watson* (Treasurer)   *EF*   *UNC*
Prefix A dated 1.3.1955 to prefix D dated 4.3.1955 .......................... £35   £50

**SC106b**  *Signatories: Sir John Craig* (Governor); *Sir William Watson* (Treasurer)
Prefix E dated 1.9.1955 to prefix N dated 14.9.1956 ........................ £25   £38

**SC106c**  *Signatories: Lord Bilsland* (Governor); *Sir William Watson* (Treasurer)
Prefix O dated 30.8.1957 to prefix B/A dated 30.11.1960 ................ £25   £38

**"C" size notes** (150mm x 70mm approximately)

*Obverse—brown with slate blue medallion at centre*
*Reverse—grey; sailing ship at centre surrounded by thistles*

|  |  | *EF* | *UNC* |
|---|---|---|---|
| **SC107a** | *Signatories: Lord Bilsland (Governor); Sir William Watson (Treasurer)* |  |  |
|  | Prefix A dated 16.11.1961 to prefix N dated 12.12.1962, and...... | £24 | £32 |
|  | Prefix A/A dated 3.2.1964 to prefix A/I dated 13.2.1964 (printer's imprint "LD") ................................................ | £24 | £32 |
|  | Prefix A/J dated 4.5.1965 to prefix A/O dated 11.5.1965 (printers imprint "LTD" ................................................ | £24 | £32 |

**SC107b** *Signatories: Lord Polwarth (Governor); J. Letham (Treasurer & General Manager)*
  Prefix A/P–A/U dated 1.6.1966 (w/o sorting symbols)............ £22 £30
  Prefix A/V–B/C dated 3.3.1967 (with sorting symbols)............ £22 £30

  Change of watermark.
**SC107c** *Signatories: Lord Polwarth (Governor); J. Letham (Treasurer & General Manager)*
  Prefix A/Z to prefix B/C dated 3.3.1967 (with sorting symbols) £22 £30

**"D" size notes** (Size 135mm x 67mm approximately)

*Obverse—multicoloured with Bank's Coat of Arms at the centre*
*Reverse—brown and purple; Shield and thistles flanked by Arms and sailing ship*

**SC108** *Signatories: Lord Polwarth (Governor); J. Letham (Treasurer & General Manager)* Prefix A/1 to A/6 dated 17.7.1968; prefix A/7 to B/1 dated 18.8.1969.................................................. £25 £35

*Obverse—mainly green; Bank's Arms at the centre, portrait of Sir Walter Scott to the right*
*Reverse—mainly green; Shield and thistles at centre flanked by sailing ship and Pallas emblem*

|  | EF | UNC |
|---|---|---|
| **SC109a** *Signatories: Lord Polwarth (Governor); T. W. Walker (Treasurer & General Manager)* | | |
| Prefix A/1 dated 10.8.1970 to prefix B/20 dated 31.8.1971 | £22 | £35 |
| Replacement note – prefix Z/1 | £50 | £80 |
| | | |
| **SC109b** *Signatories: Lord Clydesmuir (Governor); T. W. Walker (Treasurer & General Manager)* | | |
| Prefix C/1 dated 1.11.1972 to prefix C/27 dated 30.8.1973 | £18 | £28 |
| Replacement note – prefix Z/1 | £50 | £80 |
| | | |
| **SC109c** *Signatories: Lord Clydesmuir (Governor); A. M. Russell (Treasurer & General Manager)* | | |
| Prefix C/28 dated 28.10.1974 to prefix D/1 dated 3.10.1978 | £7 | £13 |
| Replacement note – prefix Z/1 and Z/2 | £30 | £55 |
| | | |
| **SC109d** *Signatories: Lord Clydesmuir (Governor); D. B. Pattullo (Treasurer & General Manager)* | | |
| Prefix D/2 dated 15.10.1979 to prefix D/31 dated 4.11.1980 | £7 | £12 |
| Replacement note – prefix Z/2 and Z/3 | £25 | £40 |
| | | |
| **SC109e** *Signatories: Sir T. N. Risk (Governor); D. B. Pattullo (Treasurer & General Manager)* | | |
| Prefix D/32 to prefix D/42 dated 30.7.1981 (with sorting symbols) and | £7 | £10 |
| Prefix D/43 dated 7.10.1983 to prefix E/1 dated 18.11.1986 (without symbols) | £5 | £9 |
| Replacement note – prefix Z/3 | £15 | £25 |
| | | |
| **SC109f** *Signatories: Sir T. N. Risk (Governor); P. Burt (Treasurer & General Manager)* | | |
| Prefix E/1 to prefix E/13 dated 19.8.1988 | £3 | £5 |
| Replacement note – prefix Z/3 | £15 | £25 |

# FIVE POUNDS

**Size** 220mm x 135mm approximately

*Obverse—brown with black value panels. Royal Arms in a panel to the left, with the Bank's Coat of Arms towards the top of the note above a grey medallion. Uniface.*

|  | F | VF |
|---|---|---|
| **SC111a** *Signatory: D. MacNeill* (Secretary)<br>Prefix 17/B dated 5.5.1894 to prefix 8/F dated 17.10.1911 ............... | | Rare |
| **SC111b** *Signatory: P. Macdonald* (Secretary)<br>Prefix 9/F dated 18.9.1912 to prefix 2/I dated 3.6.1919 .................... | £240 | £420 |
| **SC111c** *Signatory: A. J. Rose* (Secretary)<br>Prefix 3/I dated 7.10.1920 to prefix 10/L dated 19.5.1931 (approx.) | £200 | £380 |
| **SC111d** *Signatories: Lord Elphinstone* (Governor) *and G. J. Scott* (Treasurer)<br>Prefix 11/L dated 26.6.1931 (approx.) to prefix 4/M dated 25.3.1933 | £180 | £320 |
| **SC111e** *Signatories: Lord Elphinstone* (Governor) *and A. W. M. Beveridge* (Treasurer)<br>Prefix 5/M dated17.1.1935 to prefix 8/M dated 23.1.1935 ............... | £180 | £320 |

*Obverse—brown with black value panels. A Scottish thistle replaces the Royal Shield in the left hand panel. The Bank's Coat of Arms towards the top of the note above a grey medallion. Uniface.*

|  |  | VF | EF |
|---|---|---|---|
| **SC112a** | *Signatories: Lord Elphinstone* (Governor) *and A. W. M. Beveridge* (Treasurer) | | |
| | Prefix 9/M dated 9.2.1935 to prefix 14/N dated 17.3.1938 .............. | £160 | £300 |
| **SC112b** | *Signatories: Lord Elphinstone* (Governor) *and J.Macfarlane* (Treasurer) | | |
| | Prefix 15/N dated 24.4.1939 to prefix 4/P dated 16.10.1941............. | £150 | £260 |
| **SC112c** | *Signatories: Lord Elphinstone* (Governor) *and J. B. Crawford* (Treasurer) | | |
| | Prefix 5/P dated 5.6.1942 to prefix 14/R dated 26.9.1944 ................ | £120 | £230 |

**Size** 178mm x 102mm approximately

*Obverse—brown on a light brown underprint. Thistle motif in a panel to the left with the Bank's Arms at the top of the note flanked by brown value panels. Grey medallion lower centre.*
*Reverse—Dark brown. Bank's Coat of Arms on a lined background with '£5' either side.*

| **SC113** | *Signatories: Lord Elphinstone* (Governor) *and J. B. Crawford* (Treasurer) | | |
|---|---|---|---|
| | Prefix 1/A dated 3.1.1945 to prefix 10/A dated 2.3.1945 ................... | £150 | £250 |

*Obverse—brown on a light brown underprint. Thistle motif in a panel to the left with the Bank's Arms at the top of the note flanked by brown value panels. Grey medallion lower centre. Reverse—Light brown. Bank's Coat of Arms on a lined background with '£5' either side.*

VF   EF

**SC114**   *Signatories: Lord Elphinstone* (Governor) *and J. B. Crawford* (Treasurer) .
Prefix 11 / A dated 16.3.1945 to prefix 20/D dated 20.10.1947................   £80   £150

*Obverse—brown on a light brown underprint. Thistle motif in a panel to the left with the Bank's Arms at the top of the note flanked by black value panels. Grey medallion lower centre. Reverse—Light brown. Bank's Coat of Arms on a lined background with '£5' either side.*

**SC115a**   *Signatories: Lord Elphinstone* (Governor) *and J. B. Crawford* (Treasurer)
Prefix 5/E dated 5.12.1947 (possibly earlier) to prefix 10/M dated 21.11.1952
...................................................................................................................   £55   £100

**SC115b**   *Signatories: Lord Elphinstone* (Governor) *and Sir William Watson* (Treasurer)
Prefix 11/M dated 10.12.1952 to prefix 20/O dated 4.12.1953 ...............   £55   £100

*Obverse—brown on a light brown underprint. Thistle motif in a panel to the left with the Bank's Arms at the top of the note flanked by black value panels. Slate blue medallion lower centre. Reverse—Light brown. Bank's Coat of Arms on a lined background with '£5' either side.*

**SC116a**   *Signatories: Lord Elphinstone* (Governor) *and Sir William Watson* (Treasurer)
Prefix 1/A dated 1.3.1955 to prefix 6/D dated 7.4.1955 .....................   £45   £80

**SC116b**   *Signatories: Sir John Craig* (Governor) *and Sir William Watson* (Treasurer)
Prefix 7/D dated 7.4.1955 to prefix 10/G dated 3.9.1955 ...................   £45   £80

*Obverse—brown on a light brown underprint. Thistle motif in a panel to the left with the Bank's
Arms at the top of the note flanked by black value panels. Slate blue medallion lower centre.
Reverse—Dark brown. Redesigned following the merger with the Union Bank. The Bank's Shield at
the centre is flanked by two circular panels bearing the Bank's Coat of Arms to the left and the Ship
emblem to the right.*

|  |  | VF | EF |
|---|---|---|---|
| **SC117a** | *Signatories: Sir John Craig* (Governor) *and Sir William Watson* (Treasurer) | | |
| | Prefix 11/G dated 9.4.1956 to prefix 20/L dated 17.4.1956..................... | £35 | £70 |
| **SC117b** | *Signatories: Lord Bilsland* (Governor) *and Sir William Watson* (Treasurer) | | |
| | Prefix 1/M dated 1.5.1957 to prefix 20/KA dated 24.5.1960 .................. | £30 | £55 |

**Size** 140mm x 84mm approximately

*Obverse—brown on a light brown underprint. Thistle motif in a panel to the left with the Bank's
Arms at the top of the note flanked by black value panels. Slate blue medallion lower centre. "£5"
values at the bottom of the note are in hollow print.
Reverse—Dark brown. The Bank's shield at the centre is flanked by two circular panels bearing the
Bank's Coat of Arms to the left and the ship emblem to the right.*

|  |  | EF | UNC |
|---|---|---|---|
| **SC118** | *Signatories: Lord Bilsland* (Governor) *and Sir William Watson* (Treasurer) | | |
| | Prefix 1/A dated 14.9.1961 to prefix 20G dated 22.9.1961 ....................... | £45 | £60 |

*Obverse—brown on a light brown underprint. Thistle motif in a panel to the left with the Bank's Arms at the top of the note flanked by black value panels. Slate blue medallion lower centre. "£5" values at the bottom of the note are in solid print.*
*Reverse—Dark brown. The Bank's shield at the centre is flanked by two circular panels bearing the Bank's Coat of Arms to the left and the ship emblem to the right.*

|  |  | EF | UNC |
|---|---|---|---|
| **SC119a** | *Signatories: Lord Bilsland* (Governor) *and Sir William Watson* (Treasurer) | | |
| | Prefix 1/H dated 25.9.1961 to prefix 15/N dated 14.8.1962.................. | £35 | £50 |
| | Prefix A dated 7.10.1963 to prefix D dated 12.1.1965 ............................. | £35 | £50 |
| **SC119b** | *Signatories: Lord Polwarth* (Governor) *and Sir William Watson* (Treasurer) | | |
| | Prefix E dated 7.3.1966 and prefix F dated 8.3.1966 ............................... | £35 | £55 |
| **SC119c** | *Signatories: Lord Polwarth* (Governor) *and J. Letham* (Treasurer and General Manager) | | |
| | Prefix G dated 1.2.1967 and Prefix H dated 2.2.1967 (without symbols) | £35 | £55 |
| | Prefix I dated 1.11.1967 (Sorting symbols added to the reverse)........... | £40 | £60 |

**Size** 146mm x 78mm approximately

*Obverse—Multicoloured, blue, brown, green and yellow. Bank's Coat of Arms at the centre.*
*Reverse—Dark and light green. The Bank's shield at the centre is flanked by two panels bearing the Bank's Coat of Arms to the left and the ship emblem to the right.*

|  |  | EF | UNC |
|---|---|---|---|
| **SC120** | *Signatories: Lord Polwarth* (Governor) *and J. Letham* (Treasurer & General Manager) | | |
| | Prefix A dated 1.11.1968 to prefix D dated 9.12.1969............................... | £75 | £100 |

*Obverse—Mainly blue. The Bank's Coat of Arms at the centre with a portrait of Sir Walter Scott to the right*

*Reverse—Mainly blue. The Bank's shield above thistles at the centre flanked by a sailing ship and Pallas emblem.*

|  | EF | UNC |
|---|---|---|
| **SC121a** *Signatories: Lord Polwarth (Governor); T. W. Walker (Treasurer & General Manager)* | | |
| Prefix A dated 10.8.1970 to prefix K dated 2.9.1971............................ | £50 | £80 |
| Replacement note – prefix ZA.............................................................. | £75 | £120 |
| | | |
| **SC121b** *Signatories: Lord Clydesmuir (Governor); T. W. Walker (Treasurer & General Manager)* | | |
| Prefix L dated 4.12.1972 to prefix X dated 5.9.1973 ............................ | £50 | £80 |
| Replacement note – prefix ZA.............................................................. | £75 | £120 |
| | | |
| **SC121c** *Signatories: Lord Clydesmuir (Governor); A. M. Russell (Treasurer & General Manager)* | | |
| Prefix Y and prefix Z dated 4.11.1974, and | | |
| Prefix AA dated 4.11.1974 to prefix BA dated 19.10.1978 ................... | £35 | £55 |
| Replacement note – prefix ZA.............................................................. | £50 | £70 |
| | | |
| **SC121d** *Signatories: Lord Clydesmuir (Governor); D. B. Pattullo (Treasurer & General Manager)* | | |
| Prefix BB dated 28.9.1979 to prefix BS dated 28.11.1980.................... | £30 | £50 |
| Replacement note – prefix ZA and ZB ................................................. | £35 | £60 |
| | | |
| **SC121e** *Signatories: Sir T. N. Risk (Governor); D. B. Pattullo (Treasurer & General Manager)* | | |
| Prefix BT dated 27.7.1981 to prefix CK dated 25.6.1982 (with | | |
| sorting symbols)..................................................................................... | £25 | £40 |
| Prefix CL dated 13.10.1983 to prefix DZ dated 29.2.1988 (without | | |
| symbols) ................................................................................................. | £18 | £25 |
| Replacement note – prefix ZB ............................................................. | £30 | £45 |

**Size** 136mm x 70mm approximately

*Obverse—Mainly blue. The Bank's Coat of Arms at the centre with a portrait of Sir Walter Scott to the right.*
*Reverse—Mainly blue. The Bank's shield above thistles at the centre flanked by a sailing ship and Pallas emblem*

|  |  | EF | UNC |
|---|---|---|---|
| **SC122a** | *Signatories: Sir T. N. Risk (Governer) and P. Burt (Treasurer & Chief General Manager)* |  |  |
| | Prefix EA to prefix EJ dated 20.6.1990 ...................................................... | — | £22 |
| | Replacement note – prefix ZB .................................................................... | — | £35 |
| **SC122b** | *Signatories: D. B. Pattullo (Governor) and P. Burt (Treasurer & Chief General Manager)* |  |  |
| | Prefix EK dated 6.11.1991 to prefix FB dated 7.1.1994 ............................ | — | £22 |
| | Replacement note – prefix ZB .................................................................... | — | £35 |

*Obverse—Blue and multicoloured. Bank's Arms at the centre of the note with a portrait of Sir Walter Scott to the left.*
*Reverse—Blue and multicoloured. Illustration entitled "Oil and Energy" at the centre.*

| **SC123a** | *Signatories: D. B. Pattullo (Governor) and P. Burt (Treasurer & Chief General Manager)* |  |  |
|---|---|---|---|
| | Prefix AA to prefix AM dated 4.1.1995 ................................................. | — | £14 |
| | Replacement note – prefix ZZ................................................................. | | £30 |
| **SC123b** | *Signatories: D. B. Pattullo (Governor) and G. Masterton (Treasurer & Chief General Manager)* |  |  |
| | Prefix AN to prefix AZ dated 13.9.1996............................................... | — | £12 |
| | Replacement note – prefix ZZ................................................................. | — | £30 |
| **SC123c** | *Signatories: M. J. Grant (Governor) and G. Masterton (Treasurer & Chief General Manager)* |  |  |
| | Prefix BA to prefix BR dated 5.8.1998 ................................................. | — | £12 |
| | Replacement note – prefix ZZ ............................................................... | — | £30 |
| **SC123d** | *Signatories: P. Burt (Governor) and G. Mitchell (Treasurer & Managing Director)* |  |  |
| | Prefix BS to CB dated 25.6.2002 ........................................................... | — | £9 |
| | Replacement note – prefix ZZ................................................................. | — | £25 |
| **SC123e** | *Signatories: D. Stevenson (Governor) and C. Matthew (Treasurer)* |  |  |
| | Prefix CC dated 1.1.2006 and ongoing. ................................................ | — | £9.00 |
| | Replacement note – prefix ZZ................................................................. | — | £25.00 |

# TEN POUNDS

**Size** 220mm x 135mm approximately

*Obverse—brown with black value panels. Royal Arms in a Panel to the left, with the Bank's Coat of Arms towards the top of the note above a grey medallion. Uniface.*

|  | F | VF |
|---|---|---|

**SC131a** *Signatory: D. MacNeill* (Secretary)
Prefix 7/A dated 16.10.1894 to prefix 4/B dated 30.9.1909 ............... Rare

**SC131b** *Signatory: P. Macdonald* (Secretary)
Prefix 5/B dated 20.11.1912 to prefix 8/B dated 5.11.1919 ................ Rare

**SC131c** *Signatory: A. J. Rose* (Secretary)
Prefix 9/B dated 15.8.1921 to prefix 1/C dated 9.3.1929 ................... £650 £1,100

**SC131d** *Signatories: Lord Elphinstone* (Governor) *and A. W. M. Beveridge* (Treasurer)
Prefix 2/C dated 24.1.1935 ...................................................... Rare

*Obverse—brown with black value panels. A Scottish thistle replaces the Royal shield in the left hand panel. The Bank's Coat of Arms towards the top of the note above a grey medallion. Uniface.*

|  | VF | EF |
|---|---|---|

**SC132a** *Signatories: Lord Elphinstone* (Governor) *and A. W. M. Beveridge* (Treasurer)
Prefix 3/C dated 28.1.1938 .................................................... £550 £950

**SC132b** *Signatories: Lord Elphinstone* (Governor) *and J. B. Crawford* (Treasurer)
Prefix 4/C dated 16.7.1942 and prefix 5/C dated 15.10.1942 ............ £550 £950

*Obverse—brown on a light brown underprint. Thistle motif in a panel to the left with the Bank's Arms at the top of the note flanked by black value panels. Slate blue medallion lower centre. Uniface*

|  |  | VF | EF |
|---|---|---|---|
| **SC133** | *Signatories: Lord Bilsland* (Governor) *and Sir William Watson* (Treasurer) | | |
| | Prefix 6/C dated 26.9.1963 and prefix 7/C dated 27.9.1963 ............. | £220 | £360 |

**Size** 152mm x 85mm approximately

*Obverse—Mainly brown. The Bank's Coat of Arms at the centre with a portrait of Sir Walter Scott to the right*
*Reverse—Mainly brown. The Bank's shield to the right with the sailing ship and Pallas emblem in round panels.*

|  |  | EF | UNC |
|---|---|---|---|
| **SC134a** | *Signatories: Lord Clydesmuir* (Governor); *A. M. Russell* (Treasurer & General Manager) | | |
| | Prefix A dated 1.5.1974 to prefix L dated 29.9.1978............................. | £60 | £95 |
| | Replacement note – prefix ZB................................................................ | £90 | £130 |
| **SC134b** | *Signatories: Lord Clydesmuir* (Governor); *D. B. Pattullo* (Treasurer & General Manager) | | |
| | Prefix M dated 10.101979 to prefix W dated 5.2.1981.......................... | £60 | £95 |
| | Replacement note – prefix ZB................................................................ | £90 | £130 |
| **SC134c** | *Signatories: Sir T.N.Risk* (Governor); *D. B. Pattullo* (Treasurer & General Manager) | | |
| | Prefix X dated 22.7.1981to prefix CX dated 6.8.1987 .......................... | £35 | £55 |
| | Replacement note – prefix ZB................................................................ | £55 | £75 |
| **SC134d** | *Signatories: Sir T. N. Risk* (Governer) *and P. Burt* (Treasurer & Chief General Manager) | | |
| | Prefix CX dated 1.9.1989 to prefix EP dated 31.10.1990 ..................... | £28 | £40 |
| | Replacement note – prefix ZB................................................................ | £45 | £60 |

**Size** 143mm x 75mm approximately

*Obverse—Mainly brown. The Bank's Coat of Arms at the centre with a portrait of Sir Walter Scott to the right. The word "STERLING" added*
*Reverse—Mainly brown. The Bank's shield to the right with the sailing ship and Pallas emblem in round panels*

|  | EF | UNC |
|---|---|---|
| **SC135** *Signatories: Sir T. N. Risk* (Governer) *and P. Burt* (Treasurer & Chief General Manager) | | |
| Prefix EQ dated 7.5.1992 to prefix GG dated 13.4.1994 ........................ | £25 | £35 |
| Replacement note – prefix ZB and ZC(?) ............................................. | £45 | £65 |

*Obverse—Mainly brown. The Bank's Coat of Arms at the centre with a portrait of Sir Walter Scott to the left*
*Reverse—Brown and multicoloured. Illustration entitled "Distilling and Brewing" at the centre*

|  | EF | UNC |
|---|---|---|
| **SC136a** *Signatories: D. B. Pattullo* (Governor) *and P. Burt* (Treasurer & Chief General Manager) | | |
| Prefix AA to prefix BM dated 1.2.1995 ................................................ | — | £25 |
| Replacement note – prefix ZZ ............................................................. | £35 | £45 |
| **SC136b** *Signatories: D. B. Pattullo* (Governor) *and G. Masterton* (Treasurer & Chief General Manager) | | |
| Prefix BN to prefix CF dated 5.8.1997 ................................................ | — | £24 |
| Replacement note – prefix ZZ ............................................................. | £35 | £45 |
| **SC136c** *Signatories: M. J. Grant* (Governor) *and G. Masterton* (Treasurer & Chief General Manager) | | |
| Prefix CG to prefix DT dated 18.8.1998 ............................................. | — | £20 |
| Replacement note – prefix ZZ ............................................................. | £35 | £45 |
| **SC136d** *Signatories: Sir John Shaw* (Governor) *and G. Mitchell* (Treasurer & Chief General Manager) | | |
| Prefix DU dated 18.6.2001 and ongoing. ............................................. | — | £18 |

# TWENTY POUNDS

**Size** 224mm x 135mm approximately

*Obverse—brown with red value panels. Royal Arms in a panel to the left, with the Bank's Coat of Arms towards the top of the note above a grey medallion. Uniface.*

|  |  | F | VF |
|---|---|---|---|
| **SC141a** | *Signatory: D. MacNeill* (Secretary)<br>Prefix 5/B dated 26.5.1894 to prefix 6/D dated 2.9.1910................... | | Rare |
| **SC141b** | *Signatory: P. Macdonald* (Secretary)<br>Prefix 7/D dated 26.10.1911 to prefix 10/E dated 29.12.1920............ | | Rare |
| **SC141c** | *Signatory: A. J. Rose* (Secretary)<br>Prefix 1/F date unknown, to prefix 10/F dated 21.6.1932................. | £350 | £650 |
| **SC141d** | *Signatories: Lord Elphinstone* (Governor) *and G. J. Scott* (Treasurer)<br>Prefix 1/G dated 2.12.1932.................................................... | £350 | £650 |
| **SC141e** | *Signatories: Lord Elphinstone* (Governor) *and A. W. M. Beveridge* (Treasurer)<br>Prefix 2/G dated 11.1.1935 and prefix 3/G dated 16.2.1935.............. | £250 | £450 |

*Obverse—brown with red value panels. A Scottish thistle replaces the Royal Shield in the left hand panel. The Bank's Coat of Arms towards the top of the note above a grey medallion. Uniface.*

|  |  | VF | EF |
|---|---|---|---|
| **SC142a** | *Signatories: Lord Elphinstone* (Governor) *and A. W. M. Beveridge* (Treasurer)<br>Prefix 4/G dated 28.3.1936 to prefix 7/G dated 22.7.1938................ | £350 | £550 |
| **SC142b** | *Signatories: Lord Elphinstone* (Governor) *and J. Macfarlane* (Treasurer)<br>Prefix 8/G dated 16.5.1939 and prefix 9/G dated 12.9.1939.............. | £350 | £550 |
| **SC142c** | *Signatories: Lord Elphinstone* (Governor) *and J. B. Crawford* (Treasurer)<br>Prefix 10/G dated 5.6.1942 to prefix 5/J dated 11.8.1952................... | £160 | £350 |
| **SC142d** | *Signatories: Lord Elphinstone* (Governor) *and Sir W. Watson* (Treasurer)<br>Prefix 6/J dated 5.12.1952 to prefix 10/J dated 24.4.1953.................. | £150 | £320 |

*Obverse—brown with red value panels. Thistle motif in the left hand panel. The Bank's Coat of Arms towards the top of the note above a slate blue medallion. Uniface.*

|  |  | VF | EF |
|---|---|---|---|
| **S143a** | *Signatories: Sir John Craig* (Governor) *and Sir W. Watson* (Treasurer)<br>Prefix 1/A dated 6.4.1955 to prefix 5/B dated 12.6.1956................... | £100 | £180 |
| **S143b** | *Signatories: Lord Bilsland* (Governor) *and Sir W. Watson* (Treasurer)<br>Prefix 6/B dated 25.3.1958 to prefix 4/H dated 3.10.1963 ............... | £75 | £130 |

**Size** 212mm x 134mm approximately

*Obverse—brown with red value panels. Thistle motif in the left hand panel. The Bank's Coat of Arms towards the top of the note above a slate blue medallion. Uniface.*

|  |  | VF | EF |
|---|---|---|---|
| **SC144** | *Signatories: Lord Polwarth* (Governor) *and J. Letham* (Treasurer)<br>Prefix 5/H to prefix 9/H dated 5.5.1969............................................. | £130 | £230 |

**Size** 160mm x 90mm approximately

*Obverse—Mainly purple. The Bank's Coat of Arms at the centre with a portrait of Sir Walter Scott to the right*
*Reverse—Purple and red. Illustration of the Bank's head office building at the centre with the shield, sailing ship and Pallas emblem to the left.*

| | | EF | UNC |
|---|---|---|---|
| **SC145a** | *Signatories: Lord Polwarth* (Governor) *and T. W. Walker* (Treasurer & General Manager) | | |
| | Prefix A dated 1.10.1970 | £120 | £220 |
| **SC145b** | *Signatories: Lord Clydesmuir* (Governor); *T. W. Walker* (Treasurer & General Manager) | | |
| | Prefix A dated 3.1.1973 | £120 | £220 |
| **SC145c** | *Signatories: Lord Clydesmuir* (Governor); *A. M. Russel*l (Treasurer & General Manager) | | |
| | Prefix A dated 8.11.1974 and 14.1.1977 | £100 | £180 |
| **SC145d** | *Signatories: Lord Clydesmuir* (Governor); *D. B. Pattullo* (Treasurer & General Manager) | | |
| | Prefix A and B dated 16.7.1979, and prefix B dated 2.2.1981 | £80 | £130 |
| **SC145e** | *Signatories: Sir T. N. Risk* (Governor); *D. B. Pattullo* (Treasurer & General Manager) | | |
| | Prefix B dated 4.8.1981 to prefix K dated 15.12.1987 | £60 | £90 |

**Size** 150mm x 80mm approximately

*Obverse—Mainly purple. The Bank's Coat of Arms at the centre with a portrait of Sir Walter Scott to the right.*
*Reverse—Purple and red. Illustration of the Bank's head office building at the centre with the shield, sailing ship and Pallas emblem to the left*

| | | EF | UNC |
|---|---|---|---|
| **SC146** | *Signatories: D. B. Pattullo* (Governor) *and P. Burt* (Treasurer & Chief General Manager) | | |
| | Prefix K dated 1.7.1991 to prefix AU dated 12.1.1993 | £45 | £70 |

*Obverse—Mainly purple. Bank's Coat of Arms at centre with portrait of Sir Walter Scott to left.*
*Reverse—Purple, red and brown. Illustration entitled "Education and Research" at the centre.*

|  |  | EF | UNC |
|---|---|---|---|
| **SC147a** | *Signatories: D. B. Pattullo* (Governor) *and P. Burt* (Treasurer & Chief General Manager) | | |
| | Prefix AA to prefix AY dated 1.5.1995.................................................... | — | £55 |
| | Replacement note – prefix ZZ.............................................................. | £75 | £120 |
| **SC147b** | *Signatories: D. B. Pattullo* (Governor) *and G. Masterton* (Treasurer & Chief General Manager) | | |
| | Prefix AY dated 25.10.1996 to prefix CE dated 1.4.1998 ..................... | — | £45 |
| | Replacement note – prefix ZZ.............................................................. | £65 | £100 |
| **SC147c** | *Signatories: M. J. Grant* (Governor) *and G. Masterton* (Treasurer & Chief General Manager) | | |
| | Prefix CE to prefix DL dated 22.3.1999 ............................................. | — | £40 |
| | Replacement note – prefix ZZ.............................................................. | £45 | £70 |
| **SC147d** | *Signatories:Shaw* (Governor) *and G. Mitchell* (Treasurer & Managing Director) | | |
| | Prefix DM to prefix DW dated 18.6.2001 ............................................ | — | £35 |
| | Replacement note – prefix ZZ.............................................................. | £40 | £60 |
| **SC147e** | *Signatory: G. Mitchell* (Governor) | | |
| | Prefix DW (starts DW 900001) dated 26.11.2003 and ongoing.......... | — | £35 |

# FIFTY POUNDS

**Size** 156mm x 85mm approximately

*Obverse—Mainly green. Bank's Coat of Arms at centre with portrait of Sir Walter Scott to left.*
*Reverse—Green, brown and multicoloured. Illustration entitled "Arts and Culture" at the centre.*

| | | | |
|---|---|---|---|
| **SC161a** | *Signatories: D. B. Pattullo* (Governor) *and P. Burt* (Treasurer & Chief General Manager) | | |
| | Prefix AA dated 1.5.1995 ........................................................ | — | £11 |
| **SC161b** | *Signatories: M. J. Grant* (Governor) *and G. Masterton* (Treasurer & Chief General Manager) | | |
| | Prefix AA to prefix AB dated 15.4.1999............................................. | — | £90 |
| **SC161c** | *Signatories: G. Mitchell* (Governor) | | |
| | Prefix AB dated 29.1.2003 to prefix AC 500000 dated 24.9.2004...... | — | £85 |
| **SC161d** | *Signatories: D. Stevenson* (Governor) *and C. Matthew* (Treasurer) | | |
| | Prefix AC 500001 dated 1.1.2006 to and ongoing ............................. | — | £85 |

# ONE HUNDRED POUNDS

**Size** 220mm x 135mm approximately

*Obverse—brown with red value panels. Royal Arms in a panel to the left, with the Bank's Coat of Arms towards the top of the note above a grey medallion. Uniface.*

|  |  | F | VF |
|---|---|---|---|
| **SC171a** | *Signatory: D. MacNeill (Secretary)*<br>Prefix 7/C dated 12.7.1894 to prefix 1/G dated 9.12.1910 ................ |  | Rare |
| **SC171b** | *Signatory: P. Macdonald (Secretary)*<br>Prefix 2/G dated 11.12.1911 to prefix 4/H dated 17.4.1919 .............. |  | Rare |
| **SC171c** | *Signatory: A. J. Rose (Secretary)*<br>Prefix 5/H dated 7.7.1920, to prefix 8/I dated 8.6.1930..................... |  | Rare |
| **SC171d** | *Signatories: Lord Elphinstone (Governor) and G. J. Scott (Treasurer)*<br>Prefix 9/I dated 28.5.1932 and prefix 10/I dated 8.11.1932 .............. |  | Rare |
| **SC171e** | *Signatories: Lord Elphinstone (Governor) and A. W. M. Beveridge (Treasurer)*<br>Prefix 1/J dated 8.1.1935 and prefix 2/J dated 31.1.1935 .................. |  | Rare |

*Obverse—brown with red value panels. A Scottish thistle replaces the Royal Shield in the left hand panel. The Bank's Coat of Arms towards the top of the note above a grey medallion. Uniface.*

|  |  | F | VF |
|---|---|---|---|
| **SC172a** | *Signatories: Lord Elphinstone (Governor) and A. W. M. Beveridge (Treasurer)*<br>Prefix 3/J dated 23.3.1937 and prefix 4/J dated 12.8.1937 ................ |  | Rare |
| **SC172b** | *Signatories: Lord Elphinstone (Governor) and J.Macfarlane (Treasurer)*<br>Prefix 5/J dated 2.4.1940 to prefix 8/J dated 25.9.1942....................... |  | Rare |
| **SC172c** | *Signatories: Lord Elphinstone (Governor) and J. B. Crawford (Treasurer)*<br>Prefix 9/J dated 16.8.1946 to prefix 9/K dated 14.12.1951 ................ | £550 | £950 |

*Obverse—brown with red value panels. Thistle motif in the left hand panel. The Bank's Coat of Arms towards the top of the note above a slate blue medallion. Uniface.*

|  |  | VF | EF |
|---|---|---|---|
| **SC173a** | *Signatories: Sir John Craig (Governor) and Sir W. Watson (Treasurer)*<br>Prefix 10/K dated 14.9.1956 to prefix 3/L dated 3.12.1956 ............... | £500 | £900 |
| **SC173b** | *Signatories: Lord Bilsland (Governor) and Sir W. Watson (Treasurer).*<br>Prefix 4/L dated 24.3.1959 to prefix 8/N dated 30.11.1962............... | £500 | £900 |

**Size** 170mm x 100mm approximately

*Obverse—mainly red and orange. Bank's Coat of Arms centre with Sir Walter Scott to right.*
*Reverse—mainly red. Illustration of the Bank's head office building at the centre with the shield,*
*sailing ship, Ditat emblem and £100 in the four corners.*

|  | EF | UNC |
|---|---|---|

**SC174a** *Signatories: Lord Polwarth* (Governor) *and T. W. Walker* (Treasurer & General
Manager)
Prefix A dated 6.12.1971 .......................................................... £500 £750

**SC174b** *Signatories: Lord Clydesmuir* (Governor); *T. W. Walker* (Treasurer & General Manager)
Prefix A dated 6.9.1973 .......................................................... £500 £750

**SC174c** *Signatories: Lord Clydesmuir* (Governor); *A. M. Russell* (Treasurer & General Manager)
Prefix A dated 11.10.1978 ....................................................... £450 £700

**SC174d** *Signatories: Lord Clydesmuir* (Governor); *D. B. Pattullo* (Treasurer & General Manager)
Prefix A dated 26.1.1981 ....................................................... £450 £700

**SC174e** *Signatories: Sir T. N. Risk* (Governor); *D. B. Pattullo* (Treasurer & General Manager)
Prefix A dated 10.6.1982 to prefix A dated 26.11.1986 ........................ £400 £650

Size 160mm x 90mm approximately

*Obverse—mainly red and orange. Bank's Coat of Arms centre with Sir Walter Scott to right. The*
*word "STERLING" added*
*Reverse—mainly red. Illustration of the Bank's head office building at the centre with the shield,*
*sailing ship, Ditat emblem and £100 in the four corners.*

|  | EF | UNC |
|---|---|---|

**SC175** *Signatories: D. B. Pattullo* (Governor) *and P. Burt* (Treasurer & Chief General
Manager)
Prefix A dated 24.2.1990 to prefix A dated 9.2.1994 ........................... £240 £350

*Obverse — mainly red. Bank's Coat of Arms centre with Sir Walter Scott to left.*
*Reverse — red, brown and multicoloured. Illustration entitled "Leisure and Tourism" at the centre.*

|  | EF | UNC |
|---|---|---|
| **SC176a** *Signatories: D. B. Pattullo* (Governor) *and P. Burt* (Treasurer & Chief General Manager) | | |
| Prefix AA dated 17.7.1995 | — | £230 |
| Replacement note – prefix ZZ | | Rare |
| | | |
| **SC176b** *Signatories: D. B. Pattullo* (Governor) *and G. Masterton* (Treasurer & Chief General Manager) | | |
| Prefix AA dated 18.8.1997 | — | £200 |
| Replacement note – prefix ZZ | | Rare |
| | | |
| **SC176c** *Signatories: M. J. Grant* (Governor) *and G. Masterton* (Treasurer & Chief General Manager) | | |
| Prefix AA dated 19.5.1999 | — | £190 |
| Replacement note – prefix ZZ | | Rare |
| | | |
| **SC176d** *Signatory: G. Mitchell* (Governor) | | |
| Prefix AA dated 26.11.2003 and ongoing | — | £180 |
| Replacement note – prefix ZZ | | Rare |

# BRITISH LINEN BANK

Formerly known as The British Linen Company, the Bank was incorporated in 1746 during the reign of George II. The round seal with the figure of Pallas was adopted as the Company's emblem from the outset, and appears on most of the banknotes. In 1906 the name was changed to The British Linen Bank, and the first notes with the new title are dated 1907. Notes of The British Linen Bank were printed initially by Waterlow and Sons Ltd., whose banknote printing business was purchased by Thomas de la Rue in 1961. This change can be seen in the printer's imprint which appears on the notes. The British Linen Bank was merged with the Bank of Scotland in 1970.

## ONE POUND

**"A" size square notes** (150mm x 130mm approximately)

*Obverse—Blue with "B.L.B." in large red letters at centre; panel to the left; Royal Coat of Arms at the top. Uniface.*

|  | F | VF |
|---|---|---|
| **SC201a** *Signatories: F. Gordon Brown* (p. Manager) *and handsigned p. Accountant*<br>Prefix T dated 15.1.1907 and prefix U dated 26.12.1907 .................... |  | Rare |
| **SC201b** *Signatories: A. S. Aikman* (p. Manager) *and handsigned p. Accountant*<br>Prefix V dated 2.11.1908 ........................................................................ |  | Rare |
| **SC201c** *Signatories: E. G. Galletley* (p. Manager) *and handsigned p. Accountant*<br>Prefix W dated 15.7.1910 and prefix X dated 11.8.1911 ..................... | £400 | £700 |
| **SC201d** *Signatories: E. G. Galletley* (p. General Manager) *and handsigned p. Accountant*<br>Prefix Y dated 29.10.1912 and prefix Z dated 17.9.1913 .................... | £350 | £600 |

Obverse—*Blue with a red sunburst underprint and "B.L.B." in large red letters; panel at left and Royal Arms at top.*
Reverse—*Blue panel with "DITAT" emblem at centre.*

|  |  | F | VF |
|---|---|---|---|
| **SC202a** | *Signatories: E. G. Galletley* (p. General Manager) *and handsigned p. Accountant* | | |
| | Prefix A dated 23.9.1914 to prefix F dated 5.4.1918 ............................ | £180 | £320 |
| **SC202b** | *Signatories: C.J.Grant* (p. General Manager) *and handsigned p. Accountant* | | |
| | Prefix H dated 19.8.1919 to prefix L dated 31.7.1924 ......................... | £180 | £320 |

**"B" size notes.** (150mm x 85mm approximately)

Obverse—*Blue with a red sunburst underprint and "B.L.B." in large red letters; panel at left and Royal Arms at top.*
Reverse—*Blue panel with "DITAT" emblem at centre*

|  |  | VF | EF |
|---|---|---|---|
| **SC203** | *Signatory: J. Waugh* (Cashier). | | |
| | Prefix N dated 1.6.1926 to prefix Z dated 26.1.1933, and ................ | £70 | £120 |
| | Prefix A dated 3.4.1933 to prefix G dated 2.8.1934 ........................... | £65 | £110 |

*Obverse—Blue with a red sunburst underprint and "B.L.B." in large red letters; panel at left and the Bank's Coat of Arms at top.*
*Reverse—Blue panel with "DITAT" emblem at centre.*

| | VF | EF |
|---|---|---|

**SC204**  *Signatory: J. Waugh (Cashier).*
Prefix H dated 18. 1.1935 to prefix R dated 26.4.1937 ......................... £45    £85

*Obverse—Blue with a red sunburst underprint and "B.L.B." in large red letters; panel at left and the Bank's Coat of Arms at top. Silk fibres added to paper.*
*Reverse—Blue panel with "DITAT" emblem at centre.*

**SC205a**  *Signatory: J. Waugh (Cashier).*
Prefix S dated 4.7.1937 to prefix Z dated 8.11.1938, and ................... £45    £70
Prefix A dated 12.6.1939 to prefix D dated 13.11.1939, and ............. £45    £70
Prefix E/1 dated 7.3.1940 to prefix U/1 dated 7.4.1944 ................... £40    £65

**SC205b**  *Signatory: G.Mackenzie (General Manager)*
Prefix V/1 dated 4.1.1946 to prefix R/2 dated 5.8.1950 ................... £28    £45

**SC205c**  *Signatory: A. P. Anderson (General Manager)*
Prefix S/2 dated 4.6.1951 to prefix L/3 dated 12.5.1959 .................. £15    £30

*Obverse—Blue with a red sunburst underprint and "B.L.B." in large red letters; panel at left and the Bank's Coat of Arms at top. "No." is omitted from the serial number.*
*Reverse—Blue panel with "DITAT" emblem at centre.*

|  |  | VF | EF |
|---|---|---|---|
| **SC206** | *Signatory: A. P. Anderson (General Manager)* | | |
|  | Prefix M/3 to prefix P/3 dated 15.4.1960. ........................................... | £18 | £32 |

*Obverse—Blue with a red sunburst underprint and "B.L.B." in large red letters; panel at left and the Bank's Coat of Arms at top. Change of printer to Thomas de la Rue & Co. Ltd.*
*Reverse—Blue panel with "DITAT" emblem at centre.*

| **SC207** | *Signatory: A. P. Anderson* (General Manager) | | |
|---|---|---|---|
|  | Prefix Q/3 to prefix T/3 dated 30.9.1961 ........................................... | £18 | £32 |

## "C" size notes. (150mm x 70mm approximately)

*Obverse—Blue with a red sunburst underprint and "B.L.B." in large red letters; panel at left and the Bank's Coat of Arms at top.*
*Reverse—Blue panel with "DITAT" emblem at centre.*

|  |  | EF | UNC |
|---|---|---|---|
| **SC208a** | *Signatory: A. P .Anderson (General Manager)* | | |
| | Prefix U/3 to prefix Y/3 dated 31.3.1962............................................ | £28 | £40 |
| **SC208b** | *Signatory: T. W. Walker (General Manager)* | | |
| | Prefix Z/3 dated 1.7.1963 to prefix P/4 dated 13.6.1967. ................ | £25 | £40 |

*Obverse—Blue with a red sunburst underprint and "B.L.B." in large red letters; panel at left and the Bank's Coat of Arms at top—similar to previous issue.*
*Reverse—Revised blue panel with "ONE" either side of DITAT emblem at centre and sorting symbols added.*

| **SC209** | *Signatory: T. W. Walker (General Manager)* | | |
|---|---|---|---|
| | Prefix Q/4 to prefix T/4 dated 13.6.1967. ........................................ | £30 | £45 |

## "D" size notes. (Size 135mm x 67mm approximately)

*Obverse—Blue with multicoloured underprint. Portrait of Sir Walter Scott to the left.*
*Reverse—Blue panel with "ONE" either side of DITAT emblem at centre.*

| **SC210** | *Signatory: T. W. Walker (General Manager)* | | |
|---|---|---|---|
| | Prefix U/4 dated 29.2.1968 to prefix D/5 dated 20.7.1970. .............. | £24 | £35 |

# FIVE POUNDS

**Size:** 206mm x 130mm approximately

*Obverse—Blue with "B.L.B." in large red letters at centre; panel to the left; Royal Coat of Arms at the top. Uniface.*

|  |  | F | VF |
|---|---|---|---|
| **SC211a** | *Signatories: handsigned p.Manager and p.Accountant.*<br>Prefix A/3 dated 3.9.1907 to prefix H/3 dated 4.12.1911................. |  | Rare |
| **SC211b** | *Signatories: handsigned p.General Manager and p.Accountant*<br>Prefix I/3 dated 30.10.1912 to prefix M/3 dated 12.9.1915.............. | £450 | £800 |

*Obverse—Blue with a red sunburst underprint and "B.L.B." in large red letters; panel at left and Royal Arms at top.*
*Reverse—Blue panel with "DITAT" emblem at centre.*

|  |  |  | |
|---|---|---|---|
| **SC212** | *Signatories: Handsigned p.General Manager and p. Accountant.*<br>Prefix N/3 dated 1.2.1916 to prefix W/5 dated 3.8.1933 ......from £200 | £400 |

*Obverse—Blue with a red sunburst underprint and "B.L.B." in large red letters; panel at left and the Bank's Coat of Arms at top.*
*Reverse—Blue panel with "DITAT" emblem at centre.*

|  | VF | EF |
|---|---|---|
| **SC213a** *Signatories: A.Dempster (General Manager) and handsigned p. Accountant* | | |
| Prefix A/6 dated 20.12.1935 to prefix P/6 dated 30.12.1940.......... | £180 | £350 |
| **SC213b** *Signatories: G.Mackenzie (General Manager) and handsigned p. Accountant* | | |
| Prefix Q/6 dated 16.7.1941 to prefix B/7 dated 12.1.1943.............. | £180 | £350 |
| **SC213c** *Signatories: J.Waugh (Accountant and Cashier) and G. Mackenzie (General Manager)* | | |
| Prefix C/7 dated 11.2.1943 to prefix O/7 dated 28.1.1944.............. | £150 | £300 |

### Size 182mm x 100mm approximately

*Obverse—Blue with a red sunburst underprint and "B.L.B." in large red letters; panel at left and the Bank's Coat of Arms at top.*
*Reverse—Blue panel with "DITAT" emblem at centre.*

| | | |
|---|---|---|
| **SC214a** *Signatories: J. Waugh (Accountant & Cashier) and G. Mackenzie (General Manager)* | | |
| Prefix P/7 dated 29.5.1944 to prefix U/7 dated 3.11.1944............... | £100 | £180 |
| **SC214b** *Signatory: G. Mackenzie (General Manager)* | | |
| Prefix V/7 dated 10.9.1946 to prefix Z/8 dated 2.8.1950................. | £55 | £110 |
| **SC214c** *Signatory: A. P. Anderson (General Manager)* | | |
| Prefix A/9 dated 5.12.1950 to prefix Y/11 dated 4.8.1959............... | £35 | £75 |

**Size** 158mm x 90mm approximately

*Obverse—Blue with a red sunburst underprint and "B.L.B." in large red letters; panel at left and the Bank's Coat of Arms at top. Printed by De la Rue.*
*Reverse—Blue panel with "DITAT" emblem at centre.*

| | | VF | EF |
|---|---|---|---|
| **SC215** | *Signatory: A. P. Anderson* (General Manager) | | |
| | Prefix Z/11 dated 2.1.1961 and prefix A/12 dated 3.2.1961 ............ | £80 | £160 |

**Size** 140mm x 84mm approximately

*Obverse—Blue on a red sunburst underprint; portrait of Sir Walter Scott.*
*Reverse—Revised blue panel with "DITAT" emblem at centre.*

| | | EF | UNC |
|---|---|---|---|
| **SC216a** | *Signatory: A. P. Anderson* (General Manager) | | |
| | Prefix D/12 dated 21.9.1962 to prefix F/12 dated 19.11.1962.......... | £28 | £50 |
| **SC216b** | *Signatory: T. W. Walker* (General Manager) | | |
| | Prefix G/12 dated 16.6.1964 to prefix I/12 dated 18.8.1964 ............ | £28 | £50 |

**Size** 146mm x 78mm approximately.

*Obverse—Blue on a red sunburst underprint; portrait of Sir Walter Scott.*
*Reverse—Revised blue panel with "DITAT" emblem at centre.*

| | | | |
|---|---|---|---|
| **SC217** | *Signatory: T. W. Walker* (General Manager) | | |
| | Prefix K/12 dated 22.3.1968 to prefix M/12 dated 24.5.1968.......... | £40 | £60 |

## TEN POUNDS

**Size:** 206mm x 130mm approximately

*Obverse—Blue with "B.L.B." in large red letters at centre; panel to the left; Royal Coat of Arms at the top. Uniface.*

|  |  | F | VF |
|---|---|---|---|

**SC221**  *Signatories: handsigned p. Manager and p. Accountant.*
Prefix S/1 dated 30.1.1907.................................................................  Rare

*Obverse—Blue with a red sunburst underprint and "B.L.B." in large red letters; panel at left and Royal Arms at top.*
*Reverse—Blue panel with "DITAT" emblem at centre.*

**SC222**  *Signatories: Handsigned p. General Manager and p. Accountant.*
Prefix T/1 dated 15.2.1916 to prefix V/1 dated 15.3.1920............  from £650

## TWENTY POUNDS

**Size:** 206mm x 130mm approximately

*Obverse—Blue with "B.L.B." in large red letters at centre; panel to the left; Royal Coat of Arms at the top. Uniface.*

**SC231**  *Signatories: handsigned p. Manager and p. Accountant.*
Prefix X/2 dated 2.1.1907 to prefix B/3 dated 31.3.1911 ..................  Rare

*Obverse—Blue with "B.L.B." in large red letters at centre; panel to the left; Royal Coat of Arms at the top. Uniface.*

**SC232**  *Signatories: handsigned p. General Manager and p. Accountant.*
Prefix C/3 dated 20.10.1912 and prefix D/3 dated 18.11.1912 ........  Rare

*Obverse—Blue with a red sunburst underprint and "B.L.B." in large red letters; panel at left and Royal Arms at top.*
*Reverse—Blue panel with "DITAT" emblem at centre.*

**SC233**  *Signatories: Handsigned p. General Manager and p. Accountant.*
Prefix E/3 dated 3.5.1916 to prefix Z/3 dated 3.10.1935.................from £250     £450

*Obverse—Blue with a red sunburst underprint and "B.L.B." in large red letters; panel at left and the Bank's Coat of Arms at top.*
*Reverse—Blue panel with "DITAT" emblem at centre.*

|  |  | VF | EF |
|---|---|---|---|
| **SC234a** | *Signatories: A. Dempster* (General Manager) *and handsigned p.Accountant.* |  |  |
|  | Prefix Y/3 dated 6.8.1935 to prefix D/4 dated 2.8.1940 .................. £280 | | £480 |
| **SC234b** | *Signatories: G. Mackenzie* (General Manager) *and handsigned p. Accountant.* |  |  |
|  | Prefix E/4 dated 25.5.1942 to prefix K/4 dated 24.2.1945 ............... £200 | | £350 |

*Obverse—Blue with a red sunburst underprint and "B.L.B." in large red letters; panel at left and the Bank's Coat of Arms at top.*
*Reverse—Blue panel with "DITAT" emblem at centre.*

| **SC235a** | *Signatory: G. Mackenzie* (General Manager) |  |  |
|---|---|---|---|
|  | Prefix L/4 dated 2.9.1946 to prefix Q/4 dated 4.8.1949 .................. £180 | | £320 |
| **SC235b** | *Signatory: A. P.Anderson* (General Manager) |  |  |
|  | Prefix R/4 dated 12.5.1952 to prefix F/5 dated 11.12.1957 ............. £120 | | £250 |

*Obverse—Blue with a red sunburst underprint and "B.L.B." in large red letters; panel at left and the Bank's Coat of Arms at top. Printed by De la Rue.*
*Reverse—Blue panel with "DITAT" emblem at centre.*

|  |  | VF | EF |
|---|---|---|---|
| **SC236** | *Signatory: A. P. Anderson* (General Manager) |  |  |
|  | Prefix G/5 dated 14.2.1962 to prefix I/5 dated 4.4.1962 ................ | £170 | £320 |

# ONE HUNDRED POUNDS

**Size:** 206mm x 130mm approximately

*Obverse—Blue with "B.L.B." in large red letters at centre; panel to the left; Royal Coat of Arms at the top. Uniface.*

**SC241**    *Signatories: handsigned p. Manager and p. Accountant.*
         Prefix E/3 dated 3.1.1906 to prefix H/3 dated 15.5.1912.................      Rare

*Obverse—Blue with a red sunburst underprint and "B.L.B." in large red letters; panel at left and Royal Arms at top.*
*Reverse—Blue panel with "DITAT" emblem at centre.*

**SC242**    *Signatories: Handsigned p. General Manager and p. Accountant.*
         Prefix I/3 dated 7.1.1916 to prefix N/3 dated 18.7.1933..................      Rare

*Obverse—Blue with a red sunburst underprint and "B.L.B." in large red letters; panel at left and the Bank's Coat of Arms at top.*
*Reverse—Blue panel with "DITAT" emblem at centre.*

**SC243a** *Signatories: A. Dempster* (General Manager) *and handsigned p.Accountant.*
Prefix O/3 dated 24.6.1935 .................................................................. Rare

**SC243b** *Signatories: G. Mackenzie* (General Manager) *and handsigned p.Accountant.*
Prefix P/3 dated 4.2.1942 and prefix Q/3 dated 3.3.1943 ................ Rare

*Obverse—Blue with a red sunburst underprint and "B.L.B." in large red letters; panel at left and the Bank's Coat of Arms at top.*
*Reverse—Blue panel with "DITAT" emblem at centre.*

| | VF | EF |
|---|---|---|
| **SC244** *Signatory: A. P. Anderson* (General Manager)<br>Prefix R/3 dated 6.4.1951 to prefix T/3 dated 27.11.1957 ............... | £650 | £1100 |

*(Actual size 206mm x 130mm)*

*Obverse—Blue with a red sunburst underprint and "B.L.B." in large red letters; panel at left and the Bank's Coat of Arms at top. Printed by De la Rue.*
*Reverse—Blue panel with "DITAT" emblem at centre.*

| | VF | EF |
|---|---|---|
| **SC245** *Signatory: A. P. Anderson* (General Manager)<br>Prefix U/3 dated 9.5.1962 and V/3 dated 1.6.1962 ......................... | £650 | £1100 |

# THE CLYDESDALE BANK LIMITED

The Bank was founded in Glasgow in 1838 and expanded rapidly during the 19th century by absorbing a number of other Scottish banks including the Greenock Union Bank, the Edinburgh and Glasgow Bank and the Eastern Bank of Scotland. In 1919 ownership of the Bank passed to the Midland Bank who also purchased the North of Scotland Bank Ltd., but it was not until 1950 that the two Scottish Banks merged to form The Clydesdale & North of Scotland Bank Ltd. In 1987 the Clydesdale Bank was sold by the Midland Bank to the National Australia Bank, and it remains as one the three issuers of paper money in Scotland today.

## ONE POUND

### "A" size square notes  (165mm x 120mm approximately)

*Obverse—black and red. The Arms of Glasgow surrounded by three female figures at the top with further female figure to the left and right; uniface.*

|  |  | F | VF |
|---|---|---|---|
| **SC301** | *Signatories: D. Dewar* (Accountant) *and handsigned p. General Manager* |  |  |
|  | From 4.7.1882 to 30.10.1912 without prefix letter, and ...................... | £380 | £650 |
|  | Prefix A dated 8.10.1913 to prefix A dated 9.2.1921. ........................... | £220 | £400 |

*Obverse—Blue with a red overlay. Similar to previous design with the Arms of Glasgow and female figures*
*Reverse—Blue. A large panel with the Arms of Glasgow at the centre*

**SC302a** *Signatories: A. Swanson (Cashier) and J. D. Dewar (Accountant)*      *F*      *VF*
      Prefix A dated 4.1.1922 and 14.6.1922 ...................................................... £220    £380

**SC302b** *Signatories: A. Swanson* (Cashier) *and R. Young* (Accountant)
      Prefix A dated 14.3.1923 to prefix A dated 27.10.1926........................... £220    £350

**"B" size notes** (152mm x 85mm approximately)

*Obverse—Blue with red overlay. Arms of Glasgow with female figures at the top; female figures to the left and right.*
*Reverse—Blue. A large panel with the Arms of Glasgow at the centre.*

**SC303a** *Signatories: A. Swanson* (Cashier) *and R. Young* (Accountant)      *VF*     *EF*
      Prefix A dated 3.1.1927 to prefix A dated 7.10.1931.............................. £75    £140

**SC303b** *Signatories: A. Mitchell* (General Manager) *and R. Young* (Accountant & Cashier)
      Prefix A dated 2.3.1932 to prefix B dated 24.10.1945............................ £55    £90

**SC303c** *Signatories: A. Mitchell* (General Manager) *and J. W. Pairmain* (Accountant & Cashier)
      Prefix C dated 1.5.1946. ............................................................................ £85    £160

**SC303d** *Signatories: J. J. Campbell* (General Manager) *and J. W. Pairmain* (Accountant & Cashier)
      Prefix C dated 20.11.1946 to prefix C dated 3.9.1947............................. £45    £80

**SC303e** *Signatories: J. J. Campbell* (General Manager) *and R. R. Houston* (Accountant & Cashier)
      Prefix C dated 7.4.1948 to prefix C dated 14.12.1949 ............................ £45    £80

# FIVE POUNDS

**Size** 225mm x 125mm approximately

*Obverse—black with "Clydesdale Bank Limited" and value panels overlaid in red. Arms of Glasgow at the top of the note; ornate panel to the left. Uniface*

                                                                                                    F      VF

**SC304**  *Signatories: D. Dewar (Accountant) and handsigned p. General Manager*
            From 4.7.1882 (prefix unknown) to prefix Q_/B dated 9.2.1921............               Rare

*Obverse—blue with "Clydesdale Bank Limited" and value panels overlaid in red. Arms of Glasgow at the top of the note; ornate panel to the left*
*Reverse—large blue value panel with the Arms of Glasgow at the centre surrounded by "The Clydesdale Bank Limited"*

**SC305a** *Signatories: A. Swanson (Cashier) and J. D. Dewar (Accountant)*                      F      VF
            Prefix Q_/C dated 15.2.1922 to prefix R_/J dated 14.6.1922................            Rare

**SC305b** *Signatories: A. Swanson (Cashier) and R. Young (Accountant)*
            Prefix R_/K dated 31.1.1923 to prefix U_/O dated 9.12.1931..............    £250     £420

**SC305c** *Signatories: A. Mitchell (General Manager) and R. Young (Accountant & Cashier)*  VF      EF
            Prefix U_/P dated 16.11.1932 to prefix W_/H dated 27.10.1937, then    £360     £540
            *printers imprint is added to the bottom left of the note, and*

**SC305d** Prefix W_/J dated 25.5.1938 to prefix D_/A dated 24.10.1945 ...........    £280     £480

**SC305e** *Signatories: J. J. Campbell (General Manager) and J. W. Pairmain (Accountant & Cashier).*
            Prefix D_/B to prefix D_/R dated 10.7.1946 ........................    £320     £500

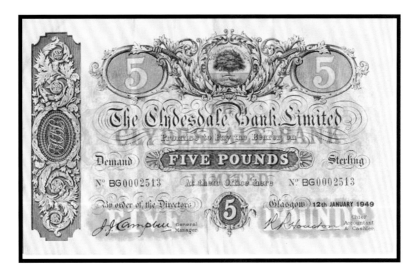

*Obverse—blue with "Clydesdale Bank Limited" and value panels overlaid in red, and with an additional light blue overlay. Arms of Glasgow at the top of the note; ornate panel to the left*
*Reverse—large blue value panel with the Arms of Glasgow at the centre surrounded by "The Clydesdale Bank Limited"*

|  | VF | EF |
|---|---|---|

**SC306a** *Signatories: J. J. Campbell (General Manager) and J. W. Pairmain (Accountant & Cashier)*
Prefix AA to prefix AQ dated 3.3.1948...................................................... £320    £550

**SC306b** *Signatories: J. J. Campbell (General Manager) and R. R. Houston (Accountant & Cashier)*
Prefix Prefix AR to prefix BG dated 12.1.1949. ....................................... £320    £550

## TWENTY POUNDS

**Size** 225mm x 125mm approximately

*Obverse—black with "Clydesdale Bank Limited" and value panels overlaid in red. Arms of Glasgow at the top of the note; ornate panel to the left. Uniface*

**SC307** *Signatories: D.Dewar (Accountant) and handsigned p. General Manager*
From 4.7.1882 (prefix unknown) to prefix P/B dated 9.6.1920 ................    Rare

*Obverse—blue with "Clydesdale Bank Limited" and value panels overlaid in red. Arms of Glasgow at the top of the note; ornate panel to the left*
*Reverse—large blue value panel with the Arms of Glasgow at the centre surrounded by "The Clydesdale Bank Limited"*

|  | F | VF |
|---|---|---|
| **SC308a** *Signatories: A. Swanson (Cashier) and J. D. Dewar (Accountant).*<br>Prefix P/C dated 15.2.1922 to prefix Q/A dated 31.1.1923 |  | Rare |

**SC308b** *Signatories: A. Swanson (Cashier) and R. Young (Accountant).*
Prefix Q/B dated 2.5.1923 to prefix Q/Z dated 3.6.1931......................from £350 £750

|  | VF | EF |
|---|---|---|
| **SC308c** *Signatories: A. Mitchell (General Manager) and R. Young (Accountant & Cashier).*<br>Prefix R/A dated 16.11.1932 to prefix U/A dated 15.11.1944.................. | £450 | £850 |

**SC308d** *Signatories: J. J. Campbell (General Manager) and J. W. Pairmain (Accountant & Cashier)*
Prefix U/B to prefix U/J dated 4.6.1947...................................................... £450 £850

## ONE HUNDRED POUNDS

**Size** 225mm x 125mm approximately

*Obverse—black with "Clydesdale Bank Limited" and value panels overlaid in red. Arms of Glasgow at the top of the note; ornate panel to the left. Uniface*

|  | F | VF |
|---|---|---|
| **SC309** *Signatories: D. Dewar (Accountant) and handsigned p.General Manager.*<br>Final prefix E/V dated 5.8.1914................................................................ |  | Rare |

*Obverse—blue with "Clydesdale Bank Limited" and value panels overlaid in red. Arms of Glasgow at the top of the note; ornate panel to the left*
*Reverse—large blue value panel with the Arms of Glasgow at the centre surrounded by "The Clydesdale Bank Limited"*

|  | F | VF |
|---|---|---|
| **SC310a** *Signatories: A. Swanson* (Cashier) *and J. D. Dewar* (Accountant)<br>Prefix E/W to prefix F/A dated 15.2.1922 |  | Rare |
| **SC310b** *Signatories: A. Swanson* (Cashier) *and R. Young* (Accountant).<br>Prefix F/B dated 16.12.1925 to prefix F/L dated 3.6.1931 ........................ |  | Rare |
| **SC310c** *Signatories: A. Mitchell* (General Manager) *and R. Young* (Accountant & Cashier).<br>Prefix F/M dated 19.6.1935 to prefix G/D dated 3.2.1943 ........................ |  | Rare |
| **SC310d** *Signatories: J. J. Campbell* (General Manager) *and J. W. Pairmain* (Accountant & Cashier).<br>Prefix G/E to prefix G/H dated 26.3.1947 ................................................ |  | Rare |

# THE CLYDESDALE & NORTH OF SCOTLAND BANK LIMITED

## ONE POUND

**"B" size notes** (152mm x 85mm approximately)

*Obverse—blue/grey with a red/orange underprint. New Coat of Arms at the top of the note; vignettes of shipping and agricultural scenes at the bottom corners.*
*Reverse—blue with an illustration of a highland river scene.*

|  | VF | EF |
|---|---|---|
| **SC311a** *Signatory: J. J. Campbell* (General Manager)............................. | | |
| Prefix A dated 1.11.1950 to prefix M dated 1.6.1955, and ......................... | £20 | £45 |
| Prefix A/N to prefix A/Q dated 1.11.1956................................................ | £20 | £45 |
| | | |
| **SC311b** *Signatory: R. D. Fairbairn* (General Manager) | | |
| Prefix A/R dated 1.5.1958 to prefix A/U dated 1.11.1960 ....................... | £20 | £50 |

**"C" size notes** (152mm x 72mm approximately)

*Obverse—mainly green with an orange/brown underprint. Coat of Arms to the right.*
*Reverse—green; illustration of a ship launching scene.*

|  | EF | UNC |
|---|---|---|
| **SC312** *Signatory: R. D. Fairbairn* (General Manager) | | |
| Prefix B/A dated 1.3.1961 to prefix B/H dated 1.2.1963......................... | £30 | £45 |

# FIVE POUNDS

**Size** 179mm x 98mm approximately

*Obverse—purple on a green and pink underprint. Illustrations of King's College, Aberdeen to the left, and Glasgow Cathedral to the right*
*Reverse—large purple panel with the new Coat of Arms at the centre with the value to the left and right*

| | | VF | EF |
|---|---|---|---|
| **SC313a** *Signatory: J. J. Campbell* (General Manager) | | | |
| Prefix A dated 2.5.1951 to prefix P dated 1.6.1955, and ........................... | | £45 | £85 |
| Prefix A/Q dated 1.11.1956 to prefix A/X dated 1.2.1958....................... | | £45 | £85 |
| | | | |
| **SC313b** *Signatory: R. D. Fairbairn* (General Manager) | | | |
| Prefix A/Y, A/Z, A/A and A/B dated 1.3.1960 ....................................... | | £45 | £85 |

**Size** 141mm x 84mm approximately

*Obverse—mainly blue with an orange/brown underprint. Coat of Arms to the right.*
*Reverse—blue; illustration of King's College, Aberdeen.*

| | | VF | EF |
|---|---|---|---|
| **SC314** *Signatory: R. D. Fairbairn* (General Manager) | | | |
| Prefix B/A dated 20.9.1961 to prefix B/M dated 1.2.1963 ....................... | | £32 | £55 |

## TWENTY POUNDS

**Size** 179mm x 98mm approximately

*Obverse—green on a pale yellow underprint. Illustrations of King's College, Aberdeen to the left, and Glasgow Cathedral to the right.*
*Reverse—large green panel with the new Coat of Arms at the centre with the value to the left and right.*

| | | *VF* | *EF* |
|---|---|---|---|
| **SC315a** *Signatory: J. J. Campbell* (General Manager) | | | |
| Prefix A dated 2.5.1951 to prefix B dated 1.2.1958...................................... | | £85 | £150 |
| | | | |
| **SC315b** *Signatory: R. D. Fairbairn* (General Manager) | | | |
| Prefix C dated 1.12.1960 to prefix E dated 1.8.1962.................................... | | £85 | £150 |

## ONE HUNDRED POUNDS

**Size** 179mm x 98mm approximately

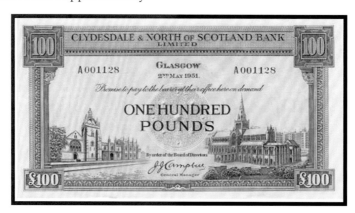

*Obverse—blue on a pale yellow/green underprint. Illustrations of King's College, Aberdeen to the left, and Glasgow Cathedral to the right.*
*Reverse—large blue panel with the new Coat of Arms at the centre with the value to the left and right.*

| | | *VF* | *EF* |
|---|---|---|---|
| **SC316a** *Signatory: J. J. Campbell* (General Manager) | | | |
| Prefix A dated 2.5.1951.............................................................................. | | £500 | £950 |
| | | | |
| **SC316b** *Signatory: R. D. Fairbairn* (General Manager) | | | |
| Prefix A dated 1.12.1960............................................................................ | | £550 | £1100 |

# CLYDESDALE BANK LIMITED

## ONE POUND

**"C" size notes** (152mm x 72mm approximately)

*Obverse — mainly green with an orange/brown underprint. Coat of Arms to the right.*
*Reverse — green; illustration of a ship launching scene.*

| | | EF | UNC |
|---|---|---|---|
| **SC317a** | *Signatory: R. D. Fairbairn* (General Manager) | | |
| | Prefix C/A dated 2.9.1963 to prefix C/K dated 3.4.1967 ......................... | £24 | £36 |
| **SC317b** | *Sorting symbols added to reverse of the notes* | | |
| | Prefix C/L dated 3.4.1967 to prefix C/U dated 1.9.1969.......................... | £24 | £36 |

**"D" size notes** (135mm x 67mm approximately)

*Obverse — green with a multicoloured underprint. Portrait of Robert the Bruce to the left.*
*Reverse — mainly green with an illustration of Robert the Bruce at the battle of Bannockburn.*

| | | EF | UNC |
|---|---|---|---|
| **SC318a** | *Signatory: R. D. Fairbairn* (General Manager) | | |
| | Prefix D/A to prefix D/F dated 1.3.1971 ...................................... | £22 | £32 |
| **SC318b** | *Signatory: A. R. MacMillan* (General Manager) | | |
| | Prefix D/G dated 1.5.1972 to prefix D/Q dated 1.8.1973......................... | £16 | £24 |
| **SC318c** | *Signatory: A. R. MacMillan* (Chief General Manager) | | |
| | Prefix D/R dated 1.3.1974 to prefix D/BT dated 27.2.1981 ..................... | £9 | £12 |

# FIVE POUNDS

**Size** 141mm x 84mm approximately

*Obverse—mainly blue with an orange/brown underprint. Coat of Arms to the right.*
*Reverse—blue; illustration of King's College, Aberdeen.*

**SC319a** *Signatory: R. D. Fairbairn (General Manager)*           *EF*   *UNC*
      Prefix C/A dated 2.9.1963 to prefix C/R dated 1.5.1967 .......................... £50   £75

**SC319b** *Sorting symbols added to reverse of the notes*
      Prefix C/S dated 1.5.1967 to prefix C/GG dated 1.9.1969....................... £50   £75

**Size** 146mm x 78mm approximately

*Obverse—blue with a multicoloured underprint. Portrait of Robert Burns to the left.*
*Reverse—mainly blue. Illustration of a field mouse and wild roses.*

**SC320a** *Signatory: R. D. Fairbairn (General Manager)*           *EF*   *UNC*
      Prefix D/A to prefix D/K dated 1.3.1971 ........................................... £50   £75

**SC320b** *Signatory: A. R. MacMillan (General Manager)*
      Prefix D/L dated 1.5.1972 to prefix D/AA dated 1.8.1973............... £50   £75

**SC320c** *Signatory: A. R. MacMillan (Chief General Manager)*
      Prefix D/AB dated 1.3.1974 to prefix D/DX dated 27.2.1981.......... £40   £60

# TEN POUNDS

**Size** 151mm x 93mm approximately

*Obverse — mainly brown with a multicoloured underprint. Coat of Arms to the right.*
*Reverse — brown; illustration of the University of Glasgow.*

**SC321**    *Signatory: R. D. Fairbairn* (General Manager)       *EF*    *UNC*
        Prefix C/A dated 20.4.1964 to prefix C/D dated 1.12.1967.................. £150    £260

**Size** 150mm x 85mm approximately

*Obverse — brown; portrait of David Livingstone to the left.*
*Reverse — brown; scene with three African slaves.*

**SC322a** *Signatory: A. R. MacMillan* (General Manager)       *EF*    *UNC*
        Prefix D/A dated 1.3.1972 to prefix D/F dated 1.8.1973 ................... £130    £200

**SC322b** *Signatory: A. R. MacMillan* (Chief General Manager)
        Prefix D/G dated 1.3.1974 to prefix D/DZ dated 27.2.1981................... £120    £180

# TWENTY POUNDS

**Size** 162mm x 93mm approximately

*Obverse—mainly red with a multicoloured underprint. Coat of Arms to the right.*
*Reverse—red; view of George Square, Glasgow.*

| | | EF | UNC |
|---|---|---|---|
| **SC323** | *Signatory: R. D. Fairbairn* (General Manager) | | |
| | Prefix C/A dated 19.11.1964 to prefix C/H dated 1.12.1967. ................. £160 | | £240 |

*Obverse—purple with a portrait of Lord Kelvin to the left.*
*Reverse—purple; illustration of Lord Kelvin's lecture room at the University of Glasgow.*

| | | EF | UNC |
|---|---|---|---|
| **SC324a** | *Signatory: A. R. MacMillan* (General Manager) | | |
| | Prefix D/A to prefix D/J dated 1.3.1972 .............................................. | £220 | £320 |
| **SC324b** | *Signatory: A. R. MacMillan* (Chief General Manager) | | |
| | Prefix D/K dated 2.2.1976 to prefix D/BG dated 27.2.1981 ............... | £160 | £260 |

# FIFTY POUNDS

**Size** 169mm x 95mm approximately

*Obverse—olive green with a portrait of Adam Smith to the left.*
*Reverse—olive green; illustration of a group of old industrial and agricultural tools with sailing ships in the background.*

| | | EF | UNC |
|---|---|---|---|
| **SC325** | *Signatory: A. R. MacMillan* (Chief General Manager) | | |
| | Prefix D/A to prefix D/Q dated 1.9.1981. ............................................. | £260 | £350 |

# ONE HUNDRED POUNDS

**Size** 162mm x 93mm approximately

*Obverse—mainly purple with a multicoloured underprint. Coat of Arms to the right.*
*Reverse—purple; river scene with bridge and hills in the background.*

| | | VF | EF |
|---|---|---|---|
| **SC326** | *Signatory: R. D. Fairbairn* (General Manager) | | |
| | Prefix C/A dated 1.2.1964 to prefix C/B dated 1.2.1968. .................... | £750 | £1250 |

**Size** 169mm x 95mm approximately

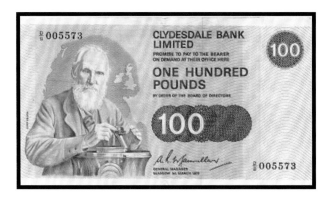

*Obverse—red with a portrait of Lord Kelvin to the left.*
*Reverse—mainly red; illustration of Lord Kelvin's lecture room at the University of Glasgow.*

|  |  | *EF* | *UNC* |
|---|---|---|---|
| **SC327a** *Signatory: A. R. MacMillan* (General Manager) | | | |
| Prefix D/A to prefix D/E dated 1.3.1972 ..................................................... | | £650 | £950 |
| | | | |
| **SC327b** *Signatory: A. R. MacMillan* (Chief General Manager) | | | |
| Prefix D/F dated 1.2.1976........................................................................... | | £650 | £950 |

# CLYDESDALE BANK PLC

## ONE POUND

**"D" size notes** (135mm x 67mm approximately)

*Obverse—green with a multicoloured underprint. Portrait of Robert the Bruce to the left.*
*Reverse—mainly green with an illustration of Robert the Bruce at the battle of Bannockburn.*

| | | EF | UNC |
|---|---|---|---|
| **SC328a** *Signatory: A. R. MacMillan* (Chief General Manager) | | | |
| Prefix D/BU to prefix D/CD dated 29.3.1982............................................ | | £9 | £12 |
| | | | |
| **SC328b** *Signatory: A. R. Cole Hamilton* (Chief General Manager) | | | |
| Prefix D/CE to prefix D/CR dated 5.1.1983 ............................................. | | £7 | £10 |
| | | | |
| **SC328c** *Sorting symbols removed from reverse of the notes* | | | |
| Prefix D/CS dated 8.4.1985 to prefix D/DK dated 25.11.1985 ................ | | £7 | £10 |
| Replacement note – prefix D/ZZ.................................................................. | | £25 | £35 |
| | | | |
| **SC328d** *Signatory: A. R. Cole Hamilton* (Chief Executive) | | | |
| Prefix D/DL dated 18.9.1987 to prefix D/DW dated 9.11.1988............... | | £5 | £7 |
| Replacement note – prefix D/ZZ.................................................................. | | £20 | £30 |

# FIVE POUNDS

**Size** 146mm x 78mm approximately

*Obverse—blue with a multicoloured underprint. Portrait of Robert Burns to the left.*
*Reverse—mainly blue. Illustration of a field mouse and wild roses.*

**SC329a** *Signatory: A. R. MacMillan* (Chief General Manager)
Prefix D/DY to prefix D/FP dated 29.3.1982.............................................. £40 £55

**SC329b** *Signatory: A. R. Cole Hamilton* (Chief General Manager)
Prefix D/FQ to prefix D/HP dated 5.1.1983.............................................. £40 £55

**SC329c** *Sorting symbols removed from reverse of the notes*
Prefix D/HQ to prefix D/JG dated 18.9.1986 ............................................ £25 £40

**SC329d** *Signatory: A. R. Cole Hamilton* (Chief Executive)
Prefix D/JH dated 18.9.1987 to prefix D/LU dated 28.6.1989................. £22 £35

**Size** 136mm x 70mm approximately

*Obverse—blue with a multicoloured underprint. Revised portrait of Robert Burns to the left.*
*Reverse—mainly blue. Illustration of a field mouse and wild roses.*

**SC330a** *Signatory: A. R. Cole Hamilton* (Chief Executive)                                    EF UNC
Prefix E/AA to prefix E/CM dated 2.4.1990.............................................. £16 £25

**SC330b** *Signatory: F. Cicutto* (Chief Executive)
Prefix E/CN to prefix E/DN dated 1.9.1994.............................................. £10 £14
Replacement note – prefix D/ZZ................................................................. rare

**SC330c** *Signatory: F. Goodwin* (Chief Executive)
Prefix E/DP dated 21.7.1966 to prefix E/DY dated 1.12.1997 ............... £9 £12

**SC330d** *Signatory: G. Savage* (Chief Executive)
Prefix E/DZ dated 19.6.2002 and ongoing................................................. — £10

*Obverse—blue with a multicoloured underprint. Portrait of Robert Burns to the left. A set of four notes, to commemorate the 200th anniversary of the poet, Robert Burns. Each note has a different Burns poem printed towards the top left corner.*
*Reverse—mainly blue. Illustration of a field mouse and wild roses.*

These were originally issued as a set with similar serial numbers—
Prefix RB, and with the first digit running sequentially.

| | | EF | UNC |
|---|---|---|---|
| **SC331** | *Signatory: F. Goodwin* (Chief Executive) | | |
| | Prefix RB dated 21.7.1996. Set of four notes with matched numbers..... | — | £70 |
| | Prefix RB dated 21.7.1996. Single note ......................................................... | — | £13 |

# TEN POUNDS

**Size** 150mm x 85mm approximately

*Obverse—brown; portrait of David Livingstone to the left.*
*Reverse—brown; scene with three african slaves.*

| | | EF | UNC |
|---|---|---|---|
| **SC341a** | *Signatory: A. R. MacMillan* (Chief General Manager) | | |
| | Prefix D/EA to prefix D/GV dated 29.3.1982................................. | £110 | £170 |
| **SC341b** | *Signatory: A. R. Cole Hamilton* (Chief General Manager) | | |
| | Prefix D/GW dated 3.1.1983 to prefix D/PZ dated 18.9.1986....... | £90 | £120 |
| | Replacement note – prefix D/ZZ....................................................... | | Rare |
| **SC341c** | *Signatory: A. R. Cole Hamilton* (Chief Executive) | | |
| | Prefix D/QA to prefix D/SW dated 18.9.1987................................ | £90 | £110 |

**Size** 150mm x 85mm approximately

*Obverse—brown on a multicoloured underprint. Revised portrait of David Livingstone to the left.*
*Reverse—mainly brown. Illustration of the birthplace of Livingstone in Blantyre.*

| | | EF | UNC |
|---|---|---|---|
| **SC342** | *Signatory: A. R. Cole Hamilton* (Chief Executive) | | |
| | Prefix D/SW dated 7.5.1988 to prefix E/GR dated 3.9.1992 .................. | £35 | £55 |
| | Replacement note – prefix D/ZZ ................................................................ | | Rare |

**Size** 143mm x 75mm approximately

Similar to previous issue, but reduced size.

*Obverse—brown on a multicoloured underprint. Portrait of David Livingstone to the left.*
*Reverse—mainly brown. Illustration of the birthplace of Livingstone in Blantyre.*

| | | EF | UNC |
|---|---|---|---|
| **SC343a** | *Signatory: A. R. Cole Hamilton* (Chief Executive) | | |
| | Prefix E/GR to prefix E/QZ dated 3.9.1992. | £30 | £45 |
| | Replacement note – prefix E/ZZ | | Rare |
| **SC343b** | *Signatory: C. Love* (Chief Executive) | | |
| | Prefix E/QZ to prefix E/VC dated 5.1.1993 | £25 | £35 |
| | Replacement note – prefix E/ZZ | | Rare |
| **SC343c** | *Signatory: F. Goodwin* (Chief Executive) | | |
| | Prefix E/VD dated 22.3.1996 to prefix E/WZ dated 27.2.1997 | £22 | £30 |
| | Replacement note – prefix E/ZZ | | Rare |

**Size** 143mm x 75mm approximately

*Obverse—brown on a multicoloured underprint. Portrait of Mary Slessor to the left.*
*Reverse—representation of Mary Slessors missionary work in Africa during the late 19th Century.*

|  |  | *EF* | *UNC* |
|---|---|---|---|
| **SC344a** | *Signatory: F. Goodwin* (Chief Executive) | | |
| | Prefix A/AA to prefix A/AK dated 1.5.1997......................................... | — | £25 |
| | Replacement note – prefix E/ZZ................................................ | | Rare |

**SC344b** Prefix NAB dated 1.5.1997 .......................................................... £65 £90
Notes with prefix NAB were encapsulated in a block of acrylic and issued to members of the Bank's staff to commemorate 10 years of ownership of the National Australia Bank. Surplus, un-encapsulated notes were subsequently issued due to a shortage of new notes, and a few have found their way onto the collectors market.

**SC344c** *Signatory: J. Wright* (Chief Executive)
Prefix A/AK dated 5.11.1998 to prefix A/CA dated 12.10.1999 ......... — £22

**SC344d** *Signatory: S. Targett* (Chief Executive)
Prefix A/CA to prefix A/CL dated 26.1.2003 ....................................... — £22

**SC344e** *Signatory: R. Pinney* (Chief Executive)
Prefix A/CL dated 25.4.2003 and ongoing ........................................... — £20
Prefix E/ZZ—replacement note................................................ £65

**SC344f** *Signatory:  D. Thorburn (Chief Operating Officer)*
Prefix A/CZ 300,001 to prefix A/DS (split at 800,000) dated 21.11.2004 £20

Similar to previous issue with commemorative overprint.

*Obverse—brown on a multicoloured underprint. Portrait of Mary Slessor to the left. Overprint to the right reads "Commemorating the year 2000"*
*Reverse—representation of Mary Slessors missionary work in Africa during the late 19th Century.*

|  |  | *EF* | *UNC* |
|---|---|---|---|
| **SC345** | *Signatory: J. Wright* (Chief Executive) | | |
| | Prefix MM dated 1.1.2000 ............................................. | — | £25 |

*Issued to commemorate the Commonwealth Games in Melbourne, March 2006. (5 million notes issued)*
*Obverse–brown on a multicoloured underprint. Portrait of Mary Slessor to the left. Overprint to the right*
*reads "Commonwealth Games – Scotland – Melbourne 2006. Proud Partner"*
*Reverse–multicoloured; stylised representation of events in the Games.*

|  | EF | UNC |
|---|---|---|
| SC346 Signatory: D. Thorburn (Chief Operating Officer). | | |
| Prefix CG/1 to CG/5 dated 15.3.2006 | --- | £18.00 |

*Obverse - brown on a multicoloured underprint. Portrait of Mary Slessor to the left. (Change of logo design)*
*Reverse—representation of Mary Slessors missionary work in Africa during the late 19th Century*

SC347   Signatory: D.Thorburn (Chief Operating Officer)
          Prefix A/DS 800,001 dated 14.3.2006 and ongoing          ----          £18.00

# TWENTY POUNDS

**Size** 162mm x 93mm approximately

*Obverse — purple with a portrait of Lord Kelvin to the left.*
*Reverse — purple; illustration of Lord Kelvin's lecture room at the University of Glasgow.*

| | | EF | UNC |
|---|---|---|---|
| **SC351a** | *Signatory: A. R. MacMillan* (Chief General Manager) Prefix D/BH to prefix D/BR dated 29.3.1982......................................... | £170 | £300 |
| **SC351b** | *Signatory: A. R. Cole Hamilton* (Chief General Manager) Prefix D/CN dated 5.1.1983 to prefix D/ED dated 8.4.1985................. | £140 | £220 |
| **SC351c** | *Signatory: A. R. Cole Hamilton* (Chief Executive) Prefix D/EE dated 18.9.1987 to prefix D/FV dated 2.8.1990. ............... | £120 | £200 |

**Size** 162mm x 93mm approximately

*Obverse — purple and orange/brown on a multicoloured underprint. Portrait of Robert the Bruce in armour to the left.*
*Reverse — purple and brown. Illustration of Robert the Bruce in full battle armour on horseback.*

| | | EF | UNC |
|---|---|---|---|
| **SC352a** | *Signatory: A. R. Cole Hamilton* (Chief Executive) Prefix E/AA dated 30.11.1990 to prefix E/NM dated 3.9.1992 ............ | £60 | £90 |
| | Replacement note – prefix E/ZZ................................................................. | | Rare |
| **SC352b** | *Signatory: C. Love* (Chief Executive) Prefix E/NN to prefix E/SR dated 5.1.1993............................................ | £60 | £90 |
| | Replacement note – prefix E/ZZ................................................................. | | Rare |

*Obverse—purple and orange/brown on a multicoloured underprint. Portrait of Robert the Bruce in armour to the left. Somewhat bolder colours and new design elements added*
*Reverse—purple and brown. Illustration of Robert the Bruce in full battle armour on horseback. Bolder colours and new design element to the left.*

| | | EF | UNC |
|---|---|---|---|
| **SC353a** | *Signatory: F. Ciccutto* (Chief Executive) | | |
| | Prefix E/SS to prefix F/AX dated 1.9.1994 | £45 | £65 |
| | Replacement note – prefix E/ZZ | | Rare |
| **SC353b** | *Signatory: F. Goodwin* (Chief Executive) | | |
| | Prefix F/AY to prefix F/BC dated 2.12.1996 | £40 | £55 |
| | Replacement note – prefix E/ZZ | | Rare |

Commemorates the Commonwealth Heads of Government meeting which took place in Edinburgh in October 1997.

*Obverse—purple and orange/brown on a multicoloured underprint. Portrait of Robert the Bruce in armour to the left.*
*Reverse—Illustrations of the Edinburgh International Conference Centre and the new Clydesdale Bank Plaza, with Edinburgh Castle in the background.*

| | | EF | UNC |
|---|---|---|---|
| **SC354** | *Signatory: F. Goodwin* (Chief Executive) | | |
| | Prefix F/BD to F/BF, and prefix C/HG dated 30.9.1997 | £35 | £50 |

*Obverse—purple and orange/brown on a multicoloured underprint. Portrait of Robert the Bruce in armour to the left. Some design elements changed.*
*Reverse—purple and brown. Illustration of Robert the Bruce in full battle armour on horseback.*

**SC355a** *Signatory: F. Goodwin* (Chief Executive)
    Prefix A/AA to A/AN dated 1.11.1997. ...................................................... £35   £55
    Replacement note – prefix E/ZZ................................................................ Rare

**SC355b** *Signatory: J. Wright* (Chief Executive)
    Prefix A/AR to A/BL dated 12.10.1999....................................................... £35   £50

**SC355c** *Signatory: G. Savage* (Chief Executive)
    Prefix A/BL to prefix A/BP dated 19.6.2002 ............................................. —   £40

**SC355d** *Signatory: S. Targett* (Chief Executive)
    Prefix A/BQ to prefix A/BW dated 26.1.2003............................................ —   £40

**SC355e** *Signatory: R. Pinney* (Chief Executive)
    Prefix A/BW dated 25.4.2003 and ongoing ............................................... —   £35

**SC355f** **Signatory: D. Thorburn (Chief Operating Officer)**
    Prefix A/CS to prefix ADK dated 21.11.2004............................................ —   £32

*EF UNC* headings appear at right of SC355a and SC356.

Comemorates the 19th Century architect Alexander "Greek" Thomson 1817–75, and Glasgow as the UK City of Architecture and Design, 1999.

*Obverse—purple and orange/brown on a multicoloured underprint. Portrait of Alexander "Greek" Thomson to the left.*
*Reverse—stylised illustration of architecture in Glasgow.*

**SC356** *Signatory: J. Wright* (Chief Executive)                *EF   UNC*
    Prefix A/AL to A/AQ, and G/AD dated 9.4.1999. ................................... £35   £50

*Obverse—purple and orange/brown on a multicoloured underprint. Portrait of Robert the Bruce in armour to the left. Similar to the 1999 issue above with additional overprint—"Commemorating the Year 2000".*

*Reverse—purple and brown. Illustration of Robert the Bruce in full battle armour on horseback.*

**SC357** *Signatory: J. Wright* (Chief Executive).        *EF   UNC*
        Prefix MM dated 1.1.2000. .............................................................................    £35   £50

*Obverse —purple and orange/brown on a multicoloured underprint. Portrait of Robert the Bruce in armour to the left. Similar to the earlier 1997 issue (SC355) with the addition of the Bank logo and extra security features.*

*Reverse—purple and brown. Illustration of the Clydesdale Bank Exchange which opened 6th. June 2005.*

**SC358** *Signatory: D. Thorburn* (Chief Operating Officer) ........................................    —    £40
        Prefix A/DK to prefix A/DP dated 6.5.2005 and ongoing
        (Series starts at A/DK 950001 and is split with ref. SC355f above)

Issued in December 2006 to commemorate the 700th. Anniversary of the enthronement of Robert the Bruce.

*Obverse— purple and orange/brown on a multicoloured underprint. Portrait of Robert the Bruce in armour to the left. Similar to the earlier issues with the addition of a shield and commemorative text to thev right.*

*Reverse—purple and brown. Picture of Robert the Bruce on horseback with commemorative text at the top.*

|  | EF | UNC |
|---|---|---|
| **SC358** *Signatory: D. Thorburn* (Chief Operating Officer) .......................................... | — | £36 |
| Prefix RB/1 dated 25.3.2005 and ongoing | | |

# FIFTY POUNDS

**Size** 169mm x 95mm approximately

*Obverse—olive green with a portrait of Adam Smith to the left.*
*Reverse—olive green; illustration of a group of old industrial and agricultural tools with sailing ships in the background.*

**SC361** *Signatory: A. R. Cole Hamilton* (Chief Executive)...........................................    *EF  UNC*
       Prefix D/R dated 3.9.1989 to prefix D/AV dated 20.4.1992......................    £140  £220

**Size** 156mm x 85mm approximately

*Obverse—green, brown and multicolour with a portrait of Adam Smith to the left.*
*Reverse—mainly green and brown; illustration of a group of old Industrial and agricultural tools with sailing ships in the background.*

**SC362a** *Signatory: F. Goodwin* (Chief Executive)                    *EF UNC*
       Prefix A/AA and A/CB dated 22.3.1996 .....................................................    £85  £120

**SC362b** *Signatory: R. Pinney* (Chief Executive)                     *EF UNC*
       Prefix A/CC dated 26.4.2003 and ongoing .................................................    —  £90

Commemorates 550 years of the University of Glasgow

*Obverse—green, brown and multicolour with a portrait of Adam Smith to the left and with an additional overprint—"University of Glasgow 1451 - 2001"*
*Reverse—mainly green and brown; illustration of a group of old Industrial and agricultural tools with sailing ships in the background.*

| | | EF | UNC |
|---|---|---|---|
| **SC363** *Signatory: S. Grimshaw* (Chief Executive) | | | |
| Prefix GU dated 6.1.2001 ................................................................................. | | £85 | £110 |

# ONE HUNDRED POUNDS

**Size** 160mm x 90mm approximately

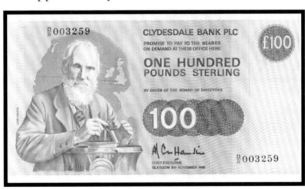

*Obverse—mainly red with a portrait of Lord Kelvin to the left.*
*Reverse—red and yellow; illustration of Lord Kelvin's lecture room at the University of Glasgow.*

| | | EF | UNC |
|---|---|---|---|
| **SC371a** *Signatory: A. R. Cole Hamilton* (Chief General Manager).......................... | | | |
| Prefix D/G to prefix D/L dated 8.4.1985 .................................................... | | £400 | £650 |
| | | | |
| **SC371b** *Signatory: A. R. Cole Hamilton* (Chief Executive) | | | |
| Prefix D/M to prefix D/R dated 9.11.1991 ................................................. | | £320 | £600 |

**Size** 162mm x 90mm approximately

*Obverse—red, purple and multicolour with a portrait of Lord Kelvin to the left.*
*Reverse—red, purple and multicolour; illustration of the University of Glasgow.*

**SC372**    *Signatory: F. Goodwin (Chief Executive)*                                                            *EF*        *UNC*
               Prefix A/AA to prefix A/AD dated 2.10.1996 ....................................        —         £190

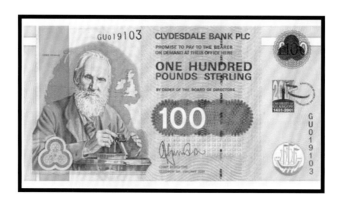

Commemorates 550 years of the University of Glasgow

*Obverse—ed, purple and multicolour with a portrait of Lord Kelvin to the left and with an additional*
*overprint—"University of Glasgow 1451–2001"*
*Reverse—red, purple and multicolour; illustration of the University of Glasgow.*

**SC373**    *Signatory: S. Grimshaw (Chief Executive)*                                                        *EF*        *UNC*
               Prefix GU dated 6.1.2001 .........................................................................        —         £220

# THE COMMERCIAL BANK OF SCOTLAND LIMITED

Founded in 1810 as The Commercial Banking Company of Scotland, the Bank developed during the 19th Century the largest branch system in Scotland. The name was changed to the Commercial Bank of Scotland Limited in 1882 by which time the bank had absorbed the Caithness Bank and the Arbroath Banking Company. In 1959 it amalgamated with the National Bank of Scotland Ltd. to form the National Commercial Bank of Scotland Limited.

## ONE POUND

**"A" size square notes** (160mm x 120mm approximately)

*Obverse—mainly black with the value in a yellow and blue underprint. Illustrations of the Bank's principal offices in Edinburgh, Glasgow and London.*
*Reverse—large blue panel with the Bank's emblem at the centre.*

|  |  | F | VF |
|---|---|---|---|
| **SC401** | *Signatories: L. M. Mackay (Accountant) and handsigned p. Cashier.* | | |
| | Prefix 18/A dated 2.1.1907 to prefix 18/E dated 2.1.1908. ............. | | Rare |

*Obverse—blue on a yellow and light blue underprint. Illustrations of the Bank's principal offices in Edinburgh, Glasgow and London*
*Reverse—large blue panel with the Bank's emblem at the centre*

|  |  | F | VF |
|---|---|---|---|
| **SC402a** | *Signatories: L. M. Mackay (Accountant) and handsigned p. Cashier* | | |
| | Prefix 18/F dated 2.1.1909 to prefix 18/Q dated 3.1.1911................ | £250 | £450 |
| **SC402b** | *Signatories: L. M. Mackay (Accountant) and G. Riddell (Cashier)* | | |
| | Prefix 19/A dated 2.1.1912 to prefix 19/Q dated 2.1.1915 (red serial Nos.) | £180 | £360 |
| | Prefix 20/A dated 2.1.1915 to prefix 20/Q dated 2.1.1917 (black serial Nos.) | £180 | £360 |
| | Prefix 21/A dated 2.1.1918 (red serial No.)........................................ | £190 | £380 |
| | Prefix 21/B dated 2.1.1918 to prefix 21/I dated 2.1.1923 (black serial Nos.). | £180 | £360 |

*Obverse—dark blue on a yellow and red underprint. Portrait of Lord Pitcairn, the first Chairman of the Bank, at lower centre*
*Reverse—dark blue panel with the Bank's Head Office building at the centre*

|  | F | VF |
|---|---|---|

**SC403**   *Signatories: R. R. Thomson (Accountant) and H. M. Roberts (Cashier)*
Prefix 22/Z dated 31.10.1924 to prefix 22/W dated 1.11.1926........   £200   £400

## "B" size notes (150mm x 85mm approximately)

*Obverse—dark blue on a yellow and red underprint. Portrait of Lord Pitcairn, the first Chairman of the Bank, at lower centre*
*Reverse—dark blue panel with the Bank's Head Office building at the centre*

|  | VF | EF |
|---|---|---|

**SC404a**   *Signatories: R. R. Thomson (Accountant) and H. M. Roberts (Cashier)*
Prefix 23A dated 1.12.1927 (Serial letter in Gothic capitals) ..........   £80   £200

**SC404b**   *Signatories: P. Irving (Accountant) and R. R. Thomson (Cashier)*
Prefix 23B dated 1.6.1928 to prefix 23C dated 1.12.1928 (Gothic capitals) £65   £140

**SC404c**   *Signatories: P. Irving (Accountant) and R. R. Thomson (Cashier)*
Prefix 23D dated 2.12.1929 to prefix 23Z dated 30.11.1936, ...........   £35   £80
(Serial letters now in Roman capitals), and
Prefix A/24 dated 2.9.1937 to prefix P/24 dated 4.5.1939..............   £35   £80

**SC404d**   *Signatories: P. Irving (Chief Accountant) and James Thomson (Cashier)*
Prefix Q/24 dated 6.8.1940 to prefix Z/24 dated 4.6.1941, and.....   £25   £55
Prefix A/25 dated 4.6.1941, and.......................................   £30   £60
Prefix 25B dated 4.6.1941 to prefix 25N dated 2.12.1944 ................   £25   £55

*Obverse—mainly purple. Portrait of Lord Cockburn in a round panel to the right.*
*Reverse—purple; large panel with the Bank's Arms at the centre.*

|  |  | EF | UNC |
|---|---|---|---|
| **SC405** | *Signatory: Sir J. M. Erskine* (General Manager) | | |
| | Prefix 26A dated 2.1.1947 to prefix 26V dated 2.1.1953 ................ | £40 | £60 |

*Obverse—mainly blue. Portrait of Lord Cockburn in a round panel to the right*
*Reverse—blue; large panel with the Bank's Arms at the centre*

|  |  | EF | UNC |
|---|---|---|---|
| **SC406** | *Signatory: I. W. Macdonald* (General Manager) | | |
| | Prefix 27A dated 2.1.1954 to prefix 27R dated 1.7.1958 ................. | £35 | £55 |

## FIVE POUNDS

**Size** 220mm x 130mm approximately

*Obverse—mainly black with the value in a yellow and blue underprint. Illustrations of the Bank's principal offices in Edinburgh, Glasgow and London*
*Reverse—large blue panel with the Bank's emblem at the centre*

**SC411**   *Signatories: handsigned p. Accountant and handsigned p. Manager*
   Prefix13/A dated 2.1.1908....................................................................   Rare

*Obverse—blue on a yellow and light blue underprint. Illustrations of the Bank's principal offices in Edinburgh, Glasgow and London*
*Reverse—large blue panel with the Bank's emblem at the centre*

|  |  | F | VF |
|---|---|---|---|
| **SC412a** | *Signatories: handsigned p. Accountant and handsigned p. Manager*..... Prefix 13/A dated 2.1.1909 to prefix 13/B dated 2.1.1913 .............. | £400 | £850 |
| **SC412b** | *Signatories: L. M. Mackay (Accountant) and handsigned p. Manager* Prefix 13/C dated 2.1.1913 to prefix 13/M dated 2.1.1923.............. | £350 | £700 |

**Size** 207mm x 130mm approximately

*Obverse—dark blue on a yellow and red underprint. Portrait of Lord Pitcairn, the first Chairman of the Bank, at lower centre*
*Reverse—dark blue panel with the Bank's head office building at the centre*

|          |                                                                                                             | F    | VF   |
|----------|-------------------------------------------------------------------------------------------------------------|------|------|
| **SC413a** | *Signatories: R. R. Thomson* (Accountant) *and handsigned p. Manager*                                     |      |      |
|          | Prefix 14/Z dated 31.10.1924 to prefix 14/W dated 1.11.1926.                                               | £250 | £450 |

|          |                                                                                                             | VF   | EF   |
|----------|-------------------------------------------------------------------------------------------------------------|------|------|
| **SC413b** | *Signatories: R. R. Thomson* (Cashier) *and A. Robb* (General Manager)                                     |      |      |
|          | Prefix 14/W dated 1.12.1928 to prefix 14/R dated 1.8.1931                                                  | £220 | £350 |
| **SC413c** | *Signatories: R. R. Thomson* (Cashier) *and Sir J. M. Erskine* (General Manager)                          |      |      |
|          | Prefix 14/R dated 30.4.1934 to prefix 14/K dated 20.11.1937                                                | £130 | £260 |
| **SC413d** | *Signatories: James Thomson* (Cashier) *and Sir J. M. Erskine* (General Manager)                          |      |      |
|          | Prefix 14/K dated 3.8.1940 to prefix 14/A dated 5.1.1943, and                                              | £100 | £220 |
|          | Prefix 15/Z dated 5.1.1943 to prefix 15/M dated 1.12.1944                                                  | £100 | £220 |

**Size** 179mm x 102mm approximately

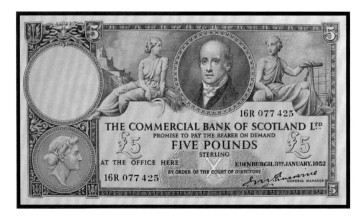

*Obverse—mainly purple. Portrait of Lord Cockburn at top flanked by two female figures representing agriculture and shipping.*
*Reverse—purple. Illustration of an Edinburgh street scene in Victorian times with the Bank's head office building in the background.*

|  |  | EF | UNC |
|---|---|---|---|
| **SC414a** | *Signatory: Sir J. M. Erskine* (General Manager) | | |
| | Prefix 16A dated 2.1.1947 to prefix 16Z dated 2.1.1953..................... | £70 | £100 |
| **SC414b** | *Signatory: I. W. Macdonald* (General Manager) | | |
| | Prefix 17A dated 2.1.1954 to prefix 17Z dated 2.1.1957, and............ | £70 | £100 |
| | Prefix 18A to prefix 18F dated 2.1.1958 .............................................. | £70 | £100 |

# TWENTY POUNDS

**Size** 220mm x 130mm approximately

*Obverse—mainly black with the value in a yellow and blue underprint. Illustrations of the Bank's principal offices in Edinburgh, Glasgow and London*
*Reverse—large blue panel with the Bank's emblem at the centre*

**SC421**   *Signatories: handsigned p. Accountant and handsigned p. Manager*
Prefix 11/A dated 2.1.1907.........................................   no known examples extant

*Obverse—blue on a yellow and light blue underprint. Illustrations of the Bank's principal offices in Edinburgh, Glasgow and London.*
*Reverse—large blue panel with the Bank's emblem at the centre.*

|  |  | F | VF |
|---|---|---|---|
| **SC422a** | *Signatories: handsigned p. Accountant and handsigned p. Manager* | | |
| | Prefix 11/A dated 3.1.1910 to prefix 11/A dated 2.1.1913 ................. | | Rare |
| **SC422b** | *Signatories: L. M. Mackay* (Accountant) *and handsigned p. Manager* | | |
| | Prefix 11/A dated 2.1.1914 to prefix 11/B dated 2.1.1923.................. | | Rare |

**Size** 207mm x 130mm approximately

*Obverse—dark blue on a yellow and red underprint. Portrait of Lord Pitcairn, the first Chairman of the Bank, at lower centre*
*Reverse—dark blue panel with the Bank's head office building at the centre*

| | F | VF |
|---|---|---|
| **SC423a** *Signatories: R. R. Thomson (Accountant) and handsigned p. Manager* | | |
| Prefix 12/Z dated 31.10.1924 and 1.5.1925............................................ | | Rare |
| **SC423b** *Signatories: R. R. Thomson (Cashier) and A. Robb (General Manager).* | | |
| Prefix 12/Z dated 1.5.1928 to prefix 12/X dated 1.8.1931. ................ | £280 | £500 |
| **SC423c** *Signatories: R. R. Thomson (Cashier) and Sir J. M. Erskine (General Manager)* | | |
| Prefix 12/X dated 31.7.1935 to prefix 12/V dated 25.10.1937 ........... | £200 | £400 |
| **SC423d** *Signatories: James Thomson (Cashier) and Sir J. M. Erskine (General Manager)* | | |
| Prefix 12/V dated 2.8.1940 to prefix 12/Q dated 4.1.1943................. | £180 | £350 |

**Size** 179mm x 102mm approximately

*Obverse—mainly blue. Portrait of Lord Cockburn at top flanked by two female figures representing agriculture and shipping*
*Reverse—blue. Illustration of an Edinburgh street scene in Victorian times with the Bank's head office building in the background*

| | VF | EF |
|---|---|---|
| **SC424a** *Signatory: Sir J. M. Erskine (General Manager)* | | |
| Prefix 13A dated 2.1.1947 to prefix 13K dated 2.1.1953 ................... | £120 | £240 |
| **SC424b** *Signatory: I. W. Macdonald (General Manager)* | | |
| Prefix 13K dated 2.1.1954 to prefix 13P dated 2.1.1958. ................... | £110 | £220 |

# ONE HUNDRED POUNDS

**Size** 220mm x 130mm approximately

*Obverse — mainly black with the value in a yellow and blue underprint. Illustrations of the Bank's principal offices in Edinburgh, Glasgow and London*
*Reverse — large blue panel with the Bank's emblem at the centre*

**SC431**  *Signatories: handsigned p. Accountant and handsigned p. Manager*
Prefix 10/A dated 2.1.1907............................................    no known examples extant

*Obverse — blue on a yellow and light blue underprint. Illustrations of the Bank's principal offices in Edinburgh, Glasgow and London.*
*Reverse — large blue panel with the Bank's emblem at the centre.*

|  |  | F | VF |
|---|---|---|---|
| **SC432a** | *Signatories: handsigned p. Accountant and handsigned p. Manager* Prefix 10/A dated 2.1.1908 to prefix 10/A dated 2.1.1913 .............. |  | Rare |
| **SC432b** | *Signatories: L. M. Mackay (Accountant) and handsigned p. Manager* Prefix 10/A dated 2.1.1914 to prefix 10/A dated 2.1.1923 .............. |  | Rare |

**Size** 207mm x 130mm approximately

*Obverse — dark blue on a yellow and red underprint. Portrait of Lord Pitcairn, the first Chairman of the Bank, at lower centre.*
*Reverse — dark blue panel with the Bank's head office building at the centre.*

|  |  | F | VF |
|---|---|---|---|
| **SC433a** | *Signatories: R. R. Thomson (Accountant) and handsigned p. Manager.* Prefix 11/Z dated 31.10.1924 and 1.12.1928. ...................................... |  | Rare |
| **SC433b** | *Signatories: R. R. Thomson (Cashier) and A. Robb (General Manager).* Prefix 11/Z dated 30.9.1937.................................................... | £650 | £1200 |
| **SC433c** | *Signatories: James Thomson (Cashier) and Sir J. M. Erskine (General Manager)* Prefix 11/Z dated 1.8.1940 to prefix 11/Y dated 2.1.1943. ............... | £550 | £1000 |

**Size** 179mm x 102mm approximately

*Obverse—mainly green. Portrait of Lord Cockburn at top flanked by two female figures representing agriculture and shipping.*
*Reverse—green. Illustration of an Edinburgh street scene in Victorian times with the Bank's head office building in the background.*

| | VF | EF |
|---|---|---|
| **SC434** *Signatory: Sir J. M. Erskine* (General Manager)<br>Prefix 12A dated 2.1.1947 to prefix 12B dated 2.1.1953 .................... | £650 | £1200 |

# THE NATIONAL BANK OF SCOTLAND LIMITED

The National Bank of Scotland was founded in 1825 and rapidly developed a branch system throughout Scotland. It absorbed the Commercial Banking Company of Aberdeen in 1833 and the Perth Union Bank in 1836. The title of the Bank was changed to The National Bank of Scotland Limited in 1882. In 1959 it merged with the Commercial Bank of Scotland Ltd. to form the National Commercial Bank of Scotland Limited.

## ONE POUND

**"A" size square notes** (160mm x 120mm approximately)

*Obverse—black lettering on a blue design with a red and yellow sunburst underprint. Royal Coat of Arms at the centre of the note; portrait of the Marquess of Lothian to the left and view of Edinburgh castle to the right.*
*Reverse—blue Elaborate panel with a view of Edinburgh at the centre.*

|  | F | VF |
|---|---|---|
| **SC501a** *Signatories: Thomas Shaw* (p. Manager) *and handsigned p. Accountant*<br>Prefix A dated 2.1.1893 to prefix D dated 2.1.1905. ............................ |  | Rare |
| **SC501b** *Signatories: W. Samuel* (p. General Manager) *and handsigned p. Accountant*<br>Prefix F dated 15.5.1908 to prefix L dated 15.5.1919...................... from £170 | | £320 |
| **SC501c** *Signatories: W. Samuel* (p. General Manager) *and A. McKissock* (Accountant)<br>Prefix L dated 11.11.1919 to prefix N dated 15.5.1924........................ £140 | | £300 |
| **SC501d** *Signatories: W. Lethbridge* (Cashier) *and A. McKissock* (Accountant)<br>Prefix N dated 15.5.1925 to prefix O dated 1.7.1926........................... £140 | | £300 |

**"B" size notes** (150mm x 85mm approximately)

*Obverse — black on a red and yellow sunburst underprint. Royal Arms at the centre; illustrations of Glasgow Cathedral to the left and the Palace of Holyroodhouse to the right.*
*Reverse — large brown panel on a red and yellow sunburst underprint with a view of Edinburgh at the centre.*

|  |  | VF | EF |
|---|---|---|---|
| **SC502a** | *Signatory: W. Lethbridge* (Cashier) ........................................................ | | |
| | Prefix A/A dated 2.11.1927 to prefix A/C dated 1.11.1929............... | £80 | £160 |
| **SC502b** | *Signatory: George Drever* (Cashier) | | |
| | Prefix A/D dated 2.2.1931 ....................................................................... | £80 | £160 |
| | *Change of printer from Waterlow & Sons Ltd to W. & A.K.Johnston Ltd.* | | |
| **SC502c** | Prefix A/D dated 2.2.1931 to prefix A/F dated 11.11.1933................ | £65 | £140 |

*Obverse — black on a red and yellow sunburst underprint. Bank's Coat of Arms at the centre; illustrations of Glasgow Cathedral to the left and the Palace of Holyroodhouse to the right.*
*Reverse — large brown panel on a red and yellow sunburst underprint with a view of Edinburgh at the centre.*

|  |  | VF | EF |
|---|---|---|---|
| **SC503a** | *Signatory: George Drever* (Cashier) | VF | EF |
| | Prefix A/G dated 12.11.1934 to prefix A/S dated 1.5.1942............... | £30 | £60 |
| **SC503b** | *Signatory: J. T. Leggat* (General Manager) | | |
| | Prefix A/T dated 15.3.1943 to prefix A/V dated 15.6.1946 .............. | £30 | £60 |
| **SC503c** | *Signatory: J. A. Brown* (General Manager) | EF | UNC |
| | Prefix A/W dated 1.3.1947 to prefix B/G dated 2.1.1953 ................. | £40 | £60 |
| | *Change of printer's imprint to W. & A. K.Johnston & G. W. Bacon Ltd.* | | |
| **SC503d** | Prefix B/H dated 1.6.1953 to prefix B/K dated 1.10.1954................. | £35 | £55 |
| **SC503e** | *Signatory: D. Alexander* (General Manager) | | |
| | Prefix B/L dated 1.3.1955 to prefix B/Z dated 2.2.1959, and ........... | £35 | £55 |
| | Prefix C/A dated 1.5.1959 ....................................................................... | | Rare |

# FIVE POUNDS

**Size** 210mm x 126mm approximately

*Obverse—blue with a red and yellow underprint. Royal Coat of Arms at the centre of the note; portrait of the Marquess of Lothian to the left and view of Edinburgh Castle to the right.*
*Reverse—blue. Elaborate panel with a view of Edinburgh at the centre.*

|  |  | F | VF |
|---|---|---|---|
| **SC511a** | *Signatories: handsigned p.General Manager and handsigned p. Accountant.* | | |
| | Prefix A dated 15.5.1909 to prefix A dated 15.5.1918 .................... from £250 | | £460 |
| **SC511b** | *Signatories: W. Samuel* (p. General Manager) *and handsigned p. Accountant* | | |
| | Prefix A dated 11.11.1919 and prefix A dated 8.7.1920 ..................... | £240 | £440 |
| **SC511c** | *Signatories: W. Lethbridge* (Cashier) *and handsigned p. Accountant* | | |
| | Prefix A dated 1.7.1927 to prefix A dated 11.11.1930........................ | £180 | £360 |
| **SC511d** | *Signatories: George Drever* (Cashier) *and handsigned p. Accountant* | | |
| | Prefix A dated 11.11.1932. .................................................................. | £150 | £320 |

*Obverse—blue with a red and yellow underprint. The Bank's Coat of Arms at the centre of the note; portrait of the Marquess of Lothian to the left and view of Edinburgh Castle to the right.*
*Reverse—blue, elaborate panel with a view of Edinburgh at the centre.*

|  | VF | EF |
|---|---|---|
| **SC512a** *Signatories: George Drever* (Cashier) *and handsigned p.Accountant*<br>Prefix A and Prefix B dated 1.7.1936 ............................................... | £180 | £320 |
| **SC512b** *Signatories: George Drever* (Cashier) *and A. A. Bremner* (Accountant)<br>Prefix B dated 1.8.1939 to prefix B dated 1.3.1941 ........................ | £160 | £270 |
| **SC512c** *Signatories: George Drever* (Cashier) *and A. A. Bremner* (Chief Accountant)<br>Prefix B dated 6.7.1942 ................................................................ | £160 | £270 |
| **SC512d** *Signatories: George Drever* (Cashier) *and J. T. Leggatt* (General Manager)<br>Prefix B dated 11.1.1943 ............................................................... | £150 | £260 |
| **SC512e** *Signatories: A.S.O.Dandie* (Cashier) *and J. T. Leggatt* (General Manager)<br>Prefix B dated 3.1.1944 to prefix C dated 2.1.1945 ....................... | £130 | £220 |
| **SC512f** *Signatories: A.S.O.Dandie* (Cashier) *and J.A.Brown* (General Manager)<br>Prefix C dated 3.6.1947 to prefix D dated 1.5.1954 ...................... | £85 | £160 |
| **SC512g** *Signatories: A.S.O.Dandie* (Cashier) *and D.Alexander* (General Manager)<br>Prefix D dated 1.7.1955 to prefix E dated 31.12.1956 .................. | £85 | £160 |

**Size** 178mm x 102mm approximately

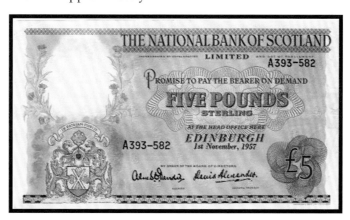

*Obverse —green, Bank's Coat of Arms to the bottom left with thistles above.*
*Reverse—green, illustration of the Forth rail bridge.*

|  | EF | UNC |
|---|---|---|
| **SC513** *Signatories: A.S.O.Dandie* (Cashier) *and D.Alexander* (General Manager)<br>Prefix A and prefix B dated 1.11.1957 .............................................. | £90 | £120 |

# TWENTY POUNDS

**Size** 210mm x 126mm approximately

*Obverse—blue with a red yellow and pink underprint. Royal Coat of Arms at the centre of the note; portrait of the Marquess of Lothian to the left and view of Edinburgh Castle to the right. Reverse—blue. Elaborate panel with a view of Edinburgh at the centre.*

|  | F | VF |
|---|---|---|
| **SC521a** *Signatories: handsigned p.General Manager and handsigned p. Accountant*<br>Prefix A dated 1.8.1914. ......................................................... |  | Rare |
| **SC521b** *Signatories: W. Lethbridge* (Cashier) *and handsigned p. Accountant*<br>Prefix A dated 1.3.1928 and 2.1.1930. ................................................ | £350 | £600 |
| **SC521c** *Signatories: George Drever* (Cashier) *and handsigned p. Accountant*<br>Prefix A dated 11.11.1932. ......................................................... | £350 | £600 |

*Obverse—blue with a red yellow and pink underprint. The Bank's Coat of Arms at the centre of the note; portrait of the Marquess of Lothian to the left and view of Edinburgh Castle to the right.*
*Reverse—blue, elaborate panel with a view of Edinburgh at the centre.*

|  | VF | EF |
|---|---|---|
| **SC522a** *Signatories: George Drever* (Cashier) *and handsigned p. Accountant* Prefix A dated 16.5.1935 to prefix A dated 1.4.1941 | £420 | £750 |
| **SC522b** *Signatories: A. A. Bremner* (Chief Accountant) *and handsigned p. Cashier* Prefix A dated 8.12.1941 and 6.7.1942 | £420 | £750 |
| **SC522c** *Signatories: George Drever* (Cashier) *and J. T. Leggatt* (General Manager) Prefix A dated 11.1.1943 | £420 | £750 |
| **SC522d** *Signatories: A. S. O. Dandie* (Cashier) *and J. T. Leggatt* (General Manager) Prefix A dated 1.6.1944 and 2.1.1945 | £380 | £450 |
| **SC522e** *Signatories: A. S. O. Dandie* (Cashier) *and J. A. Brown* (General Manager) Prefix A dated 2.6.1947 to prefix A dated 1.5.1954 | £350 | £550 |
| **SC522f** *Signatories: A. S. O. Dandie* (Cashier) *and D. Alexander* (General Manager) Prefix A dated 31.12.1956 | £340 | £530 |

**Size** 178mm x 102mm approximately

*Obverse—red, bank's Coat of Arms to the bottom left with thistles above.*
*Reverse—red, illustration of the Forth rail bridge.*

|  | VF | EF |
|---|---|---|
| **SC523** *Signatories: A. S. O. Dandie* (Cashier) *and D. Alexander* (General Manager) Prefix A dated 1.11.1957 | £110 | £220 |

# ONE HUNDRED POUNDS

**Size** 210mm x 126mm approximately

*Obverse—blue with a red yellow and pink underprint. Royal Coat of Arms at the centre of the note; portrait of the Marquess of Lothian to the left and view of Edinburgh Castle to the right. Reverse—blue. Elaborate panel with a view of Edinburgh at the centre.*

|  | *F* | *VF* |
|---|---|---|
| **SC531** *Signatories: handsigned p. General Manager and handsigned p. Accountant.* Prefix A dated 16.5.1935. ........................................................................ | | Rare |

*Obverse—blue with a red yellow and pink underprint. The Bank's Coat of Arms at the centre of the note; portrait of the Marquess of Lothian to the left and view of Edinburgh Castle to the right. Reverse—blue, elaborate panel with a view of Edinburgh at the centre.*

**SC532a** *Signatories: George Drever* (Cashier) *and J. T. Leggat* (General Manager)
Prefix A dated 11.1.1943 ........................................................................... Rare

**SC532b** *Signatories: A. S. O. Dandie* (Cashier) *and J. A. Brown* (General Manager)
Prefix A dated 2.6.1947 to prefix A dated 1.3.1952.............................. Rare

**SC532c** *Signatories: A. S. O. Dandie* (Cashier) *and D. Alexander* (General Manager)
Prefix A possibly exists........................................................................... Rare

**Size** 178mm x 102mm approximately

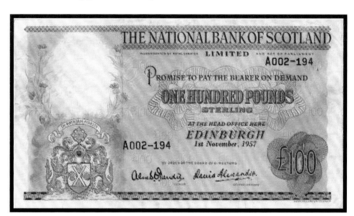

*Obverse—green, bank's Coat of Arms to the bottom left with thistles above.*
*Reverse—green, illustration of the Forth rail bridge.*

|  | *VF* | *EF* |
|---|---|---|
| *Signatories: A. S. O.Dandie* (Cashier) *and D. Alexander* (General Manager) Prefix A dated 1.11.1957........................................................................ | £650 | £1250 |

# THE NATIONAL COMMERCIAL BANK OF SCOTLAND LTD

The National Commercial Bank of Scotland Limited was formed in 1959 as the result of a merger between The Commercial Bank of Scotland Ltd. and the National Bank of Scotland Ltd. It was the largest bank in Scotland at that time. Its lifespan however was limited as in 1970 it merged with the Royal Bank of Scotland to form the Royal Bank of Scotland Limited.

## ONE POUND

**"B" size notes** (152mm x 84mm approximately)

*Obverse—blue; illustration of the Forth rail bridge*
*Reverse—blue; large panel with the Bank's Coat of Arms at the centre*

|  | EF | UNC |
|---|---|---|
| **SC601** *Signatory: D. Alexander* (General Manager) | | |
| Prefix A to prefix 1F dated 16.9.1959 ..................................................... £25 | | £35 |

**"C" size notes** (152mm x 72mm approximately)

*Obverse—green; illustration of the Forth rail bridge*
*Reverse—green; large panel with the Bank's Coat of Arms at the centre*

|  | EF | UNC |
|---|---|---|
| **SC602a** *Signatory: D. Alexander* (General Manager) | | |
| Prefix A dated 1.11.1961 to prefix 2F dated 4.1.1966 .......................... £18 | | £28 |
| **SC602b** *Electronic sorting symbols added to the reverse.* | | |
| Prefix 2G to prefix 2T dated 4.1.1967 ..................................................... £20 | | £32 |

**"D" size notes** (136mm x 68mm approximately)

*Obverse—green; illustration of the Forth rail bridge with the new Forth road bridge in the background*
*Reverse—green; large panel with the Bank's Coat of Arms at the centre*

|  | EF | UNC |
|---|---|---|
| **SC603**    *Signatory: J. B. Burke* (General Manager) | | |
| Prefix A to prefix K dated 4.1.1968........................................................ | £22 | £35 |

# FIVE POUNDS

**Size** 178mm x 102mm approximately

*Obverse—mainly green; Bank's Coat of Arms at lower right*
*Reverse—green; illustration of the Forth rail bridge*

|  | EF | UNC |
|---|---|---|
| **SC611**    *Signatory: D. Alexander* (General Manager) | | |
| Prefix A to prefix G dated 16.9.1959.................................................... | £45 | £85 |

**Size** 159mm x 90mm approximately

Similar to previous issue but smaller size
*Obverse—mainly green; Bank's Coat of Arms at lower right*
*Reverse—green; illustration of the Forth rail bridge*

|  |  | EF | UNC |
|---|---|---|---|
| **SC612** | *Signatory: D. Alexander* (General Manager) |  |  |
|  | Prefix G to prefix J dated 3.1.1961......................................... | £80 | £120 |

**Size** 140mm x 85mm approximately

*Obverse—blue on a multicoloured underprint. Bank's coat of Arms at lower centre*
*Reverse—blue; view of Edinburgh with the Castle in the background*

|  |  | EF | UNC |
|---|---|---|---|
| **SC613a** | *Signatory: D. Alexander* (General Manager) |  |  |
|  | Prefix A dated 2.1.1963 to prefix N dated 1.8.1966............................ | £35 | £50 |
| **SC613b** | *Signatory: J. B. Burke* (General Manager) |  |  |
|  | Electronic sorting symbols added to the reverse. |  |  |
|  | Prefix N to prefix R dated 4.1.1968....................................... | £40 | £65 |

# TEN POUNDS

**Size** 150mm x 90mm approximately

*Obverse—brown on a multicoloured underprint. Bank's coat of Arms at bottom centre*
*Reverse—illustration of the Tay road bridge with Dundee in the background*

|  |  | EF | UNC |
|---|---|---|---|
| **SC621** | *Signatory: D. Alexander* (General Manager) |  |  |
|  | Prefix A dated 18.8.1966........................................... | £650 | £850 |

# TWENTY POUNDS

**Size** 178mm x 102mm approximately

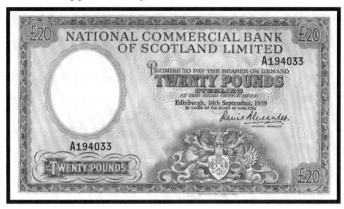

*Obverse—mainly green; Bank's Coat of Arms at lower right*
*Reverse—green; illustration of the Forth rail bridge*

|  | | EF | UNC |
|---|---|---|---|
| **SC631** | *Signatory: D. Alexander* (General Manager) | | |
|  | Prefix A dated 16.9.1959......................................................................... | £140 | £220 |

*A second printing, also prefix A and dated 1.6.1967 was prepared but not issued. One or two have come on to the market in the intervening years but they remain very rare.*

# ONE HUNDRED POUNDS

**Size** 178mm x 102mm approximately

*Obverse—mainly purple; Bank's Coat of Arms at lower right*
*Reverse—purple; illustration of the Forth rail bridge*

|  | | VF | EF |
|---|---|---|---|
| **SC641** | *Signatory: D. Alexander* (General Manager) | | |
|  | Prefix A dated 16.9.1959......................................................................... | £700 | £1250 |

# THE NORTH OF SCOTLAND & TOWN & COUNTRY BANK LIMITED

The North of Scotland Banking company was founded in Aberdeen in 1836. In 1907 the Bank merged with the Town & County Bank Limited, and from 1910 issued notes under the heading The North of Scotland & Town & County Bank Limited. In 1923 the name reverted to The North of Scotland Bank Ltd. which remained until 1950 when the Bank merged with the Clydesdale bank Ltd. to form The Clydesdale & North of Scotland Bank Limited.

## ONE POUND

**"A" size square notes  (174mm x 130mm approximately)**

*Obverse—black printing on a blue design with a yellow underprint. Illustration of the Marischal College in Aberdeen at top centre with three Coats of Arm in a panel to the left*
*Reverse—blue and yellow; Bank's Coat of Arms at the centre*

| | F | VF |
|---|---|---|
| **SC701a** *Signatories: handsigned p. Accountant and p. General Manager.* | | |
| Prefix A dated 1.3.1910 to prefix B dated 1.3.1916 | £320 | £500 |
| | | |
| **SC701b** *Signatories: handsigned p. Accountant and Mitchell Stuart* (p. General Manager). | | |
| Prefix C dated 1.3.1918 | £320 | £500 |

|  |  | F | VF |
|---|---|---|---|
| **SC701c** | *Prefix C dated 1.3.1918 with rubber stamp overprint in red,* | | |
| | *reading "Now the North of Scotland Bank Limited"* | £340 | £550 |
| | *(This rubber stamp overprint may exist on earlier dates)* | | |

|  |  | F | VF |
|---|---|---|---|
| **SC701d** | *Prefix C dated 1.3.1918 with printed overprint in black,* | | |
| | *reading "Now the North of Scotland Bank Limited"* .............................. | £360 | £600 |

## FIVE POUNDS
**Size** 217mm x 135mm approximately

*Obverse—black printing on a blue design with a yellow underprint. Illustration of the Marischal College in Aberdeen at top centre with three Coats of Arm in a panel to the left*
*Reverse—blue and yellow; Bank's Coat of Arms at the centre. Later notes have the denomination "£5" printed six times.*

|  | F | VF |
|---|---|---|
| **SC702a** *Signatories: handsigned p.Accountant and p.General Manager* | | |
| Prefix A dated 1.3.1910 to prefix A dated 1.3.1918.................................... | £400 | £650 |
| **SC702b** *Prefix A dated 1.3.1918 with rubber stamp overprint in red,* | | |
| *reading "Now the North of Scotland Bank Limited" .......................* | £400 | £650 |
| *(This rubber stamp overprint may exist on earlier dates)* | | |
| **SC702c** *Prefix A dated 1.3.1918 and 1.3.1921 with printed overprint in black,* | | |
| *reading "Now the North of Scotland Bank Limited" .......................* | £450 | £700 |

## TWENTY POUNDS
**Size** 217mm x 135mm approximately

*Obverse—black printing on a blue design with a yellow underprint. Illustration of the Marischal College in Aberdeen at top centre with three Coats of Arm in a panel to the left*
*Reverse—blue and yellow; Bank's Coat of Arms at the centre*

|  | F | VF |
|---|---|---|
| **SC703a** *Signatories: handsigned p.Accountant and p.General Manager.* | | |
| Prefix A dated 1.3.1910 to prefix A dated 1.3.1918............................... | | From £750 |
| **SC703b** *Prefix A dated 1.3.1918 with rubber stamp overprint in red, ...................* | | From £750 |
| *reading "Now the North of Scotland Bank Limited"* | | |
| *(This rubber stamp overprint may exist on earlier dates)* | | |
| **SC703c** *Prefix A dated 1.3.1918 and 1.3.1921with printed overprint in black,* | | |
| *reading "Now the North of Scotland Bank Limited" ................................* | | From £750 |

## ONE HUNDRED POUNDS

*Whilst £100 notes in this series were almost certainly printed and issued, no issued example has ever been seen. Specimens dated 1910 and 1921 exist.*

# THE NORTH OF SCOTLAND BANK LIMITED

## ONE POUND

"B" size notes  (155mm x 85mm approximately)

*Obverse—black printing on a blue design with a yellow underprint. Illustration of the Marischal College in Aberdeen at top centre with three Coats of Arm in a panel to the left. Value panels with "£1"*
*Reverse—blue and yellow; Bank's Coat of Arms at the centre*

| | F | VF |
|---|---|---|
| **SC710a** *Signatories: handsigned p. Accountant and Mitchell Stuart (p. General Manager)* Prefix D dated 1.3.1924 to prefix E dated 1.3.1926............................. | £160 | £280 |
| **SC710b** *Signatories R.W.W. (Accountant) and Mitchell Stuart (p. General Manager)* Prefix E and prefix F dated 1.3.1926 ................................................... | £160 | £280 |

*Obverse—black printing on a blue design with a yellow underprint. Illustration of the Marischal College in Aberdeen at top centre with three Coats of Arm in a panel to the left. Value panels with 1* *Reverse—blue and yellow; Bank's Coat of Arms at the centre*

| | VF | EF |
|---|---|---|
| **SC711a** *Signatories R.W.W. (Accountant) and Mitchell Stuart (p. General Manager)* Prefix F dated 1.3.1928 to prefix H dated 1.3.1932............................... | £85 | £150 |
| **SC711b** *Signatories: J.D.P. (Accountant) and R.W.Wath (p. General Manager).* Prefix J dated 1.3.1935 ............................................................................ | £85 | £150 |

*Obverse—blue on a pale yellow underprint. Illustration of King's College, Aberdeen at the centre.*
*Reverse—blue on a pale yellow underprint. Bank's Coat of Arms at the centre*

|  |  | VF | EF |
|---|---|---|---|
| **SC712a** | *Signatory: Harvey Smith (General Manager)* |  |  |
|  | Prefix A dated 1.7.1938 to prefix C dated 1.7.1940............................ | £35 | £60 |
| **SC712b** | *Signatory: G. L. Webster (General Manager)* |  |  |
|  | Prefix D dated 1.7.1945 to prefix F dated 1.7.1949............................ | £35 | £60 |

## FIVE POUNDS

**Size** 215mm x 135mm approximately

*Obverse—black printing on a blue design with a yellow underprint. Illustration of the Marischal College in Aberdeen at top centre with three Coats of Arm in a panel to the left*
*Reverse—blue and yellow; Bank's Coat of Arms at the centre with the denomination "£5" printed six times around it*

|  |  | F | VF |
|---|---|---|---|
| **SC713** | *Signatory: handsigned p. Accountant and Harvey Smith (General Manager)* |  |  |
|  | Prefix A dated 2.3.1925.......................................................................... | £480 | £700 |

**Size** 191mm x 130mm approximately

*Obverse—black printing on a blue design with a yellow underprint. Illustration of the Marischal College in Aberdeen at top centre with three Coats of Arm in a panel to the left*
*Reverse—blue and yellow; Bank's Coat of Arms at the centre with the denomination "5" printed five times around it*

|  |  | VF | EF |
|---|---|---|---|
| **SC714a** | *Signatory: handsigned p. Accountant and Harvey Smith* (General Manager) Prefix A dated 1.3.1928 to prefix A dated 1.3.1932 | £160 | £300 |
| **SC714b** | *Signatory: Thomas Brown* (Accountant) *and Harvey Smith* (General Manager) Prefix A dated 1.3.1934 | £160 | £300 |

**Size** 180mm x 98mm approximately

*Obverse—red; illustration of King's College, Aberdeen at the centre*
*Reverse—red; Bank's Coat of Arms at the centre*

|  |  | VF | EF |
|---|---|---|---|
| **SC715a** | *Signatory: Harvey Smith* (General Manager) Prefix AE dated 1.7.1940 | £120 | £240 |
| **SC715b** | *Signatory: G. L. Webster* (General Manager) Prefix BE dated 1.7.1943 to prefix EE dated 1.7.1949 | £120 | £240 |

## TWENTY POUNDS

**Size** 190mm x 130mm approximately

*Obverse—black printing on a purple design with an olive underprint. Illustration of the Marischal College in Aberdeen at top centre with three Coats of Arm in a panel to the left*
*Reverse—purple and olive; Bank's Coat of Arms at the centre with the denomination "20" printed five times around it*

|  |  | F | VF |
|---|---|---|---|
| **SC716** | *Signatory: handsigned p.Accountant and Harvey Smith* (General Manager) | | |
| | Prefix A dated 1.3.1930 and 1.3.1934 ................................................ | £250 | £450 |

**Size** 181mm x 98mm approximately

*Obverse—green on a light mauve underprint; illustration of King's College, Aberdeen at the centre*
*Reverse—green on a light mauve underprint; Bank's Coat of Arms at the centre*

|  |  | VF | EF |
|---|---|---|---|
| **SC717a** | *Signatory: Harvey Smith* (General Manager) | | |
| | Prefix AT to prefix 0ET dated 1.7.1940 ............................................... | £120 | £200 |
| **SC717b** | *Signatory: G.L.Webster* (General Manager) | | |
| | Prefix FT dated 1.7.1943 to prefix PT dated 1.7.1949 ........................ | £120 | £200 |

# ONE HUNDRED POUNDS

**Size** 190mm x 130mm approximately

*Obverse—black printing on a brown design with a green and brown underprint. Illustration of the Marischal College in Aberdeen at top centre with three Coats of Arms in a panel to the left*
*Reverse—brown and green; Bank's Coat of Arms at the centre with the denomination "100" printed five times around it*

|  |  | F | VF |
|---|---|---|---|
| **SC718** | *Signatory: handsigned p. Accountant and Harvey Smith* (General Manager) | | |
| | Prefix A dated 1.3.1930 and 1.3.1934................................................From £1,000 | | |

Size 181mm x 90mm approximately

*Obverse—dark purple on a light purple underprint; illustration of King's College, Aberdeen at the centre*
*Reverse—dark purple on a light purple underprint; Bank's Coat of Arms at the centre*

|  |  | F | VF |
|---|---|---|---|
| **SC719** | *Signatory: Harvey Smith* (General Manager) | | |
| | Prefix AC to prefix EC dated 1.7.1940. ................................................ | £650 | £1,000 |

# THE ROYAL BANK OF SCOTLAND

The Royal Bank of Scotland was founded in 1727 and immediately competed strongly with the already well established Bank of Scotland. It took over the Dundee Banking Company in 1864, and then in the 1920's and 1930's acquired several English Banks—namely Drummonds Bank in 1924, Williams Deacons Bank as well as the Western Branch of the Bank of England in 1930, and Glyn Mills & Co. in 1939. More recently, it merged with the National Commercial Bank of Scotland Ltd. in 1969 when it became The Royal Bank of Scotland Limited.

## ONE POUND

**"A" size square notes** (65mm x 120mm approximately)

*Obverse—blue on a yellow background with R.B.S. in brown/red letters at the centre. Portrait of George I flanked by Lion and Unicorn at the top. Female figures in the bottom corners. Uniface*

|  | F | EF |
|---|---|---|
| **SC801a** *Signatories: W. Templeton (Accountant) and handsigned p. Cashier*<br>Prefix P dated 2.2.1888 (and perhaps earlier) to prefix Z dated ?<br>Prefix A dated 1.11.1900 to prefix H dated 3.1.1908 ..........................From £260 | | £480 |
| **SC801b** *Signatories: D. S. Lunan (Accountant) and handsigned p. Cashier*<br>Prefix H dated 5.5.1908 to prefix Z dated 29.6.1919, and<br>Prefix A dated 24.3.1920 ......................................................... £180 | | £360 |
| **SC801c** *Signatories: D. Speed (Accountant) and handsigned p. Cashier*<br>Prefix A dated 14.5.1920 to prefix M dated 14.5.1926 ........................ £160 | | £320 |

**"B" size notes** (152mm x 85mm approximately)

*Obverse—blue on a yellow background with a red/brown underprint. Portrait of George I flanked by Lion and Unicorn at the top. Female figures in the bottom corners*
*Reverse—blue panel with illustrations of the Bank's head office buildings in Edinburgh and Glasgow*

| | | VF | EF |
|---|---|---|---|
| | *Signatories: D. Speed* (Accountant) *and handsigned p. Cashier* | | |
| **SC802a** | Suffix A dated 2.2.1927 (just over 100,000 notes issued, then .......... | | Rare |
| **SC802b** | Prefix A dated 2.2.1927 to prefix L dated 24.12.1936 ........................ | £65 | £120 |
| **SC802c** | *Signatory: D. Speed* (Chief Accountant) | | |
| | Prefix A/1 dated 2.1.1937 to prefix G/1 dated 1.7.1942, also .......... | £40 | £75 |
| | Prefix D/1 with suffix A dated 1.9.1939 ........................................ | only one known | |
| **SC802d** | *Signatory: T. Brown* (Chief Accountant). | | |
| | Prefix H/1 dated 1.3.1943 to prefix T/1 dated 1.7.1951.................... | £25 | £55 |
| **SC802e** | *Signatory: J. D. C. Dick* (Chief Accountant). | | |
| | Prefix U/1 dated 16.7.1951 to prefix X/1 dated 1.11.1952, then change of printer's imprint to "W. and A. K. Johnston and G. W. Bacon Ltd., Edinburgh" ........................................................................... | £25 | £50 |
| **SC802f** | Prefix Y/1 dated 1.4.1953 and Z/1 dated 1.8.1953, and Prefix AA dated 1.12.1953 to prefix AE dated 3.1.1955.................... | £25 | £50 |

*Obverse—blue/black on a darker yellow background with a red/brown underprint. Portrait of George I flanked by Lion and Unicorn at the top. Female figures in the bottom corners*
*Reverse—blue/black panel with illustrations of the Bank's head office buildings in Edinburgh and Glasgow*

| | | EF | UNC |
|---|---|---|---|
| **SC803** | *Signatory: W. R. Ballantyne* (General Manager) | | |
| | Prefix AF dated 1.4.1955 to prefix BS dated 1.7.1964...................... | £24 | £35 |

## "C" size notes (152mm x 72mm approximately)

*Obverse — blue/black on a yellow background with a red/brown underprint. Portrait of George I flanked by Lion and Unicorn at the top. Female figures in the bottom corners*
*Reverse — blue/black panel with illustrations of the Bank's head office buildings in Edinburgh and Glasgow*

|  | *EF* | *UNC* |
|---|---|---|
| **SC804a** *Signatory: W. R. Ballantyne* (General Manager) |  |  |
| Prefix CA dated 1.8.1964 to prefix CG dated 1.6.1965........................ | £20 | £30 |
| **SC804b** *Signatory: G. P. Robertson* (General Manager) |  |  |
| Prefix CH dated 2.8.1965 to prefix CX dated 1.11.1967...................... | £20 | £30 |

## "D" size notes (135mm x 67mm approximately)

*Obverse — mainly green on a multicoloured underprint. Portrait of David Dale to the left*
*Reverse — mainly green with illustrations of the Bank's head offices in Edinburgh and Glasgow*

|  | *EF* | *UNC* |
|---|---|---|
| **SC805** *Signatory: G. P. Robertson* (General Manager) |  |  |
| Prefix A/1 to prefix A/24 dated 1.9.1967........................................... | £20 | £30 |

# FIVE POUNDS

**Size** 228mm x 128mm approximately

*Obverse—blue on a yellow background with red/brown overprint. Blue panel to the left; portrait of George I flanked by Lion and Unicorn at the top. Uniface*

|  | F | VF |
|---|---|---|
| **SC806a** *Signatories: handsigned p. Accountant and p. Cashier.* | | |
| Various handwritten dates: | | |
| Prefix D to 26.12.1907 | | Rare |
| Prefix E from 23.12.1909 to 3.1.1922 | From £260 | £480 |

| | VF | EF |
|---|---|---|
| **SC806b** *Signatories: D. Speed (Accountant) and handsigned p. Cashier* | | |
| Prefix E dated 29.6.1923 to 10.1.1942 | From £240 | £400 |

**SC806c** *Signatories:* W. Whyte (Cashier & General Manager) *and* D. Speed (Chief Accountant)
*Signatories:* I. M. Thomson (Cashier & General Manager) *and* T. Brown (Chief Accountant)

| | | |
|---|---|---|
| Prefix F dated 1.7.1942 to 16.10.1950 | £200 | £360 |

**Size** 178mm x 104mm approximately

*Obverse—blue on a yellow background with red/brown overprint. Blue panel to the left; portrait of George I flanked by Lion and Unicorn at the top. Uniface. Similar to previous issue*

|  |  | EF | UNC |
|---|---|---|---|

**SC807a** *Signatories: I. M. Thomson (Cashier & General Manager) and J. D. C.Dick*
(Chief Accountant)
Prefix G dated 2.1.1952 to 1.7.1953 ........................................................ £90 £140

**SC807b** *Signatories: W. A. Watt and W. R. Ballantyne (joint Chief Cashiers and*
General Managers) *and J. D. C. Dick* (Chief Accountant)
Prefix G dated 1.7.1953 and 1.3.1955 ..................................................... £100 £160

**SC807c** *Signatories: W. R. Ballantyne (Cashier & General Manager) and A. G. Campbell*
(Chief Accountant)
Prefix G dated 1.4.1955 to 2.1.1964 ....................................................... £90 £140
Series traced to G34321 dated 2.1.1964

**Size** 146mm x 78mm approximately

*Obverse—blue on a yellow background with red/brown overprint. Blue panel to the left; portrait of George I flanked by Lion and Unicorn at the top. Uniface. Similar to previous issue*

|  |  | EF | UNC |
|---|---|---|---|

**SC808a** *Signatories: W. R. Ballantyne (Cashier & General Manager) and*
*A. G. Campbell* (Chief Accountant)
Prefix H dated 2.11.1964 ......................................................................... £90 £140

**SC808b** *Signatories: G. P. Robertson (Cashier & General Manager) and*
*A. G. Campbell* (Chief Accountant)
Prefix H dated 2.8.1965 and 1.10.1965. ................................................ £90 £140

*Obverse — mainly blue on a multicoloured underprint. Portrait of David Dale to the left*
*Reverse — blue. Illustration on the Bank's head office in Edinburgh*

|  | EF | UNC |
|---|---|---|
| **SC809** *Signatories: G. P. Robertson* (General Manager) *and A. G. Campbell* (Chief Accountant) | | |
| Prefix J/1 dated 1.11.1966 to prefix J/5 dated 1.3.1967 ..................... | £65 | £90 |

## TEN POUNDS

**Size** 228mm x 128mm approximately

*Obverse — blue on a yellow background with red/brown overprint. Blue panel to the left; portrait of*
*George I flanked by Lion and Unicorn at the top. Uniface*

|  | F | VF |
|---|---|---|
| **SC810** *Signatories: handsigned p. Accountant and p. Cashier* | | |
| Various hand written dated, including: | | |
| Prefix C dated 3.3.1914 to 10.4.1917, and ............................................. | | Rare |
| Prefix D dated 5.4.1921 to 1.8.1940 ......................................From £650 | | |

# TWENTY POUNDS

**Size** 228mm x 128mm approximately

*Obverse—blue on a yellow background with red/brown overprint. Blue panel to the left; portrait of George I flanked by Lion and Unicorn at the top. Uniface*

|  | *F* | *VF* |
|---|---|---|
| **SC811a** *Signatories: handsigned p. Accountant and p. Cashier*<br>Various hand written dated, including:<br>Prefix C to 1912 ................................................................ |  | Rare |
| Prefix D from 1912 to 3.1.1947 (the earlier notes have higher values) ...........................................*from £200* | | £350 |

| | *VF* | *EF* |
|---|---|---|
| **SC811b** *Signatories: I. M. Thomson* (Cashier & General Manager) *and T. Brown*<br>(Chief Accountant)<br>Prefix E dated 1.7.1947 to 2.7.1951 ................................ | £230 | £420 |

| | *F* | *VF* |
|---|---|---|
| **SC811c** *Signatories: I. M. Thomson* (Cashier & General Manager) *and J. D. C. Dick*<br>(Chief Accountant)<br>Prefix F dated 1.12.1952 ................................................. | £200 | £380 |
| **SC811d** *Signatories: W. R. Ballantyne* (General Manager) *and A. G. Campbell*<br>(Chief Accountant)<br>Prefix G dated 1.5.1957 .................................................. | £200 | £380 |
| **SC811e** *Signatories: G. P. Robertson* (General Manager) *and A. G. Campbell*<br>(Chief Accountant)<br>Prefix H ........................................................................ | | possibly exists |

# ONE HUNDRED POUNDS

**Size** 228mm x 128mm approximately

*Obverse—blue on a yellow background with red/brown overprint. Blue panel to the left; portrait of George I flanked by Lion and Unicorn at the top. Uniface*

|  |  | F | VF |
|---|---|---|---|
| **SC812a** | *Signatories: handsigned p. Accountant and p. Cashier* | | |
| | Various hand written dated, including: | | |
| | Prefix C to 1912 ..................................................................... | | Rare |
| | Prefix D from 1912 to 1.8.1940 (perhaps later).................................. from £700 | | |
| **SC812b** | *Signatories: I. M. Thomson (Cashier & General Manager) and T. Brown (Chief Accountant)* | | |
| | Prefix E dated 1.10.1949 ........................................................ | £650 | £1150 |

|  |  | VF | EF |
|---|---|---|---|
| **SC812c** | *Signatories: W. R. Ballantyne (General Manager) and A. G. Campbell (Chief Accountant)* | | |
| | Prefix F dated 1.10.1960 ........................................................ | £650 | £1050 |

*Obverse – blue on a yellow background with red/brown overprint. Blue panel to the left; portrait of George I flanked by Lion and Unicorn at the top. Uniface. (The note has guillotined rather than deckled edges).*

|  |  | | |
|---|---|---|---|
| **SC813** | *Signatories: G. P. Robertson (General Manager) and A. G. Campbell (Chief Accountant)* | | |
| | Prefix G dated 3.2.1966.......................................................... | £650 | £1050 |

# THE ROYAL BANK
# OF SCOTLAND LIMITED

## ONE POUND

**"D" size notes** (135mm x 67mm approximately)

*Obverse—mainly green. Illustration of the Forth road and rail bridges*
*Reverse—green, Bank's Coat of Arms at the centre*

|  | | EF | UNC |
|---|---|---|---|
| **SC814a** | *Signatories: A. P. Robertson and J. B. Burke* (General Managers) | | |
| | Prefix A/1 to prefix A/45 dated 19.3.1969......................................... | £16 | £25 |
| **SC814b** | *Signatory: J. B. Burke* (Managing Director) | | |
| | Prefix A/46 to prefix A/68 dated 15.7.1970..................................... | £16 | £25 |

*Obverse—green on a multicoloured underprint. Bank's Arms to the right*
*Reverse—green, illustration of Edinburgh Castle*

|  | | EF | UNC |
|---|---|---|---|
| **SC815** | *Signatory: J. B. Burke* (Managing Director) | | |
| | Prefix A/1 dated 5.1.1972 to prefix C/57 dated 1.5.1981.................. | £10 | £15 |

# FIVE POUNDS

**Size** 146mm x 79mm approximately

*Obverse—blue on a multicoloured underprint. Bank's Arms to the left*
*Reverse—blue, view over Edinburgh with the Castle at the centre*

| | EF | UNC |
|---|---|---|
| **SC816a** *Signatories: A. P. Robertson and J. B. Burke* (General Managers) Prefix A/1 to prefix A/14 dated 19.3.1969 | £50 | £75 |
| **SC816b** *Signatory: J. B. Burke* (Managing Director) Prefix A/15 to prefix A/19 dated 15.7.1970. | £50 | £75 |

*Obverse—blue on a multicoloured underprint. Bank's Arms to the right*
*Reverse—blue, illustration of Culzean Castle*

| | EF | UNC |
|---|---|---|
| **SC817** *Signatory: J. B. Burke* (Managing Director) Prefix A/1 dated 5.1.1972 to prefix B/13 dated 1.5.1981 ................. | £40 | £55 |

# TEN POUNDS

**Size** 151mm x 84mm approximately

*Obverse—brown on a multicoloured underprint. Bank's Coat of Arms at bottom centre*
*Reverse—brown, illustration of the Tay bridge*

| | | EF | UNC |
|---|---|---|---|
| **SC818** | *Signatories: A. P. Robertson and J. B. Burke* (General Managers) | | |
| | Prefix A/1 dated 19.3.1969 ................................................................. | £140 | £190 |

*Obverse—brown on a multicoloured underprint. Bank's Coat of Arms to the right*
*Reverse—brown, illustration of Glamis Castle*

| | | EF | UNC |
|---|---|---|---|
| **SC819** | *Signatory: J. B. Burke* (Managing Director) | | |
| | Prefix A/1 dated 5.1.1972 to prefix A/49 dated 1.12.1981 ................. | £75 | £100 |

# TWENTY POUNDS

**Size** 160mm x 90mm approximately

*Obverse—purple on a multicoloured underprint. Bank's Coat of Arms at bottom centre*
*Reverse—purple, illustration of the Forth road and rail bridges*

| | | EF | UNC |
|---|---|---|---|
| **SC820** | *Signatories: A. P. Robertson and J. B. Burke* (General Managers) | | |
| | Prefix A/1 dated 19.3.1969 | £180 | £250 |

*Obverse—purple on a multicoloured underprint. Bank's Coat of Arms to the right.*
*Reverse – purple. Illustration of Brodick Castle*

| | | EF | UNC |
|---|---|---|---|
| **SC821** | *Signatory: J. B. Burke* (Managing Director) | | |
| | Prefix A/1 dated 5.1.1972 to prefix A/6 dated 1.5.1981 .................. | £160 | £230 |

# ONE HUNDRED POUNDS

**Size** 160mm x 90mm approximately

*Obverse — red on a multicoloured underprint. Bank's coat of Arms at bottom centre*
*Reverse — red, illustration of the Forth road and rail bridges*

|  | *EF* | *UNC* |
|---|---|---|
| **SC822** *Signatories: A. P. Robertson and J. B. Burke* (General Managers) | | |
| Prefix A/1 dated 19.3.1969 ................................................................... | | Rare |

*Obverse — red on a multicoloured underprint.  Bank's coat of Arms to the right*
*Reverse — red, illustration of Balmoral Castle*

|  | *EF* | *UNC* |
|---|---|---|
| **SC823** *Signatory: J. B. Burke* (Managing Director) | | |
| Prefix A/1 dated 5.1.1972 to 1.5.1981 ..................................................... | £650 | £900 |

# THE ROYAL BANK OF SCOTLAND PLC

## ONE POUND

**"D" size notes** (135mm x 67mm approximately)

*Obverse—green on a multicoloured underprint. Bank's Arms to the right*
*Reverse—green, illustration of Edinburgh Castle*

|  |  | EF | UNC |
|---|---|---|---|
| **SC831a** | *Signatory: C. R. Winter* (Managing Director) | | |
| | Prefix C/58 to prefix C/66 dated 3.5.1982............................................ | £16 | £25 |
| | Sorting symbols removed from reverse. | | |
| **SC831b** | Prefix C/67 dated 1.10.1983 to prefix D/32 dated 3.1.1985 .............. | £7 | £11 |
| **SC831c** | *Signatory: C. R. Winter* (Chief Executive) | | |
| | Prefix D/33 to prefix D/67 dated 1.5.1986 ......................................... | £4.50 | £8 |
| **SC831d** | *Signatory: R. M. Maiden* (Managing Director) | | |
| | Prefix D/68 to prefix D/84 (maybe higher) dated 17.12.1986 .......... | £5 | £8 |
| | Replacement note – prefix Z/1 ........................................................... | £40 | £60 |

*Obverse—green on a multicoloured underprint. Portrait of Lord Ilay, first Governor of the Bank, to the right*
*Reverse—green on a multicoloured underprint. Illustration of Edinburgh Castle*

|  |  | EF | UNC |
|---|---|---|---|
| **SC832** | *Signatory: R. M. Maiden* (Managing Director) | | |
| | Prefix A/1 to prefix A/40 dated 25.3.1987 ......................................... | £4 | £6 |
| | Replacement note – prefix Z/1 ............................................................ | £16 | £25 |

## "E" size notes (129mm x 65mm approximately)

Similar to previous issue.

*Obverse—green on a multicoloured underprint. Portrait of Lord Ilay, first Governor of the Bank, to the right.*
*Reverse—green on a multicoloured underprint. Illustration of Edinburgh Castle.*

|  |  | EF | UNC |
|---|---|---|---|
| **SC833a** | *Signatory: R. M. Maiden* (Managing Director) |  |  |
|  | Prefix A/41 dated 13.12.1988 to prefix B/21 dated 19.12.1990......... | — | £5 |
|  | Replacement note – prefix Z/1 ............................................................ | £16 | £25 |
| **SC833b** | *Signatory: C. M. Winter* (Chief Executive) |  |  |
|  | Prefix B/22 to prefix B/51 dated 24.7.1991........................................ | — | £4 |
|  | Replacement note – prefix Z/1 ............................................................ | £16 | £25 |
| **SC833c** | *Signatory: G. R. Mathewson* (Chief Executive) |  |  |
|  | Prefix B/52 dated 24.3.1992 to prefix C/72 dated 1.10.1997 ............. | — | £3 |
|  | Replacement note – prefix Z/1 ............................................................ | £14 | £20 |
| **SC833d** | Notes printed on un-watermarked paper, sometimes known as the "headless" notes. |  |  |
|  | Prefix C/28 to prefix C/31 dated  23.3.1994...................................... | £15 | £25 |
| **SC833e** | *Signatory: G. R. Mathewson* (Group Chief Executive) |  |  |
|  | Prefix C/73 to prefix C/82 dated 30.3.1999....................................... | — | £2 |
|  | Replacement note – prefix Z/1 ............................................................ | £10 | £15 |
| **SC833f** | *Signatory: F. Goodwin* (Group Chief Executive) |  |  |
|  | Prefix C/83 dated 27.6.2000 to prefix C/97 dated 1.10.2001............. | —- | £2 |
|  | Replacement note – prefix Z/1 ............................................................ | £10 | £15 |

*Obverse—mainly Green with portrait of Lord Ilay. Similar to regular issue but with overprint to the left to commemorate the European Summit in Edinburgh, December 1992*
*Reverse—green on a multicoloured underprint. Illustration of Edinburgh Castle*

|  | EF | UNC |
|---|---|---|
| **SC834**  *Signatory: G. R. Mathewson* (Chief Executive) | | |
| Prefix EC dated 8.12.1992.................................................................... | £3.50 | £6 |

*Obverse—mainly Green with portrait of Lord Ilay. Similar to regular issue but with overprint to the left to commemorate the death of Robert Louis Stevenson 1850–94*
*Reverse—portrait of robert Louis Stevenson.*

|  | EF | UNC |
|---|---|---|
| **SC835**  *Signatory: G. R. Mathewson* (Chief Executive) | | |
| Prefix RLS dated 3.12.1994.................................................................... | £2.50 | £4 |

*Obverse—mainly Green with portrait of Lord Ilay. Similar to regular issue but with overprint to the left to commemorate the 150th anniversary of the birth of Alexander Graham Bell 1847–1922*
*Reverse—portrait of Alexander Graham Bell and a representation of his work*

|  | EF | UNC |
|---|---|---|
| **SC836**  *Signatory: G. R. Mathewson* (Chief Executive) ..................................... | | |
| Prefix AGB dated 3.3.1997 .................................................................. | £2.50 | £4 |

*Obverse—mainly Green with portrait of Lord Ilay. Similar to regular issue but with overprint to the left to commemorate the first meeting of the Scottish Parliament*
*Reverse—illustration of the Scottish Parliament building*

|  |  | EF | UNC |
|---|---|---|---|
| **SC837** | *Signatory: G. R. Mathewson* (Group Chief Executive) |  |  |
|  | Prefix SP dated 12.5.1999 ................................................................. | £2.50 | £4 |

## FIVE POUNDS

**Size** 145mm x 78mm approximately

*Obverse—blue on a multicoloured underprint. Bank's Arms to the right*
*Reverse—blue, illustration of Culzean Castle*

|  |  | EF | UNC |
|---|---|---|---|
| **SC841a** | *Signatory: C. R. Winter* (Managing Director) |  |  |
|  | Prefix B/13 dated 3.5.1982 to prefix B/36 dated 5.1.1983................ | £35 | £55 |
|  | Sorting symbols removed from reverse. |  |  |
| **SC841b** | Prefix B/37 dated 4.1.1984 to prefix B/58 dated 3.1.1985................ | £35 | £55 |
| **SC841c** | *Signatory: R. M. Maiden* (Managing Director) |  |  |
|  | Prefix B/59 to prefix B/82 (possibly higher) dated 17.12.1986....... | £35 | £55 |
|  | Replacement note – prefix Z/1........................................................... |  | Rare |

*Obverse—blue on a multicoloured underprint. Portrait of Lord Ilay to the right*
*Reverse—blue on a multocoloured underprint. Illustration of Culzean Castle*

|  |  | EF | UNC |
|---|---|---|---|
| **SC842** | *Signatory: R. M. Maiden* (Managing Director) |  |  |
|  | Prefix A/1 dated 25.3.1987 to prefix A54 dated 22.6.1988 ............... | £18 | £25 |
|  | Replacement note – prefix Z/1 ............................................................ | £35 | £50 |

**Size** 135mm x 70mm approximately

Similar to previous issue but reduced size

*Obverse—blue on a multicoloured underprint. Portrait of Lord Ilay to the right*
*Reverse—blue on a multocoloured underprint. Illustration of Culzean Castle*

|  |  | EF | UNC |
|---|---|---|---|
| **SC843a** | *Signatory: R. M. Maiden* (Managing Director) |  |  |
|  | Prefix A/55 dated 13.12.1988 to prefix B/5 dated 24.1.1990.......... | £14 | £22 |
|  | Replacement note – prefix Z/1 ............................................................ | £40 | £60 |
| **SC843b** | *Signatory: G. R. Mathewson* (Chief Executive) |  |  |
|  | Prefix B/6 dated 23.3.1994 to prefix B/57 dated 29.4.1998 ............. | £10 | £15 |
|  | Replacement note – prefix Z/1 ............................................................ | £40 | £60 |
| **SC843c** | *Signatory: G. R. Mathewson* (Group Chief Executive) |  |  |
|  | Prefix B/58 to prefix B/67 dated 30.3.1999 ...................................... | £11 | £16 |
|  | Replacement note – prefix Z/1 ............................................................ | £40 | £60 |
| **SC843d** | *Signatory: F. Goodwin* (Group Chief Executive) |  |  |
|  | Prefix B/68 to prefix B/77 dated 20.1.2005 and ongoing................ | — | £8 |
|  | Replacement note – prefix Z/1 ............................................................ | £25 | £40 |

Commemorates the Queen's Golden Jubilee.

*Obverse—similar to regular issue. Mainly blue; portrait of Lord Ilay to the right. Gold overprint "The Queen's Golden Jubilee 2002" to the left.*
*Reverse—blue and multicolour. Portrait of the Queen with an earlier portrait from 1952.*

|  |  | EF | UNC |
|---|---|---|---|
| **SC844** | *Signatory: F. Goodwin* (Group Chief Executive) |  |  |
|  | Prefix TQGJ dated 6.2.2002.................................................................... | £10 | £15 |

Issued to commemorate the 250th anniversary of the Royal and Ancient Golf Club of St. Andrews, established 1754.

|  |  |  |  |
|---|---|---|---|
| **SC845** | *Signatory: F. Goodwin* (Group Chief Executive) |  |  |
|  | Prefix R&A dated 14.5.2004................................................................... | — | £14 |

*Commemorates the 500th. Anniversary of the Royal College of Surgeons Edinburgh, 1505 –2005.*
*Obverse–similar to regular issue. Mainly blue; portrait of Lord Ilay to the right. Gold overprint*
*"500 Years The Royal College of Surgeons Edinburgh–1505–2005" to the left.*
*Reverse–as regular issue; blue on a multcoloured underprint. Illustration of Culzean Castle.*

|  |  | EF | UNC |
|---|---|---|---|
| **SC846** | *Signatory: F.Goodwin* (Group Chief Executive).................................. |  |  |
|  | Prefix RCS dated 1.7.2005. ....................................................................... | --- | £12.00 |

Issued July 2005 to commemorate the golfer Jack Nicklaus.
Obverse – similar to regular issue. Mainly blue; portrait of Lord Ilay to the right. Bear
emblem over NICKLAUS to the left. to the left.
Reverse – pictures of Jack Nicklaus with details of St. Andrews golf course.

|  |  | EF | UNC |
|---|---|---|---|
| **SC846** | *Signatory: F.Goodwin* (Group Chief Executive) |  |  |
|  | Prefix JWN dated 14.7.2005. .................................................................. | --- | £12.00 |

# TEN POUNDS

**Size** 153mm x 85mm approximately

*Obverse—brown on a multicoloured underprint. Bank's coat of Arms to the right*
*Reverse—brown, illustration of Glamis Castle*

|  |  | EF | UNC |
|---|---|---|---|
| **SC851a** | *Signatory: C. R. Winter* (Managing Director) |  |  |
|  | Prefix A/49 dated 3.5.1982 to prefix A/88 dated 3.1.1985 .............. | £65 | £100 |
| **SC851b** | *Signatory: R. M. Maiden* (Managing Director) |  |  |
|  | Prefix A/89 to prefix A/98 (possibly higher) dated 17.12.1986...... | £90 | £120 |
|  | Replacement note – prefix Z/1............................................................ |  | Rare |

*Obverse—brown on a multicoloured underprint. Portrait of Lord Ilay to the right*
*Reverse—brown on a multicoloured underprint. Illustration of Glamis Castle*

|  |  | EF | UNC |
|---|---|---|---|
| **SC852** | *Signatory: R. M. Maiden* (Managing Director) |  |  |
|  | Prefix A/1 dated 25.3.1987 to prefix B/31 dated 24.1.1990.............. | £32 | £45 |
|  | Replacement note – prefix Z/1 ........................................................... | £55 | £80 |

**Size** 142mm x 75mm approximately

Similar to previous issue but reduced size.

*Obverse—brown on a multicoloured underprint. Portrait of Lord Ilay to the right.*
*Reverse—brown on a multicoloured underprint. Illustration of Glamis Castle.*

|  |  | EF | UNC |
|---|---|---|---|
| **SC853a** | *Signatory: G. R. Mathewson* (Chief Executive) ..................................... |  |  |
|  | Prefix B/32 dated 28.1.1992 to prefix D/3 dated 23.3.1994 .............. | — | £22 |
|  | Replacement note – prefix Z/1 ........................................................... | £40 | £60 |
| **SC853b** | *Signatory: F. Goodwin* (Group Chief Executive) |  |  |
|  | Prefix D/4 dated 27.6.2000 to prefix D/5 dated 1.10.2001................ | — | £20 |
|  | Replacement note – prefix Z/1 ........................................................... | £35 | £50 |

## TWENTY POUNDS

**Size** 160mm x 90mm approximately

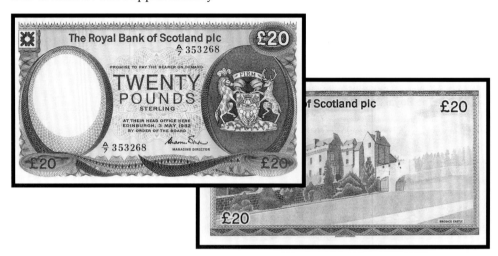

*Obverse—purple on a multicoloured underprint. Bank's Coat of Arms to the right.*
*Reverse—purple, illustration of Brodick Castle*

| | | EF | UNC |
|---|---|---|---|
| **SC861** | *Signatory: C. R. Winter* (Managing Director) | | |
| | Prefix A/6 dated 3.5.1982 to prefix ? dated 3.1.1985........................ | £90 | £130 |

*Obverse—purple on a multicoloured underprint. Portrait of Lord Ilay to the right*
*Reverse—purple on a multicoloured underprint. Illustration of Brodick Castle*

| | | EF | UNC |
|---|---|---|---|
| **SC862** | *Signatory: R. M. Maiden* (Managing Director) | | |
| | Prefix A/1 dated 25.3.1987 to prefix A/3 dated 24.1.1990............... | £60 | £80 |
| | Replacement note – prefix Z/1........................................................... | £100 | £160 |

**Size** 150mm x 80mm approximately

Similar to previous issue but reduced size

*Obverse—purple on a multicoloured underprint. Portrait of Lord Ilay to the right.*
*Reverse—purple on a multicoloured underprint. Illustration of Brodick Castle.*

|  |  | EF | UNC |
|---|---|---|---|
| **SC863a** | *Signatory: C. M. Winter* (Chief Executive) |  |  |
|  | Prefix A/4 to prefix A/8 dated 27.3.1991 ......................................... | £45 | £60 |
|  | Replacement note – prefix Z/1 ............................................................ | £85 | £120 |
| **SC863b** | *Signatory: G. R. Mathewson* (Chief Executive) |  |  |
|  | Prefix A/9 dated 28.1.1992 to prefix B/3 dated 29.4.1998............... | £35 | £50 |
|  | Replacement note – prefix Z/1 ............................................................ | £55 | £80 |
| **SC863c** | *Signatory: G. R. Mathewson* (Group Chief Executive) |  |  |
|  | Prefix B/4 to prefix B/27 dated 30.3.1999 ........................................ | £35 | £50 |
|  | Replacement note – prefix Z/1 ............................................................ | £55 | £80 |
| **SC863d** | *Signatory: F. Goodwin* (Group Chief Executive) |  |  |
|  | Prefix B/29 to prefix B/56 dated 27.6.2000 ...................................... | — | £32 |
|  | Replacement note – prefix Z/1 ............................................................ | £35 | £60 |

Commemorative issue for the 100th birthday of Her Majesty the Queen Mother.

*Obverse—similar to regular issue . Portrait of Lord Ilay to the right. Gold Crown and Commemorative*
*text to the left.*
*Reverse—purple and multicolour. Portrait of the Queen Mother with Glamis Castle in the*
*background.*

|  |  | EF | UNC |
|---|---|---|---|
| **SC864** | *Signatory: F. Goodwin* (Group Chief Executive) |  |  |
|  | Prefix QETQM dated 4.8.2000 ........................................................... | —- | £45 |

# FIFTY POUND NOTES

## Size 150mm x 85mm approximately

*Obverse–mainly green on a multicoloured underprint. Portrait of Lord Islay to the right.*
*Reverse–green and multicoloured. Illustration of Inverness Castle*

|  | EF | UNC |
|---|---|---|
| SC874 *Signatory: F.Goodwin* (Group Chief Executive) |  |  |
| Prefix A/1 dated 14.9.2005 and ongoing......................................................... | — | £85 |
| Prefix Z/1 – replacement note........................................................................... | £100 | £150 |

*Obversve–mainly green on a multicoloured underprint. Portrait of Lord Islay to the right.*
*Reverse–mainly green. Illustrations of the new RBS headquarters at Gogarburn.*

|  | EF | UNC |
|---|---|---|
| SC875 *Signatory: F.Goodwin* (Group Chief Executive) |  |  |
| Prefix RBS dated 14.9.2005 ................................................................................ | — | £130 |

# ONE HUNDRED POUNDS

**Size** 160mm x 90mm approximately

*Obverse—red on a multicoloured underprint. Bank's coat of Arms to the right.*
*Reverse—red, illustration of Balmoral Castle*

|  | EF | UNC |
|---|---|---|
| **SC881** *Signatory: C. R. Winter* (Managing Director)<br>Prefix A/1 dated 3.5.1982 and 3.1.1985 ............................................. | £400 | £600 |

*Obverse—red on a multicoloured underprint. Portrait of Lord Ilay to the right*
*Reverse—red on a multicoloured underprint. Illustration of Balmoral Castle*

|  | EF | UNC |
|---|---|---|
| **SC882a** *Signatory: R. M. Maiden* (Managing Director) |  |  |
| Prefix A/1 dated 25.3.1987 and 24.1.1990.......................................... | £250 | £380 |
| Prefix Z/1 Replacement Note ............................................................... |  | Rare |
| **SC882b** *Signatory: G. R. Mathewson* (Chief Executive) |  |  |
| Prefix A/1 dated 28.1.1992 to prefix A/2 dated 30.9.1998 ................ | — | £200 |
| Prefix Z/1 Replacement Note ............................................................... | £300 | £400 |
| **SC882c** *Signatory: G. R. Mathewson* (Group Chief Executive) |  |  |
| Prefix A/2 dated 30.3.1999....................................................................... | — | £160 |
| Prefix Z/1 Replacement Note ............................................................... | £220 | £320 |
| **SC882d** *Signatory: F. Goodwin* (Group Chief Executive) |  |  |
| Prefix A/2 dated 27.6.2000....................................................................... | — | £160 |
| Prefix Z/1 Replacement Note ............................................................... | £200 | £30 |

# THE UNION BANK
# OF SCOTLAND LIMITED

The title of The Union Bank of Scotland was adopted by the former Glasgow Union Banknig
Company in 1843. In 1905 the contract for printing the Bank's notes was secured by Waterlow
& Sons Limited; earlier notes had been printed by Perkins Bacon. The banknotes of the Union
Bank of Scotland changed relatively little over the years with the most significant design change
coming in 1949 just six years before the Bank was absorbed by the Bank of Scotland.

## ONE POUND

**"A" size square notes** (150mm x 130mm approximately)

*Obverse—Blue with a large red "ONE" overlaid in red at the centre. The Bank's Coat of Arms is at
the top of the note with twin equestrian statues in the lower corners.*
*Reverse—Large blue panel with the figure '1' circled by "The Union Bank of Scotland Limited"*

|  |  | F | VF |
|---|---|---|---|

**SC901a** *Signatories: J. R. Wood* (Accountant) *and handsigned p. Cashier* .........
Prefix A dated 6.4.1905 to prefix A dated 1.5.1907. ...........................    Rare

**SC901b** *Signatories: G. H. Moritz* (Accountant) *and handsigned p. Cashier*
Prefix B dated 2.1.1908 and 28.9.1909 .................................................    Rare

**SC901c** *Signatories: John Alexander* (Accountant) *and handsigned p. Cashier*
Prefix B dated 12.2.1910 to prefix D dated 20.8.1913. ....................... £350    £600

**SC901d** *Signatories: J. F. McCrindle* (Accountant) *and handsigned p. Cashier*
Prefix D dated 3.8.1914 to prefix H dated 10.12.1920 ....................... £250    £480

*Obverse—Blue with a large red "ONE" overlaid in red at the centre and with additional red and yellow sunburst overlay. The Bank's Coat of Arms is at the top of the note with twin equestrian statues in the lower corners.*
*Reverse—Large blue panel with the figure "1" circled by "The Union Bank of Scotland Limited".*

|  | F | VF |
|---|---|---|

**SC902**    *Signatories: N. L. Hird* (General Manager) *and J. F. McCrindle* (Cashier)
Prefix A dated 1.10.1921 and prefix B dated 2.10.1923. ................... £350    £600

## "B" size notes (150mm x 85mm approximately)

*Obverse—Blue with a large red "ONE" overlaid in red at the centre and red and yellow sunburst overlay. The Bank's Coat of Arms is at the top with twin equestrian statues in the lower corners.*
*Reverse—Blue panel with the figure "1" circled by "The Union Bank of Scotland Limited".*

|  | VF | EF |
|---|---|---|

**SC903a**   *Signatories: N. L. Hird* (General Manager) *and J. F. McCrindle* (Cashier)
Prefix A dated 2.6.1924 to prefix C dated 3.10.1927 ............................ £80    £140

**SC903b**   *Signatories: N. L. Hird* (General Manager) *and J. F. McCrindle* (Chief Accountant)
Prefix D dated 2.1.1929 to prefix F dated 5.12.1931 .......................... £60    £110

**SC903c**   *Signatories: N. L. Hird* (General Manager) *and J. D. Wink* (Chief Accountant)
Prefix G dated 1.6.1933 to prefix I dated 31.3.1936 ............................. £45    £80

**SC903d**   *Signatories: N. L. Hird* (General Manager) *and M. J. Wilson* (Cashier)
Prefix K dated 12.2.1937 to prefix V dated 28.9.1945 .......................... £35    £55

**SC903e**   *Signatories: J. A. Morrison* (General Manager) *and M. J. Wilson* (Cashier)
Prefix V dated 20.3.1946 to prefix X dated 1.6.1948 ........................... £35    £55

*Obverse—blue with a large red "ONE" at the centre and with a red and yellow sunburst overlay. Redesigned Coat of Arms to the left and sailing ship emblem to the right.*
*Reverse—mainly blue with an illustration of an industrial scene on the river Clyde.*

|  | VF | EF |
|---|---|---|
| **SC904a** *Signatory: J. A. Morrison* (General Manager) |  |  |
| Prefix A dated 1.3.1949 to prefix G dated 1.9.1953. | £35 | £55 |
| **SC904b** *Signatory: Sir William Watson* (General Manager) |  |  |
| Prefix H dated 1.6.1954 | £80 | £140 |

# FIVE POUNDS

**Size** 196mm x 130mm approximately

*Obverse—Blue with a large red "FIVE" overlaid in red at the centre. The Bank's Coat of Arms is at the top of the note with twin equestrian statues in the lower corners.*
*Reverse—Large blue panel with the figure "5" circled by "The Union Bank of Scotland Limited".*

|  | F | VF |
|---|---|---|
| **SC911** *Signatories: handsigned p. Accountant and handsigned p. Cashier* |  |  |
| Prefix A dated 25.2.1905 to prefix C dated 18.8.1920 | £480 | £850 |

*Obverse—Blue with large red 'FIVE' at the centre and red and yellow sunburst overlay.*
*The Bank's Coat of Arms is at the top of the note with twin equestrian statues in the lower corners.*
*Reverse—Large blue panel with the figure "5" circled by "The Union Bank of Scotland Limited".*

|  |  | F | VF |
|---|---|---|---|
| **SC912a** | *Signatories: N. L. Hird* (General Manager) *and handsigned p. Cashier* | | |
| | Prefix A dated 5.4.1921 and 4.5.1923 ................................................ | £320 | £550 |
| **SC912b** | *Signatories: N. L. Hird* (General Manager) *and J. F. McCrindle* (Cashier) | | |
| | Prefix A dated 4.8.1923 to prefix B dated 15.1.1927........................... | £280 | £480 |
| **SC912c** | *Signatories: N. L. Hird* (General Manager) *and J. F. McCrindle* (Chief Accountant) | | |
| | Prefix B dated 6.7.1928 to 4.5.1932...................................................... | £220 | £380 |
| **SC912d** | *Signatories: N. L. Hird* (General Manager) *and J. D. Wink* (Chief Accountant) | | |
| | Prefix C dated 2.2.1933 to 18.5.1936 .................................................... | £140 | £260 |
| **SC912e** | *Signatories: N. L. Hird* (General Manager) *and M. J. Wilson* (Cashier) | VF | EF |
| | Prefix C dated 18.8.1937 to prefix G dated 31.8.1944........................ | £160 | £350 |
| **SC912f** | *Signatories: J. A. Morriso*n (General Manager) *and M. J. Wilson* (Cashier) | | |
| | Prefix G dated 12.9.1946 to prefix H dated 3.5.1949 ......................... | £160 | £350 |

**Size** 182mm x 100mm approximately

*Obverse—blue with a large red "FIVE" at the centre and with a red and yellow sunburst overlay. Redesigned Coat of Arms to the left and sailing ship emblem to the right.*
*Reverse—mainly blue with an illustration of an industrial scene on the river Clyde.*

| | | VF | EF |
|---|---|---|---|
| **SC913a** | *Signatory: J. A. Morrison (General Manager)* | | |
| | Prefix A dated 17.7.1950 to prefix C dated 1.10.1953 ........................ | £80 | £130 |
| **SC913b** | *Signatory: Sir William Watson (General Manager)* | | |
| | Prefix D dated 2.4.1954.......................................................................... | £250 | £450 |

# TEN POUNDS

**Size** 196mm x 130mm approximately

*Obverse—Blue with a large red "TEN" overlaid in red at the centre. The Bank's Coat of Arms is at the top of the note with twin equestrian statues in the lower corners.*
*Reverse—Large blue panel with the figure "10" circled by "The Union Bank of Scotland Limited".*

| | | F | VF |
|---|---|---|---|
| **SC921** | *Signatories: handsigned p. Accountant and handsigned p. Cashier* | | |
| | Prefix A dated 4.4.1905 to prefix A dated 6.8.1920. ............................ | | Rare |

*Obverse—Blue with large red "TEN" at the centre and red and yellow sunburst overlay. The Bank's Coat of Arms is at the top of the note with twin equestrian statues in the lower corners.*
*Reverse—Large blue panel with the figure "10" circled by "The Union Bank of Scotland Limited".*

| | | | |
|---|---|---|---|
| **SC922a** | *Signatories: N. L. Hird (General Manager) and J. F. McCrindle (Cashier)* | | |
| | Prefix A dated 3.8.1923.......................................................................... | | Rare |
| **SC922b** | *Signatories: N. L. Hird (General Manager) and J. F. McCrindle (Chief Accountant)* | | |
| | Prefix A dated 4.7.1928.......................................................................... | | Rare |
| **SC922c** | *Signatories: N. L. Hird (General Manager) and J. D. Wink (Chief Accountant)* | | |
| | Prefix A dated 8.12.1933 and 8.7.1935................................................... | | from £600 |

# TWENTY POUNDS

**Size** 196mm x 130mm approximately

*Obverse—Blue with a large red "TWENTY" overlaid in red at the centre. The Bank's Coat of Arms is at the top of the note with twin equestrian statues in the lower corners.*
*Reverse—Large blue panel with the figure "20" circled by "The Union Bank of Scotland Limited".*

|  | F | VF |
|---|---|---|

**SC931** *Signatories: handsigned p. Accountant and handsigned p. Cashier*
Prefix A dated 31.3.1905 to prefix A dated 4.6.1920............................ Rare

*Obverse—Blue with large red 'TWENTY' at the centre and red and yellow sunburst overlay. The Bank's Coat of Arms is at the top of the note with twin equestrian statues in the lower corners.*
*Reverse—Large blue panel with the figure "20" circled by "The Union Bank of Scotland Limited".*

|  | F | VF |
|---|---|---|
| **SC932a** *Signatories: handsigned p. General Manager and p. Cashier* <br> Prefix A dated 2.8.1923 to prefix A dated 14.8.1935 .......................... | £380 | £550 |
| **SC932b** *Signatories: handsigned p. General Manager and p. Chief Accountant..* <br> Prefix A dated 31.5.1937 to prefix B dated 2.1.1942........................... | £240 | £380 |
| **SC932c** *Signatories: N. L. Hird (General Manager) and M. J. Wilson (Cashier)* <br> Prefix B dated 30.4.1942 to prefixB dated 10.7.1944.......................... | £180 | £350 |

|  | VF | EF |
|---|---|---|
| **SC932d** *Signatories: J. A. Morrison (General Manager) and M. J. Wilson (Cashier)* <br> Prefix B dated 2.12.1946 and 1.9.1947 ................................................ | £300 | £500 |

**Size** 182mm x 100mm approximately

*Obverse—Blue with a large red "TWENTY" at the centre and with a red and yellow sunburst overlay.*
*Redesigned Coat of Arms to the left and sailing ship emblem to the right.*
*Reverse—Mainly blue with an illustration of an industrial scene on the river Clyde.*

|  |  |  | F | VF |
|---|---|---|---|---|
| **SC933** | *Signatory: J. A. Morrison (General Manager)* | | | |
| | Prefix A dated 1.9.1950 to prefix A dated 1.5.1953............................ | | £200 | £350 |

# ONE HUNDRED POUNDS

**Size** 196mm x 130mm approximately

*Obverse—Blue with a large red "£100" overlaid in red at the centre, flanked by twin equestrian stat-*
*ues. The Bank's Coat of Arms is at the top of the note.*
*Reverse—Large blue panel with the figure "100" circled by "The Union Bank of Scotland Limited".*

|  |  | F | VF |
|---|---|---|---|
| **SC941** | *Signatories: handsigned by the Accountant and Cashier* | | |
| | Prefix A dated 7.4.1905 to prefix A dated 2.4.1919............................ | | Rare |

*Obverse—Blue with a large red "£100" overlaid in red at the centre, flanked by twin equestrian stat-*
*ues. Red and yellow sunburst overlay. The Bank's Coat of Arms is at the top of the note.*
*Reverse—Large blue panel with the figure "100" circled by "The Union Bank of Scotland Limited".*

|  |  | | |
|---|---|---|---|
| **SC942a** | *Signatories: handsigned p. General Manager and p. Cashier* | | |
| | Prefix A dated 1.8.1923 to prefix A dated 20.5.1936............................ | | Rare |
| **SC942b** | *Signatories: handsigned p. General Manager and p. Chief Accountant.* | | |
| | Prefix A dated 1.3.1939 to prefix A dated 2.1.1942............................ | | Rare |
| **SC942c** | *Signatories: J. A. Morrison (General Manager) and M. J. Wilson (Cashier)* | *VF* | *EF* |
| | Prefix A dated 18.2.1947 ......................................................... | £900 | £1500 |

**Size** 185mm x 105mm approximately

*Obverse—Blue with a large red "ONE HUNDRED" at the centre and with a red and yellow sunburst overlay. Redesigned Coat of Arms to the left and sailing ship emblem to the right.*
*Reverse—Mainly blue with an illustration of an industrial scene on the river Clyde.*

|  | VF | EF |
|---|---|---|
| **SC943a** *Signatory: J. A. Morrison* (General Manager) | | |
| Prefix A dated 9.10.1950 and 10.3.1952.............................................. | £900 | £1500 |
| | | |
| **SC943b** *Signatory: Sir William Watson* (General Manager) | | |
| Prefix A dated 1.10.1954. Only 100 printed ....................................... | | Rare |

# *The International Bank Note Society*

Founded in 1961 as a non-profit making society, The International Bank Note Society (IBNS) aims to encourage collectors of paper money and to provide them with an organisation in which they can get to know one another.

With regular meetings, newsletters and a quarterly journal, the society helps collectors to keep abreast of recent developments and initiatives.

Mail bid auctions are also held as are congresses in both the UK and overseas.

For further information on how to join *the* Society for paper money collectors contact:

**Clive Rice
25 Copse Side, Binscombe
Godalming, Surrey
GU7 3RU
E-mail: ibnsuk@onetel.com**

# Provincial private banks

**P**ROVINCIAL PRIVATE BANKS have a poor historical reputation, which is to a great extent quite undeserved. Many banking histories originate from or were commissioned by the later joint stock banking companies. It may be the case that they had a vested interest in emphasising their own illustrious contribution and then minimising the innovations and achievements of the private banks. In this short article ROGER OUTING looks at their note issues.

Provincial private banks performed an invaluable function in supporting the commencement of the English industrial revolution. They did so at a time when the Bank of England never stirred itself from the confines of Threadneedle Street and when London private Banks were completely focused on London.

Provincial private banks developed banking practices and procedures and familiarised the emerging business community with what we would today refer to as "financial services". The subsequent failures of private banks, of which there were plenty, was a consequence of the fact that they were operating at the very edge of economic and commercial innovation and their size was limited to six partners in order to protect the Bank of England from competition. The provincial private banks were inventing and creating the business of banking and doing so under artificial constraints. Failures in these circumstances should not be a surprise.

Whilst there were plenty of failures it can be easily overlooked that a great many private banks did prosper for long periods. They often went on to provide the foundation upon which joint stock banks could subsequently build and become successful. Private banks were the essential precursors to joint stock banks. Private banks and joint stock banks should be regarded as sequential developments within a single system of banking that developed over a 200-year period.

## The Original "Big Five"

The term "Big Five" normally refers to Barclays, Lloyds, Midland, National Provincial, and Westminster Banks who, after 1900, came to collectively dominate English banking. The table opposite lists an "Original Big Five"—namely the first five provincial private banks to establish themselves.

The table tells a quite remarkable story in that none of these five innovators failed. They all maintained their commercial viability and independence for at least 100 years, sometimes longer. These private banks then became part of the joint stock movement in the latter half of the nineteenth century and so established themselves within the modern banking institutions with which we are familiar. The table illustrates that these private banks were an essential part of the origins of the modern banking system and should not be regarded merely as a failed relic of past economic

development. Each of the "Original Big Five" issued their own banknotes and provided account facilities serviced by the use of cheques. Their early banknotes or cheques rarely become available to collectors although 19th century examples can be located.

The subsequent growth in provincial private banks can be summarised as follows:

1750—12 provincial banks established.
1797—230 provincial banks established.
1810—721 provincial banks established.

Clearly there was an explosive expansion in the provision of banking facilities throughout provincial England and Wales. By 1820 every town of substance had its own local bank with its own local banknote issues. It is from this period that material becomes available to present day collectors.

### Newcastle Exchange Bank

Illustrated above is a £5 note, dated 3rd March 1803, from the firm of Surtees, Burdon & Brandling of the Newcastle Exchange Bank. This Bank was established by Aubone Surtees and Rowland Burdon in 1768 and progressed through 35 years of successful trading before failing in 1803. Notes of £1, £5 and £10 are known for the whole trading period although it is the later issues, as illustrated, which are more readily available.

This £5 note has a vignette of The Exchange Building, Newcastle and the intertwined counterfoil printing at the extreme left margin is printed in blue. Handwritten elements, date etc., are also in blue ink. This makes it a two-colour banknote, which was unusual at the time. It is hand signed by the principal partner, "John Surtees". It will be noted that the name of the bank, the Newcastle Exchange Bank, is not printed on the banknote. However it will be found in the watermark that

| The Original Big Five | | | |
|---|---|---|---|
| Year Link | Town | Name | *M o d e r n* |
| 1685 | Derby | Crompton, Newton & Co. | Nat. West. |
| 1688 | Nottingham | Thomas Smith | Nat. West. |
| 1700 | Dover | Fector & Minet | Nat. West. |
| 1716 | Gloucester | James Wood | Lloyds |
| 1737 | Stafford | John Stevenson | Lloyds |

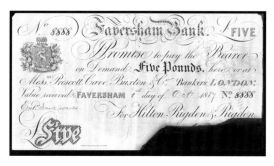

reads, "The Newcastle Exchange Bank, Surtees B & B". This combined use of high quality vignette, two colours and watermarking makes this note a more technically sophisticated product that Bank of England notes of the same period.

The banks demise illustrates an inherent weakness of private banks based upon a family partnership. In 1800 Aubone Surtees, original founder of the bank had died in his ninetieth year. His two sons, Aubone and John, carried on the partnership and were joined by John Brandling. When the original founder of a bank departs it often seems that the experience and wisdom that made the bank successful is also lost. This seems to the case here for 3 years later the Exchange Bank failed. Debts of £234,000 were announced in 1811 and total repayments were just 8/1d in the pound. The final 8d was not paid until 1832.

An interesting footnote is that notes of the Exchange Bank, to a face value of over £200,000, were auctioned off in Durham in 1807. This auction was a matter of business speculation and not an indication of collector interest. There is no record of the prices realised.

Whilst competently managed by the original founder the Newcastle Exchange Bank did successfully provide a banking service to local businesses. The subsequent partners were entirely honourable but apparently did not have the expertise necessary to maintain the trading viability of the business.

### Faversham Bank

Shown opposite is a £5 note dated 1st October 1887, from the firm of Hilton, Rigden & Rigden of the Faversham Bank (also known as Faversham Commercial Bank). This note has an additional feature that became standard during the 19th century namely a reference to a London banker, which in this case was, "Prescott, Cave, Buxton & Co.". Most private banks had a London banker acting as agent and this was usually indicated on the banknote issues. Also this note is "cut cancelled" with the signature being cut out of the note as a form of cancellation. Many notes can be found with this form of cancellation.

In Victorian England when banknotes passed through a commercial or retail firm they were often hand stamped with that firm's name. Consequently this Faversham £5 note carries two faint hand stamps (not visible in illustration) of "Bartlett, Baker & Confectioner, Market Place, Faversham" and "London County Banking Co, Knightsbridge". This gives some indication of the both local and the more distant travels that this individual note has actually made. Many banknotes of the period carry such hand stamps. Other banknotes can be found which carry bankruptcy hand stamps that record the final travails of a failed bank.

Provincial banknotes that are "cut cancelled" carry retail or bankruptcy hand stamps are all quite collectable. Collectors who insist on "uncirculated" notes may be missing the point that collecting English Provincial banknotes is rather more about preserving social history than accumulating a complete "set" of something or other.

The Faversham Bank was taken over by Prescott's in 1892, which then passed to the Union of London & Smiths in 1903, which then passed to the National Provincial in 1918, and so to National

Westminster in 1968. An example of a private bank being independently successful for almost 100 years before becoming part of the national banking structure that is with us today.

The provincial private banks also began to develop and spread the habit of using cheques. Provincial Clearing Houses were often established to support the efficient exchange of cheques in a manner duplicating the London experience.

### Ipswich Cheque

Illustrated below is a cheque on the firm of Alexanders, Maw & Co. of the Ipswich & Needham Market Bank and dated "Oct 7th 1873". There is no mention of the name of the bank on the cheque—a mildly irritating feature of some private bank cheques. The cheque is wholly printed in red on special security paper designed to resist alteration to the cheque values, as cheque forgery was a significant problem at the time. As a further security device the cheque is watermarked with "East Malling, Kent" which is the mark of Waterlow & Sons, Security Printers, who printed this cheque.

The Ipswich & Needham Market Bank was established in 1744, and enjoyed over 150 years of independent and successful trading before becoming a founder member of the banking institution now known as Barclays Bank.

### End of the Road

The demise of private banks was achieved in stages that encompassed almost 100 years. Firstly, legislation in 1826 allowed joint stock banks, other than the Bank of England, for the first time. Secondly, the Bank Charter Act 1844 placed restrictive prohibitions on the issue of banknotes. Finally, company law in 1858 allowed limited liability to be applied to banks. The accumulative effect of this legislation, and the amalgamation process which it triggered off, will be considered in more detail next month when the history of joint stock banking is dealt with.

By 1900 the banknote issues of the private banks were a minor amount of the total money supply. The very last private bank of issue was the firm of Fox, Fowler and Co. who had conducted a banking business at Wellington, Somerset, since 1787. This longstanding private bank finally relinquished its independent existence and its banknote issue when it amalgamated with Lloyds Bank in 1921. These final banknote issues are highly prized by collectors today.

During the 19th century in Great Britain many towns and cities and even villages had banks which issued their own notes. These are known as "Provincial" notes and are eagerly sought after, especially by local historians. The notes illustrated here are a selection which appeared at a Spink auction and are illustrated here with their kind permission.

# Books
## for the banknote collector

On the following pages is a list of books of interest to the banknote collector. They are listed under their area of main interest and by author alphabetically. Many of the titles are out of print but can often be acquired from your favourite numismatic bookseller.

### General

IAN ANGUS, *Paper Money*, London, 1974.

COURTNEY L. COLLING Guide & checklist of World Notgeld 1914–1947, 2000.

JOE CRIBB, *Money: From Cowrie Shells to Credit Cards*, London 1986.

LESLIE DUNKLING and ADRIAN ROOM, *The Guinness Book of Money*, Enfield, 1990.

W. KRANISTER, The *Moneymakers International*, Cambridge, 1989.

BARRY KRAUSE, *Collecting Paper Money for Pleasure and Profit.*

MONETARY RESEARCH INSTITUTE *Bankers Guide to Foreign currency*, Housten TX, 2001.

COLIN NARBETH, ROBIN HENDY AND CHRISTOPHER STOCKER, *Collecting Paper Money and Bonds*, London, 1979.

COLIN NARBETH, *Encyclopedia of Paper Money*, London, 1967.

JOHN ORNA-ORNSTEIN, *The Story of Money*, London, 1997.

ALBERT PICK, *Briefmarkengeld*, Brunswick, 1970.
*Papiergeld*, Brunswick, 1967.
*Papiergeldkatalog Europa seit 1900*, Munich, 1973.
*Paper Money Catalogue of the Americas*, Munich, 1973.
*Standard Catalog of World Paper Money*, 3 vols., Krause Publications, Iola, 1998.

FRED REINFELD, *The Story of Paper Money.*

JOHN E. SANDROCK, *World Paper Money Collection*, New York, various editions.

FRED SCHWANN, *Collecting Paper Money*, New York, 1996.

NEIL SHAFER, *The Wonderful World of Paper Money*, 1972.
*Let's Collect Paper Money*, 1976.

GEORGE J. STEN, *Banknotes of the World*, 2 vols, Menlo Park, 1967.
*Encyclopedia of World Paper Money*, New York, 1965.

### Military Invasion and Occupation Notes

JAMES MACKAY, *Banknotes at War*, London, 1977.

CARLTON F. SCHWAN, *Military Payment Certificates World War II Allied Military Currency*, Ohio, 1974.

CARLTON F. SCHWAN AND JOSEPH E. BOLING, *World War II Military Currency*, Ohio, 1978.

JAMES RUTLANDER, *Allied Military Currency*, New York, 1968.

NEIL SHAFER, *Philippine Emergency and Guerrilla Currency of World War II*, Racine, 1974.

ARLIE SLABAUGH, *Japanese Invasion Money*, Chicago, 1977.

GASTONE SOLLNER, *Moneta d'Occupazione e di Liberazione della IIa Guerra Mondiale*, Mantua, 1965.

ZVI STAHL, *Jewish Ghettos' and Concentration Camps' Money (1933-45)*, Israel, 1990.

RAYMOND TOY, *World War II Allied Military Currency*, San Diego, 1969.

RAYMOND TOY AND BOB MEYER, *World War II Axis Military Currency*, Tucson, 1967.

BENJAMIN WHITE, *The Currency of the Great War*, London, 1921.

JOHN F. YARWOOD, *A Guide to British Military Tokens*, Horsham, Australia, 1998.

### Algeria

PAUL DUGENDRE, *Catalogue des Billets de la Banque de l'Algerie et de la Tunisie*, Paris, 1953.

### Angola

LUIS M.R. DE SOUSA, *O Papel-Moeda em Angola*, Luanda, 1969.

### Argentina

JOSE MARIA MUNARI, *Papel Moneda Argentina 1935-1967*, Buenos Aires, 1967.

### Australia

GREG MCDONALD, *Australian Coins and Banknotes*, Umina Beach, 1985.

ALAN NICHOLSON, *Australian Banknote Catalogue*, Melbourne, 1979.

DION H. SKINNER, *Rennick's Australian Coins and Banknotes Guide*, Adelaide, 1980.

P. STEELE, *Collect Australian Coins and Banknotes*, Dubbo NSW, 1988.

G. W. TOMLINSON, *Australian Bank Notes 1817–1963*, Melbourne, 1963.

MICHAEL VORT-RONALD, *Collect Australian Banknotes*, Dubbo NSW, 1998.

### Austria

ALBERT PICK AND R. RICHTER, *Oesterreich Banknoten und Staatspapiergeld ab 1759*, Berlin, 1972.

### Baltic States

A. PLATBARZDIS, *Coins and Notes of Estonia, Latvia, Lithuania*, Stockholm, 1968.

M. TITUS, *Paper Currencies of Estonia*, Menlo Park, 1971.

### Belgium

J. DE MEY, *Le Papier-Monnaie Belge d'Outremer, 1896-1963*, Brussels, 1976.
*Le Papier-Monnaie Belge, 1814–1976*, Brussels, 1976.

IBNS, *Paper Money of the 20th Century: Belgium and Colonies*, St. Louis, 1975.

FRANCOIS MORIN, *Catalogue des Billets de Banque Belge 1900 a 1974*, Brussels, 1974.
*Cataloge des Billets de Banque de Congo etc*, Boom, 1974.

## Bolivia

LUIS A. ASBUN-KARMY, *Monedas de Bolvia*, La Paz, 1977.

## Brazil

BANCO DO BRASIL, *Cedulas Brasileiras*, Rio de Janeiro, 1965.

ALVARO GONCALVES, *Catalogo de Cedulas e Moedas Brasileiras*, Sao Paulo, 1969.

DALE A. SEPPA, *The Paper Money of Brazil*, Chicago, 1976.

VIOLO LISSA, *Catalogo do Papel-Moeda do Brasil*, Brasilia, 1981.

DOS SANTOS TRINGUEIROS, *Dinhero do Brasil*, Rio de Janeiro, 1966.

A. TODISCO, *Catalogue of Brazilian Banknotes*, IBNS, 1961.

## British West Africa

RICHARD J. FORD, *British West African Currency Board Bank Notes*, Walton-on-the-Naze, 1970.

## Burma

M. ROBINSON AND L.A. SHAW, *The Coins and Banknotes of Burma*, Manchester, 1980.

## Canada

BANK OF CANADA, *The Story of Canada's Currency*, Ottawa, 1981.

*The National Currency Collection and the Bank of Canada Currency Museum*, n.d.

J.E. CHARLTON, *Standard Catalogue of Canadian Paper Money*, Toronto, 1980.

HANS ZOELL, *Simplified Catalog of Canadian-Newfoundland Coins and Paper Money*, 1961.

## Chile

JOSE M. GALETOVIC AND HECTOR BENAVIDES, *El Billete Chileno*, Santiago, 1973.

## China

W.H. LU, *Paper Money Catalogue of the People's Republic of China and Macau*, Kuala Lumpur, 1998.

KING-ON MAO, *History of Chinese Paper Currency*, Hong Kong, 1968-77.

*History of Paper Currency of the People's Republic of China*, Hong Kong, 1972.

WARD D. SMITH AND BRIAN MATRAVERS, *Chinese Banknotes*, Menlo Park, USA, 1970.

HSU YIH TZON, *The Illustrated Encyclopedia of the Chinese Banknotes*, Taipei, 1981.

## Colombia

YASHA BERESINER AND EDOUARDO DARGENT, *Catalogue of the Paper Money of Colombia and Peru*, London 1973.

ERNESTO CALLEJOS, *Catalogo de Billetes Emitidos...de Colombia*, Medellin, 1978.

## Cuba

NEIL SHAFER, *Cuban Paper Money 1857-1968*, St. Louis, 1970.

## Cyprus

MAJOR F. PRIDMORE, *Modern Coins and Notes of Cyprus*, London, 1974.

## Denmark

AXEL RUBOW, *Nationalbankens Historie 1878-1908*, Copenhagen, 1920.

FROVIN SIEG, *Seddelkatalog 1874-1976*, Ulbjerg, 1977.

## El Salvador

ALCEDO F. ALMANZAR AND BRIAN R. STICKNEY, *The Coins and Paper Money of El Salvador*, San Antonio, 1973.

ENRIQUE FRANKE, *The Banknotes of the Republic of El Salvador*, San Salvador, 1974.

## England

W. MARSTON ACRES, *The Bank of England from Within*, Oxford, 1931.

DAVID BEVAN, *A Guide to Collecting English Banknotes*, New Malden, 1970.

BRYAN BURKE, *Nazi Counterfeiting of British Currency in World War II*, San Bernardino, 198.7

G. CHANDLER, *Four Centuries of Banking*, 2 vols, 1964-68.

SIR JOHN CLAPHAM, *The Bank of England: A History*, Cambridge, 1944.

W. CRICK AND J. WADSWORTH, *A Hundred Years of Joint-Stock Banking*, London, 1958.

VINCENT DUGGLEBY, *English Paper Money*, London, 2002.

PHILIP GEDDES, *Inside the Bank of England*, London, 1987.

G. L. GRANT, *Standard Catalogue of Provincial Banks and Banknotes*, London, 1977.

T. GREGORY, *The Westminster Bank Through a Century*, London, 1936.

VIRGINIA HEWITT AND J. M. KEYWORTH, *As Good as Gold*, London, 1987.

C. R. JOSSET, *Money in Britain*, Newton Abbott, 1971.

JAMES MACBURNIE, *The Story of the Yorkshire and Lancashire Bank*, Manchester, 1922.

A.D. MACKENZIE, *The Bank of England Note*, Cambridge, 1953.

P. W. MATTHEWS AND A. W. TUKE, *The History of Barclays Bank*, London, 1926.

DAVID M. MILLER, *Bank of England and Treasury Notes 1694-1970*, Newcastle, 1970.

COLIN NARBETH, *Collect British Banknotes*, London, 1970.

R. S. SAYERS, *The Bank of England, 1891-1944*, Cambridge, 1976.

H. WITHERS, *National Provincial Bank, 1833-1933*, London, 1933.

## Egypt

MAGDY HANAFY, *The Egyptian Currency Note*, Cairo, 2006

## Finland

ERKKI BORG, *Suomessa Kaytetet Rahat*, Helsinki, 1976

FINLANDS BANK, *Inhemska Sedeltyper in Finland, 1809-1951*, Helsinki, 1952.

HANNU PAATELA, *Research Collection of Bank Notes Used in Finland 1662-1978*, Helsinki, 1978.

KURT PETTERSON, *Suomen Rahojen Hinnasta 1811 1979*, Helsinki., 1979.

TUKKO TOLVIO, *The Coins and Banknotes of Finland*.

## France

JEAN LAFAURIE AND RAYMOND HABREKORN, *Catalogue des Emissions Officielles Francaises de Papier-Monnaie 1797-1952*, Auxerre, 1953-4.

M. MUSZYNSKI, *Les Billets de la Banque de France*, Villiers sur Marne, 1975 .

J. PIROT, *Catalogue of Tokens of Municipalities and Cities* (France and ex-colonies, 1914-18), Paris, 2006
ARGUS THIMONIER, *Monnaies et Billets Francxe depuis 1774*, Paris, 1960.

## Germany

KURT JAEGER AND ULLRICH HAEVECKER, *Die Deutschen Banknoten seit 1871*, Cologne, 1979.
ARNOLD KELLER. *Das Papiergeld des Ersten Weltkrieges*, Berlin, 1957.
*Das Papiergeld des Zweiten Weltkrieges*, Berlin, 1953.
*Das Papiergeld der Deutschen Kolonien*, Munster, 1967.
KAI LINDMAN, serienscheine, Sassenburg, 2000.
MANFRED MULLER AND ANTON GEIGER, *Das papiergeld der Deutschen Eisenbahnen und der Reichspost*, Frankenthal, 2000
ALBERT PICK AND J. RIXEN, *Papiergeld Spezialkatalog Deutschland 1874-1980*, Berlin, 1982.

## Gibraltar

D.C. DEVENISH, *Currency Notes of Gibraltar*, London, 1969.

## Greece

PAUL G. PYLARINOS, *Greek Paper Money*, Athens, 1976.
A. TARASSOULEAS, *Paper Money of Greece*, Athens, 1982.

## Greenland

PETER FLENSBORG, *Gronlandske Pengesedler, 1803-1967*, Copenhagen, 1970.

## Guatemala

ODIS H. CLARK, *Paper Money of Guatemala, 1834-1946*, San Antonio, 1971.
DWIGHT MUSSER, *The Paper Money of Guatemala*, USA, 1959.

## Hawaii

MAURICE M. GOULD AND KENNETH BRESSETT, *Hawaiian Coins, Tokens and Paper Money*, Racine, 1961.
GORDON MEDCALF AND ROBERT FONG, *Hawaiian Money and Medals*, Kailua, 1967.
*Paper Money of the Kingdom of Hawaii 1859-1905*, Honolulu, 1966.
AND RONALD RUSSELL, *Hawaiian Money Standard Catalog*, Honolulu., 1978.

## Hungary

RICHARD A. BANYAI, *The Legal and Monetary Aspects of the Hungarian Hyper-inflation*, Tucson, 1971.
MIHALY KUPA AND BELA AMBRUS, *Magyarorszag Papirpenzei*, Budapest, 1964.
*Paper Money of Hungary 1803-1918*, Budapest, 1963.

## Iceland

FINNUR KOLBEINSSON, *Islenzkar Myntir*, Reykjavik, 1978.

## India

KISHORE JHUNJHUNWALA, *Indian Paper Money Since 1950*, Mumbai, 1998.

## Indonesia

DONALD L. FOLTZ, *Paper Money of the Republic of Indonesia*, Indianapolis, 1970.

## Ireland

G. BARROW, *The Emergence of the Irish Banking System*, Dublin, 1975.
MÁRTAN MAC DEVITT, *Irish Banknotes, Irish Government Paper Money from 1928*, Dublin, 1999.
*Irish Banknotes, Irish Paper Money 1783-2001*, Dublin, 2004.
DEREK YOUNG, *Guide to the Currency of Ireland, Legal tender Notes 1928-1972*, Dublin, 1972.
*Guide to the Currency of Ireland, Consolidated Bank Notes, 1929-1941*, Dublin, 1977.

## Isle of Man

ISLE OF MAN BANK, *100 Years of Banking*, Douglas, 1965.
ERNEST QUARMBY, *Banknotes & Banking in the Isle of Man 1788-1970*, London, 1971.
PILCHER RALFE, *Sixty Years of Banking, 1865-1925*, Douglas, 1926.

## Israel

SYLVIA HAFFNER, *The History of Modern Israel's Money from 1917-1967*, San Diego, 1968.
A.H. KAHAN, *Israel's Money and Medals*, New York, 1976.

## Italy

CESARE BOBBA, *Carta Moneta Italiane, Asti*, 1974.
*Catalogo della Carta-Moneta d'Occupazione*, Asti, 1975.
MARIO DE FANTI, *Carta-Moneta Italiana, 1866-1961*, Casciano, 1966　.
LUIGI DE ROSA, *Il Banco di Napoli Istituto di Emissione*, Naples, 1976.
LIBERO MANCINI, *Catalogo Italiano della Cartamoneta 1746-1966*, Bologna, 1966.
ADOLFO MINI, *La Carta Moneta italiana 1746-1960*, Palermo, 1967.
GASTONE SOLLNER, *Catalogo della Carta-Moneta Italiana dal 1866 ad Oggi*, Milan, 1964.

## Jamaica

JEROME REMICK, *Jamaican Banknotes*, St. Louis, 1968.

## Japan

BANKOKU KAHEI KENKYUKAI, *Government and Bank of Japan Issues and Military Issues*, Tokyo, 1970.
IBNS, *Paper Money of the 20th Century: Japan*, St. Louis, 1981.
Y. OHASHI, *Nippon Shihei Taikei Zukan*, Tokyo, 1957.

## Katanga

PETER SYMES, *The Bank Notes of Katanga*, Kirkcaldy, 1998.

## Korea

BANK OF KOREA, *The History of Korean Money*, Seoul, 1969.
KIM IN SIK, *Illustrated Catalog of Korean Currency*, Seoul, 1978.

## Luxembourg

FERN WICTOR, *Monnaies et Essais-Monnaies du Grand-Duche de Luxembourg 1796-1965*, Luxembourg, 1965.

## Malaysia

IBNS, *Paper Money of the 20th Century*: Malaysia, Dallas, 1973.

K. C. BOON, *Standard Price Guide of Malaysian Banknotes and Coins 1939-2002*, Kuala Lumpur, 2003.

C.C. LOW, *Malaya Banknote Catalog,* Racine, 1967.

WILLIAM SHAW AND ALI KASSIM HAJI, *Paper Currency of Malaysia*, etc, Kuala Lumpur, 1971.

SARON SINGH, KASSIM HAJI, C.C. LOW AND TONY LYE FONG, *Standard Catalogue of Coins and Banknotes of Malaysia*, etc, Kuala Lumpur, 1976.

STEPHEN TAN, *Standard Catalogue of Malaysia, Singapore, Brunei Coins and Paper Money*, 1998.

## Maldive Islands

TIM J. BROWDER, *Maldive Islands Money*, Santa Monica, 1969.

## Malta

EMMANUEL SAID, *Malta Coin, Banknote and Medal Catalogue*, Valletta, 1982.

## Mexico

DOUGLAS AND DUANE, *The Complete Encyclopedia of Mexican Paper Money*, Iola, 1982.

CARLOS GAYTAN, *Billetes de Mexico*, Mexico City, 1965.

*Paper Curency of Mexico*, California, 1975.

## Monaco

RAYMOND DE VOS, *History of the Monies, Medals and Tokens of Monaco*, New York, 1977.

## Mongolia

E.D. GRIBANOV, *The Currency of the Mongolian People's Republic*, St. Louis, 1965.

## Morocco

M. MUSZYNSKI AND H. SCHWEIKERT, *Le Papier-Monnaie du Maroc*, Paris, 1974.

## Mozambique

BANCO NACIONAL ULTRAMARINO, *Papel-Moeda Para Mocambique, 1877-1973*, Lisbon, 1978.

COLIN R. OWEN, *The Banknotes of Mozambique*, Benoni, 1976.

## Netherlands

J. MEVIUS AND F.G. LELIVELT, *De Nederlandse Bankbiljetten van 1814 tot Heden*, Amsterdam, 1981.

## New Zealand

HOWARD MITCHELL, *Catalogue of New Zealand Banknotes*, Auckland, 2006.

ALISTAIR F. ROBB, *Catalogue of the Trading Bank Notes of New Zealand*, Wellington, 2006.

## Nicaragua

BRIAN STICKNEY AND ALCEDO ALMANZAR, *The Coins and Paper Money of Nicaragua*, USA, 1974.

## Norway

KARL SAETHRE AND HANS GUNNAR ELDORSEN, *Norske Pengesedler*, Loddefjord, Norway, 2003.

## Papua New Guinea

DR WILLIAM J.D. MIRA, *From Cowrie to Kina,* Sydney, 1986.

## Paraguay

DALE A. SEPPA, *Paraguayan Paper Money*, Chicago, 1974.

## Peru

EDUARDO DARGENT, *El Billete en el Peru*, Lima, 1979.

## Philippines

NEIL SHAFER, *A Guide Book of Philippines Paper Money*, Racine, 1964.

## Poland

TADEUSZ JABLONSKI, *Polski Pieniadz Papierowny*, 1794-1948, Warsaw, 1964.

MARIAN KOWLSKI, *Katalog Banknotow Polskich 1916-1972*, Warsaw, 1973.

## Portugal

FRANCISCO MALAFAYA, *Catalogo de Notafilia Portugal*, Porto, 1977.

## Romania

V. COMAN, *Katalog der Rumanischen Banknoten*, Munster, 1967.

COL. R. IOAN DOGARU, *Catalogul Monedelor si Bancnotelar Romanesti*, Bucharest, 1978.

OCTAVIAN LUCHIAN, *Monede si Bancnote Romanesti*, Bucharest, 1977.

## Russia

C. DENIS, *Catalogue des Monnaies Russes*, Paris, 1927.

N. KARDAKOFF, *Katalog der Geldscheine von Russland und der Baltischen Staaten*, Berlin, 1953.

LEONID Z. KATS and VALERY P. MALYSHEV, *Encyclopedia of Russian Paper Money 1769-1995*, St Petersburg, 1998.

DMITRI KHARITONOV, *Jewish Paper Money in Russia*, Prague, 2004.

PENTII LAURILA, *Soviet Paper Money and Bonds Used as Currency 1895-1990*, Tornio, Finland, 1990.

N. NAVOLOCHKIN, *Soviet Numismatics*, Moscow, 1970.

## Scotland

JAMES L. ANDERSON, *The Story of the Commercial Bank of Scotland*, Edinburgh, 1910.

BANKING MEMORABILIA, *Registers of the National Bank of Scotland*, Carlisle, 2004.

C. W. BOASE, A Century of Banking in Dundee, Edinburgh, 1867.

JOHN BUCHANAN, *Glasgow Banking in Olden Times*, Glasgow, 1884.

ALEX CAMERON, *The Bank of Scotland 1695-1995, A Very Singular Institution*, Edinburgh, 1995.

S.G. CHECKLAND, *Scottish Banking: A History 1695-1973*, Glasgow, 1975.

DENNET *Scottish banknote catalogue*, Norwich, 2001

JAMES DOUGLAS, *Scottish Banknotes*, London, 1975. *20th Century Scottish Banknotes, Vols. 1 & 2*, Carlisle, 1984. Revised 2002.

SIR WILLIAM FORBES, *Memoirs of a Banking-House*, Edinburgh, 1859.

WILLIAM GRAHAM, *The One Pound Note in Scotland*, Edinburgh, 1911. *The Bank Note Circulation of Scotland*, Edinburgh, 1926.

TREVOR JONES, *20th Century Scottish Banknotes: Clydesdale Bank*, Carlisle, 1998.

ALEXANDER KEITH, *The North of Scotland Bank 1836-1936*, Aberdeen, 1936.

ANDREW W. KERR, *A History of Banking in Scotland*, London, 1884.

CHARLES A. MALCOLM, *The History of the British Linen Bank*, Edinburgh, 1950.

C. MUNN, *The Scottish Provincial Banking Companies, 1747-1864*, Edinburgh, 1981.

NEIL MUNRO, *The History of the Royal Bank of Scotland 1727-1927*, Edinburgh, 1928.

ROBERT PRINGLE, *20th Century Scottish Banknotes: Royal Bank*, Carlisle, 1986.

ROBERT S. RAIT, *The History of the Union Bank of Scotland*, Glasgow, 1930.

J.M. REID, *The History of the Clydesdale Bank*, Glasgow, 1938.

## South Africa

W. BERGMAN, *A History of the Regular and Emergency Paper Money Issues of South Africa*, Cape Town, 1971.

HAROLD P. LEVIUS, *Catalogue of South African Paper Money since 1900*, Johannesburg, 1972.

## South East Asia

COLIN BRUCE, *Standard Guide to South Asian Coins and Paper Money Since 1556*, Iola, 1982.

HOWARD A. DANIEL, *The Catalogue and Guidebook of Southeast Asian Coins and Currency*, Ohio, 1978.

## Spain

IBNS, *Paper Money of the 20th Century: Spanish Civil War*, St. Louis, 1978.

FLORIAN R. VELEZ-FRIAS AND JORGE A. VILA, *Catalogo del papel Moeda Espanol*, Madrid, 1975.

JOSE A. VICENTE, *Catalogo de Billetes Espanoles 1783-1977*, Madrid, 1977.
*Catalogo Basico Monedas y Billetes 1869-1977*, Madrid, 1978.

## Sri Lanka

H.W. CODRINGTON, *Ceylon Coins and Currency, 1924*, reprinted London 1999.

## Surinam

THEO VAN ELMPT, *Surinam Paper Currency, 1760-1957*, London, 1998.

## Sweden

SVEN FLODBERG, *Katalog over Sveriges Sedlar, 1858-1971*, Lund, 1972.

A. PLATBARZDIS, *Sveriges Sedlar 1661-1961*, Lund, 1963.
*Sveriges Sedlar Enskilda Bankernas Sedlar 1831-1902*, Lund, 1965.

LENNART WALLEN AND BJARNE AHLSTROM, *Sveriges Sedlar*, Stockholm, 1978.

## Switzerland

URS GRAF, *Das Papiergeld der Schwiz, 1881-1068*, Munser, 1970 .

## Syria

ADNAN JAROUEH, *The Encyclopedia of Syrian Paper Money*, 2006

## Thailand

BANK OF THAILAND, *Banknotes of Thailand*, Bangkok, 1972.

SILAS LITTLE, *Banknotes of Thailand*, Falls Church, USA, 1973.

## Turkey

DR MINE EROL, *Osmanli Imparatorlugunda Kagit Para*, Ankara, 1970.

CUNEYT OLCER, *50 Yilin Turk Kagit Paralari*, Istanbul, 1973.

## USA

FREDERICK BART, *Comprehensive Catalog of United States Paper Money Errors*.

ELVIRA and VLADIMIR CLAIN-STEFANELLI, *American Banking*, Washington, 1975.

GROVER CRISWELL, *Confederate States of America Paper Money*, Florida, 1976.

W. P. DONLON, *United States Large Size Paper Money*, Utica, 1970.

RICHARD DOTY, *America's Money, America's Story*, Iola, 1998.

ROBERT FRIEDBERG, *Paper Money of the United States*, New York, various editions.

GENE HESSLER, *Comprehensive Catalog of US Paper Money US Essay, Proof and Specimen Notes*, 1979. the Engraver's Line

RON HORSTMAN, *Collecting National Bank Notes*.

CHESTER L. KRAUSE AND ROBERT F. LEMKE, *United States Paper Money*, Iola, 1999.

ERIC P. NEWMAN, *The Early Paper Money of America*, Iola, 1998.

ARLIE R. SLABAUGH *Confederate States Paper Money*, Iola, 2000.

## Ukraine

DMITRI KHARITONOV, *Ukrainian Paper Money*, 2005

## Uruguay

DALE A. SEPPA, *Uruguayan Paper Moneh*, Chicago, 1974.

## Wales

IVOR WYNNE JONES, *Money Galore—the Story of the Welsh Pound*, Landmark, 2004.

## Yemen

PETER SYMES, MURRAY HANEWICH AND KEITH STREET, *The Bank Notes of the Yemen*, Chester, 1998.

## Yugoslavia

VOJISLAV MIHAILOVIC AND DRAGSOLAV GLOGONJAC, *Katalog Novca Srbije I Crne Gore 1868-1918*, Belgrade, 1973.

DIMITRI SPAJIC, *Paper Money of the Yugoslavian States*, USA, 1969.

## Cheques and Postal Orders

STEPHEN CRIBB, *The Standard Catalogue of Postal Orders*, Ruislip, 1984.

JAMES DOUGLAS, *Collect British Cheques*, London, n.d. (c. 1981)
*A Collector's Guide to Cheques and Bills of Exchange*, Carlisle, n.d.

HOWARD LUNN, *Promotional Postal Orders*, Nottingham,. N.d. [1990].

ROGER OUTING, *The Cheques of Barclays Bank*, Huddersfield, 2004.

DAVID SHAW, *A Collector's Guide to British Cheques*, Shrewsbury, 1986.

# Museums and Libraries

Listed below are the Museums and Libraries in the UK which have coin collections and many also have banknotes or items of notaphilic interest on display or available to the general public. However, before setting off on a long journey it is advisable to contact the museum you wish to visit to check that any notes they have are available for viewing.

**A**

Anthropological Museum, University of Aberdeen, Broad Street, **Aberdeen,** AB9 1AS (01224 272014).

Curtis Museum (1855), High Street, **Alton,** Hants (01420 2802).

Ashburton Museum, 1 West Street, **Ashburton,** Devon.

Ashwell Village Museum (1930), Swan Street, **Ashwell,** Baldock, Herts.

Buckinghamshire County Museum (1862), Church Street, **Aylesbury,** Bucks (01296 88849).

**B**

Public Library and Museum (1948), Marlborough Road, **Banbury,** Oxon (01295 259855).

Museum of North Devon (1931), The Square, **Barnstaple,** EX32 8LN (01271 46747).

Roman Baths Museum, Pump Room, **Bath,** Avon (01225 461111 ext 2785).

Bagshaw Museum and Art Gallery (1911), Wilton Park, **Batley,** West Yorkshire (01924 472514).

Bedford Museum (1961), Castle Lane, **Bedford** (01234 353323).

Ulster Museum (1928), Botanic Gardens, **Belfast** BT9 5AB (01232 381251).

Berwick Borough Museum (1867), The Clock Block, Berwick Barracks, Ravensdowne, **Berwick**. TD15 1DQ (01289 330044).

Public Library, Art Gallery and Museum (1910), Champney Road, **Beverley,** Humberside (01482 882255).

City Museum and Art Gallery (1861), Chamberlain Square, **Birmingham** B3 3DH (0121 235 2834).

Blackburn Museum, Museum Street, **Blackburn,** Lancs (01254 667130).

Museum Collection, Town Hall, **Bognor Regis,** West Sussex.

Museum and Art Gallery,(1893), Civic Centre, **Bolton,** Lancashire (01204 22311 ext 2191).

Art Gallery and Museum, Central Library, Oriel Road, **Bootle,** Lancs.

Roman Town and Museum (1949) Main Street, **Boroughbridge,** N. Yorks. YO2 3PH (01423 322768).

The Museum (1929), The Guildhall, **Boston,** Lincs (01205 365954).

Natural Science Society Museum (1903), 39 Christchurch Road, **Bournemouth,** Dorset (01202 553525).

Bolling Hall Museum (1915), Bolling Hall Road, **Bradford,** West Yorkshire BD4 7LP (01274 723057).

Cartwright Hall Museum and Art Gallery (1904), Lister Park, **Bradford,** West Yorkshire BD9 4NS (01274 493313).

Museum and Art Gallery (1932), South Street, **Bridport,** Dorset (01308 22116).

The City Museum (1820), Queen's Road, **Bristol** BS8 1RL (0117 9 27256).

District Library and Museum (1891), Terrace Road, **Buxton,** Derbyshire SK17 6DU (01298 24658).

**C**

Fitzwilliam Museum (1816), Department of Coins and Medals, Trumpington Street, **Cambridge** (01223 332900).

National Museum & Galleries of Wales, Cathays Park, **Cardiff** (029 20397951).

Guildhall Museum (1979), Greenmarket, **Carlisle,** Cumbria (01228 819925).

Tullie House (1877), Castle Street, **Carlisle,** Cumbria (01228 34781).

Chelmsford and Essex Museum (1835), Oaklands Park, Moulsham Street, **Cheltenham,** Glos CM2 9AQ (01245 353066).

Town Gate Museum (1949), **Chepstow,** Gwent.

Grosvenor Museum (1886), Grosvenor Street, **Chester** (01244 21616).

Public Library (1879), Corporation Street, **Chesterfield,** Derbyshire (01246 2047).

Red House Museum (1919), Quay Road, **Christchurch,** Dorset (01202 482860).

Colchester and Essex Museum (1860), The Castle, **Colchester,** Essex (01206 712931/2).

**D**

Public Library, Museum and Art Gallery (1921), Crown Street, **Darlington,** Co Durham (01325 463795).

471

Borough Museum (1908), Central Park, **Dartford,** Kent (01322 343555).

Dartmouth Museum (1953), The Butterknowle, **Dartmouth,** Devon (01803 832923).

Museum and Art Gallery (1878), The Strand, **Derby** (01332 255586).

Museum and Art Gallery (1909), Chequer Road, **Doncaster,** South Yorkshire (01302 734293).

Dorset County Museum(1846), **Dorchester,** Dorset (01305 262735).

Central Museum (1884), Central Library, St James's Road, **Dudley,** West Midlands (01384 453576).

Burgh Museum (1835), The Observatory, Corberry Hill, **Dumfries** (01387 53374)**.**

Dundee Art Galleries and Museums (1873). Albert Square, **Dundee** DD1 1DA (01382 23141).

The Cathedral Treasury (995 AD), The College, **Durham** (0191-384 4854).

Durham Heritage Centre, St Mary le Bow, North Bailey, **Durham** (0191-384 2214).

**E**

Royal Museum of Scotland (1781), Queen Street, **Edinburgh** EH1 (0131 225 7534).

Royal Albert Memorial Museum (1868), Queen St, **Exeter** EX4 3RX (01392 265858).

**G**

Hunterian Museum (1807), Glasgow University, University Avenue, **Glasgow** G12 8QQ (041 339 8855).

Art Gallery and Museum (1888), Kelvingrove, **Glasgow** G3 (0141 357 3929).

Museum of Transport (1974), Kelvin Hall, Bunhouse Road, **Glasgow** G3 (0141 357 3929).

City Museum and Art Gallery (1859), Brunswick Road, **Gloucester** (01452 524131).

Guernsey Museum and Art Gallery, St Peter Port, **Guernsey** (01481 726518).

Guildford Museum (1898), Castle Arch, **Guildford,** Surrey GU1 3SX (01483 444750).

**H**

Gray Museum and Art Gallery, Clarence Road, **Hartlepool,** Cleveland (01429 268916).

Public Museum and Art Gallery (1890), John's Place, Cambridge Road, **Hastings,** East Sussex (01424 721952).

City Museum (1874), Broad Street, **Hereford** (01432 268121 ext 207).

Hertford Museum (1902), 18 Bull Plain, **Hertford** (01992 582686).

Honiton and Allhallows Public Museum (1946), High Street, **Honiton,** Devon (01404 44966).

Museum and Art Gallery (1891), 19 New Church Road, **Hove,** East Sussex (01273 779410).

Tolson Memorial Museum (1920), Ravensknowle Park, **Huddersfield,** West Yorkshire (01484 541455).

Hull and East Riding Museum (1928), 36 High Street, **Hull** (01482 593902). *Celtic, Roman and medieval coins and artifacts from local finds. Some later coins including tradesmen's tokens.*

**I**

The Manx Museum, Douglas, **Isle of Man** (01624 675522).

**J**

Jersey Museum, Weighbridge, St Helier, **Jersey** (01534 30511).

**K**

Dick Institute Museum and Art Gallery (1893), Elmbank Avenue, **Kilmarnock,** Ayrshire (01563 26401).

**L**

City Museum (1923), Old Town Hall, Market Square, **Lancaster** (01524 64637).

City Museum (1820), Municipal Buildings, The Headrow, **Leeds,** West Yorkshire (01532 478279).

Leicester Museum and Art Gallery (1849), New Walk, **Leicester** (01533 554100).

Pennington Hall Museum and Art Gallery, **Leigh,** Lancashire.

Museum and Art Gallery (1914), Broadway, **Letchworth,** Herts (01462 65647). *Ancient British coins minted at Camulodunum, Roman, me*

City Library, Art Gallery and Museum (1859), Bird Street, **Lichfield,** Staffs (01543 2177).

Liverpool Museum(1851), William Brown Street, **Liverpool** L3 8EN (0151 207 0001).

Bank of England Museum, Threadneedle Street, **London** EC2 (020-7601 5545).

British Museum(1752), HSBC Coin Gallery, Great Russell Street, **London** WC1 (020-7636 1555).

British Numismatic Society (1903), Warburg Institute, Woburn Square, **London** WC1.

Cuming Museum (1906), Walworth Road, **London** SE17 (020-7703 3324/5529).

Gunnersbury Park Museum (1927), Acton, **London** W3.

Horniman Museum and Library (1890), **London** Road, Forest Hill, London SE23 (020-7699 2339).

Imperial War Museum, Lambeth Road, **London** SE1 6HZ (020-7416 5000).

Sir John Soane's Museum (1833), 13 Lincoln's Inn Fields, **London** WC2 (020-7405 2107).

National Maritime Museum, Romney Road, Greenwich, **London** SE10 (020-8858 4422).

Victoria and Albert Museum (1852), South Kensington, **London** SW7 (020-7938 8441).

Ludlow Museum (1833). The Assembly Rooms. Castle Square, **Ludlow** (01584 873857).

Luton Museum and Art Gallery (1927), Wardown Park, **Luton,** Beds (01582 36941).

**M**

Museum and Art Gallery (1858), **Maidstone,** Kent (01622 754497).

The Manchester Museum (1868), The University, **Manchester** M13 (0161-275 2634).

Margate Museum (1923), The Old Town Hall, Market Place, **Margate,** Kent (01843 225511 ext 2520).

Montrose Museum and Art Gallery (1836). Panmure Place, **Montrose,** Angus DD10 8HE (01674 73232).

**N**

Newark-on-Trent Museum (1912), Appleton Gate, **Newark,** Notts (01636 702358).

Newbury District Museum, The Wharf, **Newbury,** Berkshire (01635 30511).

**O**

Heberden Coin Room, Ashmolean Museum (1683), **Oxford** (01865 278000).

**P**

Peterborough Museum (1881), Priestgate, **Peterborough**, Cambs (01733 340 3329).

City Museum and Art Gallery (1897), Drake Circus, **Plymouth**, Devon (01752 264878).

Waterfront Museum, 4 High Street, **Poole**, Dorset (01202 683138). *(view by appointment).*

City Museum (1972), Museum Road, Old **Portsmouth** PO1 (023 80827261).

Harris Museum and Art Gallery (1893), Market Square, **Preston**, Lancashire (01772 58248).

**R**

Reading Museum and Art Gallery, (1883) Blagrave Street, **Reading**, Berks (01734 399809).

Rochdale Museum (1905), Sparrow Hill, **Rochdale**, Lancs (01706 41085).

Municipal Museum and Art Gallery (1893), Clifton Park, **Rotherham** (01709382121).

**S**

Saffron Walden Museum (1832) (1939), Museum Street, **Saffron** Walden, Essex (01799 522494).

Salisbury and South Wiltshire Museum (1861), The Cathedral Close, **Salisbury,** Wilts (01722 332151).

Scarborough Museum (1829), The Rotunda, Vernon Road, **Scarborough**, North Yorkshire (01723 374839).

Shaftesbury and Dorset Local History Museum (1946), 1 Gold Hill, **Shaftesbury**, Dorset (01747 52157).

City Museum (1875), Weston Park, **Sheffield** (0114 2 768588).

Rowley's House Museum, Barker Street, **Shrewsbury**, Salop (01743 361196).

Museum of Archaeology (1951), God's House Tower, Town Quay, **Southampton**, Hants (023 8022 0007).

Botanic Gardens Museum, Churchtown, **Southport,** Lancs (01704 87547).

Southwold Museum (1933), St Bartholomew's Green, **Southwold**, Suffolk (01502 722375).

Stamford Museum (1961), Broad Street, **Stamford,** Lincs (01780 66317).

Municipal Museum (1860), Vernon Park, Turncroft Lane, **Stockport**, Cheshire (0161 474 4460)

Stroud Museum (1899), Lansdown, **Stroud**, Glos (01453 376394).

Museum and Art Gallery (1846), Borough Road, **Sunderland,** Tyne & Wear (0191 514 1235).

Swansea Museum (1835), Victoria Road, **Swansea**, W. Glamorgan, SA1 1SN (0792 653765).

**T**

Tamworth Castle and Museum (1899), The Holloway, **Tamworth**, Staffs (01827 63563).

Somerset County Museum, Taunton Castle, **Taunton**, Somerset (01823 255510/320200). C

Thurrock Local History Museum (1956), Civic Square, **Tilbury**, Essex (01375 390000 ext 2414).

Royal Cornwall Museum (1818), River Street, **Truro,** Cornwall (01872 72205).

**W**

Wakefield Museum (1919), Wood Street, **Wakefield,** West Yorkshire (01924 295351).

Epping Forest District Museum, 39/41 Sun Street, **Waltham Abbey**, Essex EN 9.

Warrington Museum and Art Gallery (1848). Bold Street, **Warrington**, Cheshire, WA1 1JG (01925 30550).

Worcester City Museum (1833), Foregate Street, **Worcester** (01905 25371).

Wells Museum (18903), 8 Cathedral Green, **Wells,** Somerset (01749 3477).

Municipal Museum and Art Gallery (1878), Station Road, **Wigan**, Lancashire.

City Museum (1851), The Square, **Winchester**, Hants (01962 848269).

Wisbech and Fenland Museum (1835), Museum Square, **Wisbech,** Cambridgeshire (01945 583817).

**Y**

The Museum of South Somerset (1928), Hendford, **Yeovil**, Somerset (01935 24774).

Castle Museum (1938), **York** (01904 653611).

The Yorkshire Museum (1823), **York** (01904 629745).

# Club directory

Most numismatic societies encompass banknotes in their agenda and many have regular speakers on the subject. Details given here are the names of the Numismatic Clubs or Societies, their dates of foundation, venue, days and times of meetings. Meetings are usually monthly unless otherwise stated. Finally, the telephone number of the club secretary is given; the names and addresses of club secretaries are withheld for security reasons, but full details may be obtained by writing to the Secretary of the British Association of Numismatic Societies, Philip Mernick, c/o Bush Boake Allen Ltd, Blackhorse Lane, London E17 5QP.

**Banbury & District Numismatic Society** (1967). Banbury British Rail Working Mens Club. 2nd Mon (exc Jul & Aug), 19.45. (01295 254451).

**Bath & Bristol Numismatic Society** (1950). Fry's Club, Keynsham, Bristol. 2nd Thu, 19.30. (0117 9039010).

**Bedford Numismatic Society** (1966). RAF Association Club, 93 Ashburnham Road, Bedford MK40 1EA. 3rd Mon, 19.30. (01234 228833/358369).

**Bexley Coin Club** (1968). St Martin's Church Hall, Erith Road, Barnehurst, Bexleyheath, Kent. 1st Mon (exc Jan & Aug), 20.00. (0208 303 0510).

**Birmingham Numismatic Society** (1964). Friend's Meeting House, Linden Lane, Bourneville,Birmingham. 1st Wed, 19.45. (0121 308 1616).

**Matthew Boulton Society** (1994). PO Box 395, Birmingham B31 2TB (0121 781 6558 fax 0121 781 6574).

**Banknote Society of Scotland** (2006). St. Mary's Cathedral, Edinburgh. Thrice yearly. (01416 420132).

**Bradford & District Numismatic Society** (1967). East Bowling Unity Club, Leicester Street, Bradford, West Yorkshire. 3rd Mon, 19.00. (01532 677151).

**Brighton & Hove Coin Club** (1971). Methodist Church Hall, St Patrick's Road, Hove, East Sussex. Last Wed (exc Dec), 20.00. (01273 419303).

**British Cheque Collectors' Society** (1980). John Purser, 71 Mile Lane, Cheylesmore, Coventry, West Midlands CV3 5GB.

**British Numismatic Society** (1903). Warburg Institute, Woburn Square, London WC1H 0AB. Monthly (exc Jul, Aug & Dec), 18.00. (01223 332918)

**Cambridgeshire Numismatic Society** (1946). Friends' Meeting House, 12 Jesus Lane (entrance in Park Street), Cambridge, CB5 8BA. 3rd Mon, Sept–June, 19.30. (01480 210992).

**Chester & North Wales Coin & Banknote Society** (1996). Liver Hotel, 110 Brook Street, Chester. 1st Tue, 20.00. (0151 478 4293)

**Cheltenham Numismatic Society,** The Reddings & District Community Association, North Road, The Reddings, Cheltenham. 3rd Mon, 19.45 (01242 673263)

**Coin Correspondence Club** (1988). Postal only. A.H. Chubb, 49 White Hart Lane, Barnes, London SW13 0PP. (0181-878 0472).

**Crawley Coin Club** (1969). Furnace Green Community Centre, Ashburnham Road, Furnace Green, Crawley, West Sussex. 1st Tue, 20.00. (01293 548671).

**Crewe & District Coin & Medal Club** (1968). Memorial Hall, Church Lane, Wistaston, Crewe, 2nd Tue (exc Jan & July), 19.30. (01270 569836).

**Darlington & District Numismatic Society** (1968). Darlington Arts Centre, Vane Terrace, Darlington, Co Durhm. 3rd Wed, 19.30. (01609 772976).

**Derbyshire Numismatic Society** (1964). The Friends' Meeting House, St Helens Street, Derby. 3rd Mon (exc August), 19.45. (01283 211623).

**Devon & Exeter Numismatic Society** (1965). The Courtenay Room, Sthe St. James Centre, Stadium Way, Exeter, Devon. 3rd Tue, 19.30. (01392 469111).

**Edinburgh Numismatic Society** (1996). Department of History and Applied Arts, Royal Museum of Scotland, Chambers Street, Edinburgh EH1 1JF. 3rd Mon, 19.30. (0131 225 7534).

**Enfield & District Numismatic Society** (1969). Millfield House Arts Centre, Silver Street, Edmonton, London N18 1PJ. 3rd Mon, 20.00. (0181-340 0767).

**Essex Numismatic Society** (1966). Chelmsford & Essex Museum, Moulsham Street, Chelmsford, Essex. 4th Fri (exc Dec), 20.00. (01277 656627). www.essexcoins.org.uk

**Glasgow & West of Scotland Numismatic Society** (1947). Woodside Halls, 26 Glenfarg Street, Glasgow, G3. 2nd Thu, Oct-May, 19.30. (0141 633 2564).

**Harrow & North West Middlesex Numismatic Society** (1968). Harrow Arts Centre, Hatch End Harrow, Middlesex. 2nd and 4th Mon, 20.00. (020 8952 8765).

**Havering Numismatic Society** (1967). Fairkytes Arts Centre, Billet Lane, Hornchurch, Essex. 1st Tue, 19.30. (01708 704201).

**Hayes & District Coin Club.** The United Reformed Church Hall, Swakeleys Road, Ickenham, Middlesex. 3rd Thu, 19.45. (0181-422 9178).

**Horncastle & District Coin Club** (1963). Bull Hotel, Bull Ring, Horncastle, Lincs. 2nd Thu (exc Aug), 19.30. (01754 2706).

**Huddersfield Numismatic Society** (1947). Huddersfield Library, Princess Alexandra Walk, Huddersfield, West Yorkshire. 1st Mon (exc Jul & Aug), 19.30. (01484 226300).

**Hull & District Numismatic Society** (1967). The Young People's Institute, George Street, Hull. Monthly (exc Aug & Dec), 19.30. (01482 441933).

**International Bank Note Society** (1961). General Secretary Clive Rice, 25 Copse Side, Binscombe, Godalming, Surrey GU7 3RU (ibnsuk@onetel.com).

**International Bank Note Society, London Branch** (1961). Victory Services Club, 63–79 Seymour Street, London W1. Last Thu (exc Dec), 18.00. (020-8360 2759).

**International Bank Note Society, East Midlands Chapter** (1995). Wollaton Park Community Association, Harrow Road, Wollaton Park. Bi-monthly. (0115 928 9720).

**International Bank Note Society, Scottish Chapter** (1995). West End Hotel, Palmerston Place, Edinburgh. Last Sat (exc Dec), 14.30 (0141 642 0132).

**International Bank Note Society, North West Chapter** (1974). Burnley. Last Sat (exc Dec), 14.30.

**Ipswich Numismatic Society** (1966). Ipswich Citizens Advice Bureau, 19 Tower Street, Ipswich, Suffolk. 3rd Wed, 19.30. (01473 728653).

**Kent Towns Numismatic Society** (1913). Adult Education Centre, 9 Sittingbourne Road (Maidstone) and King's School Preparatory School, King Edward Road (Rochester). 1st Fri of month, 19.30 alternately at Maidstone and Rochester. (01622 843881).

**Kingston Numismatic Society** (1966). King Athel-stan's School, Villiers Road, Kingston-upon-Thames, Surrey. 3rd Thu (exc Jan), 19.30. (020-8397 6944).

**Lancashire & Cheshire Numismatic Society** (1933). Manchester Central Library, St Peter's Square, Manchester M2 5PD. Monthly, Sep-June, Wed (18.30) or Sat (14.30). (0161 485 2415).

**Lincolnshire Numismatic Society** (1932). Grimsby Bridge Club, Bargate, Grimsby, South Humberside. 4th Wed (exc Aug), 19.30.

**London Numismatic Club** (1947). Warburg Institute, Woburn Square, London. Monthly, 18.30. (01223 332918).

**Loughborough Coin & Search Society** (1964). Wallace Humphry Room, Shelthorpe Community Centre, Loughborough, Leics. 1st Thu, 19.30. (01509 261352).

**Merseyside Numismatic Society** (1947). The Lecture Theatre, Liverpool Museum, William Brown Street, Liverpool L3 8EN. Monthly (exc July & Aug), 19.00. (0151-929 2143).

**Mid Lanark Coin Circle** (1969). Hospitality Room, The Civic Centre, Motherwell, Lanarkshire. 4th Thu, Sep–Apr (exc Dec), 19.30. (0141-552 2083).

**Monmouthshire Numismatic Society.** W. R. Lysaght Institute, Corporation Road, Newport. 2nd Wed, 19.30. (029 20 561564)

**Morecambe & Lancaster Numismatic Society.** Monthly, 19.30. (01524 411036).

**Newbury Coin & Medal Club** (1971). Monthly, 20.00. (01635 41233).

**Northampton Coin & Medal Society** (1969). Old Scouts RFC, Rushmere Road, Northampton. 3rd Mon, 20.00.

**Norwich Coin & Medal Society** (1967). The White Horse, Trowse. 3rd Mon, 19.30. (01603 419430).

**Numismatic Society** of **Nottinghamshire** (1948). The Cecil Roberts Room, Central Library, Angel Row, Nottingham NG1 6HP. 2nd Tue (Sep-Apr), 19.30. (0115 9257674).

**Nuneaton & District Coin Club** (1968). United Reformed Church Room, Coton Road, , Nuneaton, Warwickshire. 2nd Tue, 19.30. (01203 371556).

**Orders & Medals Research Society** (1942). National Army Museum, Royal Hospital Road, Chelsea, London SW3. Monthly, 14.30. (020-8680 2701).

**Ormskirk & West Lancashire Numismatic Society** (1970). Eagle & Child, Ormskirk. Lancs. 1st Thu, 20.15. (01704 531266).

**Peterborough & Districts NS** (1967). Belsize Community Centre, Celta Road, Woodston, Peterborough, Cambs. Last Tue (exc July & Aug), 19.30. (01753 567763).

**Plymouth Numismatic Society** (1970). Mutley Conservative Club, Mutley Plain, Plymouth, Devon. 4th Wed (exc Dec), 19.30. (01752 480394).

**Postal Order Society,** Mal Tedds, 1 Fairham Court, Wilford, Nottingham, NG11 7EN (0115 981 5639).

**Preston & District Numismatic Society** (1965). Eldon Hotel, Eldon Street, Preston, Lancs. 1st and 3rd Tue, 20.00. (012572 66869).

**Reading Coin Club** (1964). Abbey Baptist Church, Abbey Square, Reading. 1st Tue, 20.00. (0118 9860053).

**Redbridge Numismatic Society** (1968). Gants Hill Library, Cranbrook Road, Ilford, Essex. 4th Wed, 19.30. (020-8554 5486).

**Rochford Hundred Numismatic Society.** Civic Suite, Rayleigh Town Hall, Rayleigh, Essex. 2nd Thu, 20.00. (01702 230950).

**Romsey Numismatic Society** (1969). Romsey WM Conservative Club, Market Place, Romsey, Hants SO5 8NA. 4th Fri (exc Dec), 19.30. (01703 253921).

**Rotherham & District Coin Club** (1982). Rotherham Art Centre, Rotherham, South Yorkshire. 1st Wed, 19.00. (01709 528179).

**Royal Mint Coin Club,** PO Box 500, Cardiff CF1 1HA (01443 222111).

**Royal Numismatic Society** (1836). Society of Antiquaries, Piccadilly, London W1. Monthly (Oct-June), 17.30. Joe Cribb, Coins and Medals, British Museum, London WC1B 3DG (020-7323 8585).

**Rye Coin Club** (1955). Rye Further Education Centre, Lion Street, Rye, East Sussex. 2nd Thu (Oct-Dec, Feb-May), 19.30. (01424 422974).

**St Albans & Hertfordshire Numismatic Society** (1948). St Michael's Parish Centre, Museum Entrance, Verulamium Park, St Albans, Herts AL3 4SL. 2nd Tue (exc Aug), 19.30. (01727 862060).

**Sheffield Numismatic Society.** Telephone for venue. 2nd Wed, 19.00. (0114 2817129)

**South East Hants Numismatic Society.** Havant Conservative Club, East Street, Havant. 2nd Fri. (02392 389419).

**South Manchester Numismatic Society** (1967). Nursery Inn, Green Lane, Heaton Mersey, Stockport. Fortnightly Mon, 20.00. (0161-4763184).

**S. Wales & Monmouthshire Numismatic Society** (1958). The W. R. Lysaght Institute, Corporation Road, Newport. 2nd Wed, 19.30. (029 20561564).

**Torbay & District Coin Club** (1967). British Rail Social Club, Brunel Road, Newton Abbott, Devon TQ12 4PB. 1st Tue, 1945. (01803 326497).

**Tyneside Numismatic Society** (1954). RAFA Club, Eric Nelson House, 16 Berwick Road, Gateshead, Tyne & Wear. 2nd Wed, 19.30. (0161 825824).

**Wessex NS** (1948). The Edward Wright Room, Beaufort Community Centre, Beaufort Road, Southbourne, Bournemouth, Dorset. 2nd Thurs (exc Aug), 19.45. (020 7731 1702).

**Wiltshire Numismatic Society** (1965). Raven Inn, Poulshot, Nr Devizes, Wiltshire. 3rd Mon, Mar-Dec, 20.00. (01380 828453).

**Worthing & District Numismatic Society** (1967). Berkeley Hotel, Marine Parade, Worthing, West Sussex BN11 3QQ. 3rd Thu, 19.30. (01634 260114).

**Yorkshire Numismatic Society** (1909). Swarthmore College, Woodhouse Square, Leeds. 1st Sat (exc Jan, Aug & Dec) (0113 3910848).

**Society activities and featured every month in the "Diary Section" of COIN NEWS**

# directory of
# Auctioneers

Listed here are the major UK auction houses which handle coins, medals, banknotes and other items of numismatic interest. Many of them hold regular public auctions, whilst others handle numismatic material infrequently.

**Baldwin's Auctions Ltd**

11 Adelphi Terrace, London WC2N 6BJ (020-7930 6879 fax 020-7930 9450). Website: www.baldwin.sh.

**Banking Memorabilia**

PO Box 14, Carlisle CA3 8DZ (0169 7476465). Email: memorabilia74@btinternet.com.

**Bloomsbury Auctions**

Bloomsbury House, 24 Maddox Street, London W1S 1PP. (020 7495 9494 fax: 020 7495 9499). E-mail: info@bloomsburyauctions.com www.bloomsbury.com.

**Bonhams/Glendining's**

Montpelier Street, Knightsbridge, London SW7 1HH. (020 7393 3914). www.bonhams.com.

**A. F. Brock & Company**

269 London Road, Hazel Grove, Stockport, Cheshire SK7 4PL (0161-456 5050/5112). Website: www.afbrock.co.uk.

**Corbitts**

5 Moseley Sreet, Newcastle upon Tyne NE1 1YE (0191-232 7268 fax 0191-261 4130).

**Croydon Coin Auctions**

PO Box 201, Croydon, Surrey CR9 7AQ (020-8656 4583. www.croydoncoinauctions.co.uk.

**Dix Noonan Webb**

16 Bolton Street, Piccadilly, London W1J 8BQ (020 7499 5022 fax 020 7499 5023) Website www.dnw.co.uk.

**Downies**

11 & 12 Block Arcade, 98–100 Elizabeth Street, Melbourne, Vic, 3000, Australia. www.downies.com.

**Dublin Coins Auction**

5 St Assam's Park, Raheny, Dublin 5, Ireland (00 353 868 714 880) DA3 8JJ. (01474 871464).

**Dundee Philatelic Auctions**

15 King Street, Dundee DD1 1JD. (01382 224946).

**Edinburgh Coin Shop**

11 West Crosscauseway, Edinburgh EH8 9JW (0131 668 2928 fax 0131 668 2926).

**B. Frank & Son**

3 South Avenue, Ryton, Tyne & Wear NE40 3LD (0191 413 8749 fax 0191 413 2957). E-mail: bfrankandson@aol.com.

**Kleeford Coin Auctions**

19 Craythorns Crescent, Dishforth, Thirsk YO7 3LY. (tel/fax 01845 577977).

**Lakeland Coin Auctions**

Agricultural Hotel, Penrith, Cumbria (venue). (01946 832693, www.lakelandcoinauctions.co.uk).

**Lockdale Coins**

37 Upper Orwell Street, Ipswich IP4 1BR. (01473 218588). www.lockdales.co.uk.

**London Coins Auction**

4–6 Upper Street South, New Ash Green, Kent DA3 8JJ. (01474 871464) www.londoncoins.co.uk.

**Morton and Eden**

45 Maddox Street, London, W1S 2PE. (020 7493 5344 fax: 020 7495 6325). www.mortonandeden.com.

**Neales**

192–194 Mansfield Road, Nottingham NG1 3HU (0115 9624141 fax 0115 9856890).

**Noble Numismatics Pty Ltd**

169 Macquarie Street, Sydney 2000, Australia. (+61 2 9233 6009). E-mail: info@noble.net.au.

**Spink & Son Ltd**

69 Southampton Row, Bloomsbury, London WC1B 4ET (020 7563 4000 fax  20 7563 4066). www.spink-online.com.

**Tennants**

The Auction Centre, Leyburn, North Yorkshire, DL8 5SG. www.tennants.co.uk.

**Warwick & Warwick**

Chalon House, Scarbank, Millers Road, Warwick CV34 5DB (01926 499031 fax 01926 491906). Email info@warwickandwarwick.com

476

# directory of
# Dealers

The dealers listed below have comprehensive stocks of papermoney, unless otherwise stated. Specialities, where known, are noted. Many of those listed are postal dealers only, so to avoid disappointment always make contact by telephone or mail in the first instance, particularly before travelling any distance.

**Abbreviations:**
ADA—Antiquities Dealers Association
ANA—American Numismatic Association
BADA—British Antique Dealers Association
BNTA—British Numismatic Trade Association
IAPN—International Association of Professional Numismatists
IBNS—International Bank Note Society
P—Postal only
L—Publishes regular lists
F—Fairs

**A. Ackroyd** (IBNS)
62 Albert Road, Parkstone, Poole, Dorset BH12 2DB (tel/fax 01202 739039). *P. L. Banknotes, cheques etc.*

**David Allen Coins and Collectables**
PO Box 125, Pinner, Middlesex HA5 2TX (020 866 6796). *P. L. British and world coins, tokens, banknotes.*

**Keith Austin/KABC** (IBNS)
PO Box 89, Carlisle, Cumbria CA3 0GH (01228 819149). L. *Banknotes.* E-mail: kaustin@kabc.freeserve. co.uk

**Banking Memorabilia** (IBNS)
PO Box 14, Carlisle, Cumbria (0169 747 6465). 09.00– 18.00 (not Sun). *Cheques, banknotes, related ephemera. auctions.*

**Bath Stamp and Coin Shop** (BNTA)
Pulteney Bridge, Bath, Avon BA2 4AY (01225 463073). Mon-Sat 09.30–17.30. *British, world coins and banknotes.*

**R. P. & P. J. Beckett**
Maesyderw, Capel Dewi, Llandyssul, Dyfed SA44 4PJ. E-mail: orders@rppjbeckett.com Fax 01559 395631 *P. World crowns, coin sets and banknotes.*

**Berkshire Coin Centre**
35 Castle Street, Reading, Berkshire RG1 7SB (01734 575593). 10.00–16.00 weekdays, half-day Sat. *British and world coins and banknotes.*

**Barry Boswell** (IBNS)
24 Townsend Lane, Upper Boddington, Daventry, Northants NN11 6DR (01327 261877). *P. L. British and world banknotes.* E-mail: Barry.Boswell@btinternet. com.

**A. F. Brock & Company**
269 London Road, Hazel Grove, Stockport, Cheshire SK7 4PL (0161 456 5050/5112). Mon-Sat 09.30–17.30. Website: www.afbrock.co.uk

**E. J. & C. A. Brooks** (BNTA, IBNS)
44 Kiln Road, Thundersley, Essex SS7 1TB (01268 753835). Any time up to 23.00. *L. British coins and banknotes.*

**Iain Burn** (IBNS)
2 Compton Gardens, 53 Park Road, Camberley, Surrey GU15 2SP (01276 23304). *England and Treasury notes.*

**Cambridge Stamp Centre Ltd**
9 Sussex Street, Cambridge CB4 4HU (01223 63980). Mon-Sat 09.00–17.30. *British coins and banknotes.*

**M. Coeshaw**
PO Box 115, Leicester LE3 8JJ (0116 2873808). *P.*

**Coin & Collectors Centre**
PO Box 22, Pontefract, West Yorkshire WR8 1YT (01977 704112). *P. British coins and banknotes.*

**Coincraft** (ANA, IBNS)
44/45 Great Russell Street, London WC1B 3LU (020 7636 1188 and 020 7637 8785 fax 020 7323 2860). Mon-Fri 09.30–17.00, Sat 10.00–14.30. *L (newspaper format). Coins and banknotes.* www.coincraft.com.

**Coinote Services Ltd**
74 Elwick Road, Hartlepool TS26 NYL (01429 273044). *P. L. Coins and banknotes 1615 todate. Accessories and books.*

**The Collector**
242 High Street, Orpington, Kent BR6 0LZ (01689 890045). Mon-Sat 09.30–17.00 (closed Tue). *Coins, medals, banknotes, badges, militaria, cigarette cards etc*

**Collectors' Forum**
237 South Street, Romford, Essex RM1 2BE (01708 723357). Mon-Sat 09.30-18.00 Thu 09.30-14.00. *British coins, medals and banknotes.*

**Collectors Gallery** (BNTA, IBNS)
22 The Parade, St Marys Place, Shrewsbury SY1 1DL (01743 272140 fax 01743 366041). Mon-Fri 09.00– 18.00, half-day Sat. *Coins and banknotes. Accessories and related books. Stockist of Abafil Coin Cases.* www. collectors-gallery.co.uk.

**Corbitts** (BNTA)
5 Mosley Street, Newcastle Upon Tyne NE1 1YE (0191 232 7268 fax: 0191 261 4130). *Dealers and auctioneers of all coins, medals and banknotes.*

**G. D. Courtenay**
58 New Peachey Lane, Uxbridge, Middlesex UB8 3SX. *P. L. Coins, medals, tokens and banknotes.*

**Davidson Monk Fairs**
PO Box 201, Croydon, Surrey CR9 7AQ (020 8656 4583). *Organiser of bi-monthly fairs at Jurys Hotel, 16-22 Great Russell Street, London WC1.*

**Paul Davies Ltd** (ANA, BNTA, IAPN)
PO Box 17, Ilkley, West Yorkshire LS29 8TZ (01943 603116). *P. World coins and banknotes.*

**Dei Gratia**
PO Box 3568, Buckingham MK18 4ZS (01280 848000). *P. L. Pre-Roman to modern coins, antiquities, banknotes.*

**Clive Dennett** (BNTA, IBNS)

66 St Benedicts Street, Norwich, Norfolk NR2 4AR (01603 624315). Mon-Fri 09.00–17.30, Sat 09.00–16.00 (closed Thu). *L. World paper money.*

**C. J. Denton** (ANA, BNTA, FRNS)

PO Box 25, Orpington, Kent BR6 8PU (01689 873690). *P. World coins.*

**Dorset Coin Co Ltd** (BNTA)

193 Ashley Road, Parkstone, Poole, Dorset BH14 9DL (01202 739606, fax 01202 739230). *P. L. Separate coin and banknote lists.*

**Duncannon Partnership**

4 Beaufort Road, Reigate, RH2 9DJ (01737 244222 fax: 01737 224743) *Suppliers of albums, coin products and accessories.*

**Edinburgh Coin Shop** (ANA) (BNTA)

11 West Crosscauseway, Edinburgh EH8 9JW (0131 668 2928 fax 0131 668 2926). Mon-Sat 10.00–17.30. *L. World coins, medals and banknotes. Postal auctions.*

**Ely Stamp & Coin Shop**

27 Fore Hill, Ely, Cambs CB7 1AA (01353 663919). Mon, Wed-Sat 09.30–17.30. *World coins, medals and banknotes.*

**Jos Eijsermans (Eijsermans Events, Maastricht Fair)**

PO Box 1145, D–47547, Bedburg-Hau, Germany (+49 2821 71166–69 Fax: 2821 71166–71) e-mail: Eijsermans-Events@planet.nl. *Organisers of Papermoney, Bond and Share fair–Maastricht.*

**Evesham Stamp & Coin Centre**

Magpie Antiques, Paris House, 61 High Street, Evesham, Worcs WR11 4DA (01386 41631). Mon-Sat 09.00–17.30. *British coins and banknotes.*

**Richard N. Flashman**

54 Ebbsfleet Walk, Gravesend, Kent, DA11 9EW. *L. P. British banknotes.*

**Format of Birmingham Ltd** (ANA, BNTA, IAPN, IBNS)

Second Floor, Burlington Court, Lower Temple Street Birmingham B2 4JD (0121 643 2058). Mon-Fri 09.30-7.00. *L. Coins, tokens and medals.*

**B. Frank & Son** (ANA, IBNS)

3 South Avenue, Ryton, Tyne & Wear NE40 3LD (0191 413 8749). *P. L. Banknotes and cheques, coins of the world. Organiser of the North of England Coin & Banknote fair.* E-mail: bfrankandson@aol.com

**John Gaunt**

21 Harvey Road, Bedford MK41 9LF (01234 217685). By appointment. *Numismatic books.*

**Kate Gibson** (IBNS)

P.O. Box 819 Camberly, GU16 6ZU (01276 24954. *L World banknotes.* www.katespapermoney.co.uk.

**Glance Back Books**

17 Upper Street, Chepstow, Gwent NP6 5EX (01291 626562). 10.30–17.30. *World coins, medals, banknotes.*

**K. Goulborn**

Rhyl Coin Shop, 12 Sussex Street, Rhyl, Clwyd (01745 338112 or 01745 344856). *P. L. British coins and banknotes.*

**Ian Gradon** (IBNS)

PO Box 359, Durham, DH7 6WZ. (0191 3719 700). www.worldnotes.co.uk. *P. L. World bank notes.*

**Granta Stamp & Coin Shop**

28 Magdalene Street, Cambridge CB3 0AF (01223 315044) Mon-Sat 10.30-18.30. *English coins and banknotes.*

**Grantham Coins** (BNTA)

PO Box 60, Grantham, Lincs (01476 870565). *P. L. English coins and banknotes.*

**Eric Green—Agent in UK for Ronald J. Gillio Inc,**

1013 State Street, Santa Barbara, California, USA (020 8907 0015, Mobile 0468 454948). *Gold coins, banknotes*

**Ian Haines**

PO Box 45, Hereford, HR2 7YP (01432 268178). *P. L. British and foreign coins and banknotes.*

**A. D. Hamilton & Co** (ANA, BNTA)

7 St Vincent Place, Glasgow G1 5JA (0141 221 5423, fax 0141 248 6019). Mon-Sat 09.00-17.30. *British and World coins and banknotes.* Website: www. adhamiltons.com

**John Harvey** (IBNS)

PO Box 118, Bury St. Edmunds, IP33 2NE (01284 761894). *British Isles, Scotland, Channel Islands.*

**Craig Holmes**

6 Marlborough Drive, Bangor, Co Down BT19 1HB. *P. L. Low cost banknotes of the world.*

**R. G. Holmes**

11 Cross Park, Ilfracombe, Devon EX34 8BJ (01271 864474). *P. L. Coins, modern world crowns and foreign banknotes.*

**Homeland Holding Ltd** (IBNS)

Homeland, St John, Jersey, Channel Islands JE3 4AB (01534 65339). Mon-Fri 09.00-2.00. *World coins.*

**HTSM Coins**

26 Dosk Avenue, Glasgow G13 4LQ. *P. L. British and foreign coins and banknotes.*

**Intercol London** (ANA, BNTA, IBNS)

43 Templars Crescent, London N3 3QR (020 8349 2207 or 020 7354 2599). *P. Paper money of the world.*

**Peter Ireland Ltd** (BNTA, IBNS)

31 Clifton Street, Blackpool, Lancs FY1 1JQ (01253 21588 fax 0253 300232). Mon-Sat 09.00-17.30.*British and world coins, medals and tokens (some banknotes).*

**JAK (J. R. Leonard Ltd)** (IBNS)

31 Vapron Road, Mannamead, Plymouth, Devon PL3 5NJ (01752 665405). *P. L. GB and Commonwealth banknotes.*

**Richard W. Jeffery**

Trebehor, Porthcurno, Penzance, Cornwall TR19 6LS (01736 871263). *P. British and world coins and banknotes.*

**KB Coins** (BNTA)

50 Lingfield Road, Martins Wood, Stevenage, Herts SG1 5SL (01438 312661). 09.00–18.00 by appointment only. *L. Mainly British coins and banknotes.*

**Peter Licence**

31 Reigate Way, Wallington, Surrey SM6 8NU (020 8688 5297). *P. British and World coins.*

**Lindner Publications Ltd**

3a Hayle Industrial Park, Hayle, Cornwall TR27 4DX. Mon—Fri 09.00–13.00. *L. Manufacturers of albums, cabinets and accessories.* Website: www. stampaccessories.net.

**Lockdale Coins**

36 Upper Orwell Street, Ipswich IP4 1HP, (01473 218588), 168 London Road South, Lowestoft NR33 0BB, (01502 568468). L. (Shop's open 9.30–4.30 Mon–Sat). *World coins, medals, banknotes and accessories.* Website: www.lockdales.co.uk.

**London Coins**

4–6 Upper Street South, New Ash Green, Kent DA3 8JJ. (01474 871464) www.londoncoins. co.uk. *British and world coins.*

**Clive Maxwell-Yates**

21 Nicolas Road, Chorlton Manchester, M21 1LG (0161 881 7015). *P. L. World banknotes.*

**Michael Coins**

6 Hillgate Street, London W8 7SR (020 7727 1518). Mon-Fri 10.00-17.00. *World coins and banknotes.*

**Graeme & Linda Monk** (ANA, BNTA)

PO Box 201, Croydon, Surrey, CR9 7AQ (020 8656 4583 fax 020 8656 4583). *P. Fair organisers.*

**Peter Morris**

1 Station Concourse, Bromley North Station, Bromley, BR1 1NN or PO Box 223, Bromley, BR1 4EQ (020 8313 3410 Fax: 020 8466 8502). Mon-Fri 10.00–18.00, Sat 0900-14.00 or by appointment. *L. British and world coins and banknotes, numismatic books.* Website: www. petermorris.co.uk.

**Colin Narbeth & Son Ltd** (ANA, IBNS)

20 Cecil Court, Leicester Square, London WC2N 4HE (020 7379 6975). Mon-Sat 10.30-17.00. *World banknotes.* Website: www.colin-narbeth.com.

**New Forest Leaves**

Bisterne Close, Burley, Ringwood, Hants BH24 4BA (014253 3315). *Publishers of numismatic books.*

**Michael O'Grady** (IBNS)

PO Box 307, Pinner, Middlesex HA5 4XT (020 8428 4002). *P. British and world paper money.* E-mail: mike@ogrady.clara.co.uk

**Roger Outing**

P.O Box 123, Huddersfield HD8 9WY (01484 860419). *British & World Banknotes, Cheques & banking memorabilia.*

**Penrith Coin & Stamp Centre**

37 King Street, Penrith, Cumbria CA11 7AY (01768 64185). Mon-Sat 09.00–17.30. *World coins and notes.*

**Pentland Coins** (IBNS)

Pentland House, 92 High Street, Wick, Caithness KW14 L5. *P. British, world coins and world banknotes.*

**Pettinaro Bros.**

G. C. Pettinaro, Piaza dela Riscossa, 16 int. 50, CH– 6900 Lugano-Cassarate, Canton Ticino, Switzerland. (+41 91 970 2852) email: giovanni.pettinaro@gmail. com. *World banknotes.*

**John Pettit Pty Ltd**

GPO Box 4593, Sydney 2001, Australia. (00612 9235 0888) www.johnpettit.com. *P. L. Rare banknote specialist*

**Phil Phipps** (IBNS)

PO Box 139, Tiverton, Devon EX16 0AU (07850 864554). *P. L. World and German banknotes.* E-mail: p.p.phipps@tesco.net.

**David Pratchett**

Trafalgar Square Collectors Centre, 7 Whitcomb Street, London WC2H 7HA. (020 7930 1979). Mon-Fri 10.00–7.30. *Specialist in world coins and banknotes.* Website: www.coinsonline.co.uk.

**Pomexport (No. One Money Man)**

P.O Box, Ridgefield Park, New Jersey, 07660 (1 201 641 6641 fax: 1 201 641 1700) *Wholesale Paper Money, Stocks , Bonds Coins, Medals & Tokens.*

**Quentin Freres**

18 Rue Saint Gilles, 75003 Paris, France (33 1 42 713794, fax 33 1 42 713754). email quentin@worldnet. fr. *Specialists in world banknotes.*

**George Rankin Coin Co Ltd** (ANA, BNTA)

325 Bethnal Green Road, London E2 6AH (020 7729 1280 fax 020 7729 5023). Mon-Sat 10.00-18.00 (half-day Thu). *World coins and banknotes.*

**Mark T. Ray** (Collectors World)

188 Wollaton Road, Wollaton Road, Wollaton, Nottingham NG8 1HJ (0115 9280347) *P. British coins and banknotes.*

**Scottish Banknotes**

Sconser, Isle of Skye, IV48 8TD (01478 650450) E-mail: johnaunc@aol.com. *Scottish Banknotes*

**Scot Mint**

5 Main Street, Ayr, Scotland, KA8 8BU. (01292 268244 Fax: 01292 268626). e-mail: rob@scotmint.com *Medals, Badges, Militaria, Banknotes Coins, Collectables & Accessories*

**Safe Albums (UK) Ltd**

Freepost (RG 1792), Wokingham, Berks RG11 1BR (01734 328976 fax 01734 328612). *P. Banknote albums, coin holders, etc.*

**Simmons Gallery** (ANA, BNTA, IBNS)

P.O Box 104, Leystone, London E11 IND (0207 8989 8097 fax 020 7831 2090). *Organisers of the London Coin Fair, Cumberland Hotel, Marble Arch, London W1. L. Coins, tokens and medals.* Website: simmonsgallery. co.uk.

**E. Smith** (ANA, IBNS)

PO Box 348, Lincoln LN6 0TX (01522 684681 fax 01522 689528). *P. Organiser of the Morley, Leeds, monthly coin fair. World coins and paper money.*

**Spink & Son Ltd** (ANA, BNTA, IAPN, IBNS)

69 Southampton Row, Bloomsbury, London WC1B 4ET (020 7563 4000 Fax: 020 7563 4066). Mon-Sat 09.30–17.30. *Ancient, medieval and modern world coins, orders, medals and decorations, banknotes and numismatic books—new and secondhand.*

Website: www.spink.com.

**Stamp & Collectors Centre**

404 York Town Road, College Town, Camberley, Surrey GU15 4PR (01276 32587 fax 01276 32505). Mon, Tue, Thu, Sat 09.00–17.00, Wed, Fri 09.00–1900. *World coins, medals and banknotes.*

**Mel Steinberg & Son**

P.O Box 752, San Anselmo, CA94979 (415 897 1654) E-mail: melsteinberg@mindspring.com. *World Banknotes*

**Sterling Coins & Medals**

2 Somerset Road, Boscombe, Bournemouth, Dorset BH7 6JH (01202 423881). Mon-Sat 09.30–16.30 (closed Wed). *World coins and banknotes.*

**Vera Trinder Ltd**

38 Bedford Street, Strand, London WC2E 9EU (020 7836 2365/6). Mon-Fri 08.30-17.30. *L. Catalogues and books, albums, envelopes, cases and accessories.*

**Vista World Banknotes**

5 Greenfields Way, Burley-in-Wharfdale, Ilkley, W.Yorks, LS29 7RB. *World Notes list.* E-mail: vistabanknotes@barclays.net.

**Pam West, British Notes** (IBNS, ANA, PCDA)

PO Box 257, Sutton, Surrey SM3 9WW (020 8641 3224). *P. L. English banknotes, British banknotes accessories.* Website: west-banknotes.co.uk.

**West Essex Coin Investments** (BNTA, IBNS)

Croft Cottage, Station Road, Alderholt, Fordingbridge, Hants SP6 3AZ (01425 656 459). *P. L. British and World coins and paper money.*

**R & J White** (IBNS)

29 Shortacre, Basildon, Essex SS14 2LR (01268 522923). *P. L. Banknotes and world ephemera.*

**Trevor Wilkin**

PO Box 182, Cammeray, NSW, Australia (0061 2 9438 5040. <trevorsnotes@bigpond.com>. *P. L. World banknotes. Specialist in polymer notes.*

**wrb-banknotes**

P.O Box 52, Downham Market, PE38 0WX. E-mail: rdennettnotes@aol.com

**Barry Wright**

54 Dooley Drive, Bootle, Merseyside. L3O 8RT. *P. L. World banknotes.*

**Ye Olde Banknote Shoppe**

www.oldbanknotehop.co.uk, email jim@oldbanknoteshop.co.uk. *UK and world banknotes and coins.*

# Banks, Mints and numismatic
# Bureaux
## of the world

Many national banks and mints operate numismatic bureaux and sales agencies from which coins, notes and other numismatic products may be obtained direct. The conditions under which purchases may be made vary considerably. In many cases at the present time bureaux will accept orders from overseas customers quoting their credit card number and its expiry date; but in others payment can only be made by certified bank cheque, or international money order, or by girobank. Cash is seldom, if ever, acceptable. It is best to write in the first instance to enquire about methods of payment.

**A**

National Mint, Baghe Arg, Kabul, Afghanistan

Bank Mille Afghan, Kabul, Afghanistan

Banque d'Algerie, Sucursale d'Alger, 8 Boulevard Carnot, Alger, Algeria

Banco de Angola, Luanda, Daroal, Angola

Casa de Moneda de la Nacion, Avenida Antartica, Buenos Aires, BA, Argentina

Royal Australian Mint, Department of the Treasury, Canberra, ACT, Australia

GoldCorp Australia, Perth Mint Buildings, GPO Box M924, Perth, Western Australia 6001

Oesterreichsiches Hauptmunzamt, Am Heumarkt 1, A-1031 Wien, Postfach 225, Austria

Oesterreichische Nationalbank, A-1090 Wien, Otto Wagner-platz 3, Austria

**B**

Treasury Department, PO Box 557, Nassau, Bahamas (*coins*)

Ministry of Finance, PO Box 300, Nassau, Bahamas (*banknotes*)

Bank of Bahrain, PO Box 106, Manama, Bahrain

Eastern Bank, PO Box 29, Manama, Bahrain

Monnaie Royale de Belgique, Avenue de Pacheco 32, B-1000 Bruxelles, Belgium

Banque Nationale de Belgique SA, Caisse Centrale, Bruxelles, Belgium

Banque de Bruxelles SA, 2 Rue de la Regence, Bruxelles 1, Belgium

Casa de la Moneda, Potosi, Bolivia

Banco Central de Bolivia, La Paz, Bolivia

Casa da Moeda, Praca da Republica 173, Rio de Janeiro, Brazil

Hemus FTO, 7 Vasil Levski Street, Sofia C-1, Bulgaria

Banque de la Republique, Bujumbura, Burundi

**C**

Banque Centrale, Douala, Boite Postale 5.445, Cameroun

Royal Canadian Mint, 320 Sussex Drive, Ottawa 2, Ontario, Canada K1A 0G8

Casa de Moneda, Quinta Normal, Santiago, Chile

Casa de Moneda, Calle 11 no 4-93, Bogota, Colombia

Numismatic Section, The Treasury, Avarua, Rarotonga, Cook Islands

Banco Centrale de Costa Rica, Departamento de Contabilidad, San Jose, Costa Rica, CA

Central Bank of Cyprus, PO Box 1087, Nicosia, Cyprus

Artia, Ve Smekach 30, PO Box 790, Praha 1, Czech Republic

**D**

Den Kongelige Mønt, Amager Boulevard 115, København S, Denmark

Danmarks Nationalbank, Holmens Kanal 17, 1060 København K, Denmark

Banco Central de Santo Domingo, Santo Domingo, Dominican Republic

**E**

Banco Central, Quito, Ecuador

Mint House, Abbassia, Cairo, Egyptian Arab Republic

Exchange Control Department, National Bank of Egypt, Cairo, Egyptian Arab Republic

Banco Central de la Republica, Santa Isabel, Equatorial Guinea

Commercial Bank of Ethiopia, Foreign Branch, PO Box 255, Addis Ababa, Ethiopia

**F**

Currency Board, Victoria Parade, Suva, Fiji

Suomen Rahapaja, Katajanokanlaituri 3, Helsinki 16, Finland

Suomen Pankki, PO Box 10160, Helsinki 10, Finland

Hotel de Monnaie, 11 Quai de Conti, 75-Paris 6e, France

**G**

Banque Centrale Libreville, Boite Postale 112, Gabon

Verkaufstelle fur Sammlermunzen, D-638 Bad Homburg vdH, Bahnhofstrasse 16–18, Germany

Staatliche Munze Karlsruhe, Stephanienstrasse 28a, 75 Karlsruhe, Germany

Staatliche Munze Cannstatt, Taubenheimerstrasse 77, 7 Stuttgart-Bad, Germany

Bayerisches Hauptmunzamt, Hofgraben 4, 8 Munich, Germany

Hamburgische Munze, Norderstrasse 66, 2 Hamburg 1, Germany

Bank of Ghana, PO Box 2674, Accra, Ghana

Pobjoy Mint, Mint House, 92 Oldfields Road, Sutton, Surrey SM1 2NW

Royal Mint, Llantrisant, Mid Glamorgan, Wales, CF7 8YT

Royal Mint Coin Club, PO Box 500, Cardiff, CF1 1HA

Bank of Greece, Treasury Department, Cash, Delivery & Despatch Division, PO Box 105, Athens, Greece

Casa Nacional de Moneda, 6a Calle 4-28, Zona 1, Ciudad Guatemala, Republica de Guatemala CA

States Treasury, St Peter Port, Guernsey, Channel Islands

Bank of Guyana, PO Box 658, Georgetown, Guyana

**H**

Banque Nationale de la Republique d'Haiti, Rue Americaine et Rue Fereu, Port-au-Prince, Haiti

Banco Central de Honduras, Tegucigalpa DC, Honduras CA

State Mint, Ulloi utca 102, Budapest VIII, Hungary

Artex, PO Box 167, Budapest 62, Hungary

Magyar Nemzeti Bank, Board of Exchange, Budapest 54, Hungary

**I**

Sedlabanki Islands, Reykjavik, Iceland

Indian Government Mint, Bombay 1, India

Arthie Vasa, Keabajoran Baru, Djakarta, Indonesia

Perum Peruri, Djakarta, Indonesia

National Mint, Tehran, Iran

Bank Markazi Iran, Tehran, IranCentral Bank of Iraq, PO Box 64, Baghdad, Iraq

Central Bank of Ireland, Dublin 2, Republic of Ireland

The Treasury, Government Buildings, Prospect Hill, Douglas, Isle of Man

Israel Stamp and Coin Gallery, 4 Maze Street, Tel Aviv, Israel

Istituto Poligraphico e Zecca dello Stato, Via Principe Umberto, Roma, Italy

**J**

Decimal Currency Board, PO Box 8000, Kingston, Jamaica

Mint Bureau, 1 Shinkawasakicho, Kita-ku, Osaka 530, Japan

Numismatic Section, Treasury Department, St Helier, Jersey

Central Bank of Jordan, Amman, Jordan

Banque Nationale du Liban, Rue Masraf Loubnan, Beirut, Lebanon

**K**

Central Bank, PO Box 526, Kuwait

**L**

Bank of Lithuania, Cash Department, Gedimino av. 6, 2001 Vilius, Lithuania

Caisse Generale de l'Etat, 5 Rue Goethe, Luxembourg Ville, Grande Duche de Luxembourg

**M**

Institut d'Emission Malgache, Boite Postale 205, Tananarive, Madagascar

Central Bank of Malta, Valletta 1, Malta

Casa de Moneda, Calle del Apartado no 13, Mexico 1, DF, Mexico

Le Tresorier General des Finances, Monte Carlo, Principaute de Monaco

Banque de l'Etat du Maroc, Rabat, Morocco

Banco Nacional Ultramarino, Maputo, Republica de Mocambique

British Bank of the Middle East, Muscat

**N**

Royal Mint, Dharahara, Katmandu, Nepal

Nepal Rastra Bank, Katmandu, Nepal

Rijks Munt, Leidseweg 90, Utrecht, Netherlands

Hollandsche Bank-Unie NV, Willemstad, Breedestraat 1, Curacao, Netherlands Antilles

Central Bank of Curacao, Willemstad, Curacao, Netherlands Antilles

The Treasury, Private Bag, Lambton Quay, Wellington, New Zealand

Banco de Nicaragua, Departamento de Emison, La Tresoria, Apartada 2252, Managua, Nicaragua

Nigerian Security Printing and Minting Corporation, Ahmadu Bello Road, Victoria Island, Lagos, Nigeria

Central Bank of Nigeria, Tinubu Square LB, Lagos, Nigeria

Norges Bank, Oslo, Norway

Den Kongelige Mynt, Hyttegaten, Konigsberg, Norway

**P**

Pakistan State Mint, Baghban Pura, Lahore 9, Pakistan

National Development Bank, Asuncion, Paraguay

Casa Nacional de Moneda, Calle Junin 791, Lima, Peru

Central Bank of the Philippines, Manila, Philippines

Bank Handlowy w Warszawie, Ul. Romuald Traugutta 7, Warsaw, Poland

Desa Foreign Trade Department, Al. Jerozolimskie 2, Warszawa, Poland

Casa da Moeda, Avenida Dr Antonio Jose de Almeida, Lisbon 1, Portugal

**R**

Cartimex, 14-18 Aristide Briand St, PO Box 134-135, Bucharest, Roumania

Bank of Foreign Trade, Commercial Department, Moscow K 16, Neglinnaja 12, Russian Federation

Banque Nationale du Rwanda, Boite Postale 351, Kigali, Republique Rwandaise

**S**

Numismatic Section, Box 194, GPO, Apia, Samoa

Azienda Autonoma di Stato Filatelica-Numismatica, Casalla Postale 1, 47031 Repubblica di San Marino

Banque Internationale pour le Commerce, 2 Avenue Roume, Dakar, Senegal

Bank of Yugoslavia, PO Box 1010, Belgrade, Serbia

The Treasury, PO Box 59, Victoria, Seychelles

Bank of Sierra Leone, PO Box 30, Freetown, Sierra Leone

The Singapore Mint, 249 Jalan Boon Lay, Jurong, Singapore

South African Mint, PO Box 464, Pretoria, South Africa

Government Printing Agency, 93 Bukchang Dong, Chungku, Seoul, Republic of South Korea

Fabrica Nacional de Moneda y Timbre, Jorge Juan 106, Madrid 9, Spain

Bank of Sri Lanka, PO Box 241, Colombo, Sri Lanka

Hong Kong and Shanghai Banking Corporation, PO Box 73, Colombo 1, Sri Lanka

Sudan Mint, PO Box 43, Khartoum, Sudan

Bank of Sudan, PO Box 313, Khartoum, Sudan

Bank of Paramaribo, Paramaribo, Suriname

Kungelige Mynt och Justeringsverket, Box 22055, Stockholm 22, Sweden

Eidgenossische Staatskasse, Bundesgasse 14, CH-3003, Berne, Switzerland

Central Bank of Syria, Damascus, Syrian Arab Republic

**T**

Central Mint of China, 44 Chiu Chuan Street, Taipei, Taiwan, ROC

Royal Thai Mint, 4 Chao Fah Road, Bangkok, Thailand

Numismatic Section, The Treasury, Nuku'alofa, Tonga

Central Bank of Trinidad and Tobago, PO Box 1250, Port of Spain, Trinidad

Banque Centrale de Tunisie, Tunis, Tunisia

State Mint, Maliye Bakanligi Darphane Mudurlugu, Istanbul, Turkey

**U**

Bank of Uganda, PO Box 7120, Kampala, Uganda

Numismatic Service, US Assay Office, 350 Duboce Avenue, San Francisco, CA, 94102, USA

Office of the Director of the Mint, Treasury Department, Washington, DC, 20220, USA

Philadelphia Mint, 16th and Spring Garden Streets, Philadelphia, PA, 19130, USA

Franklin Mint, Franklin Center, Pennsylvania, 19063, USA

Banco Central del Uruguay, Cerrito 351, Montevideo, RO del Uruguay

**V**

Ufficio Numismatico, Governatorato dello Stato della Citta de Vaticano, Italy

Banco Central de Venezuela, Caracas, Venezuela

**Y**

Yemen Bank, Sana'a, Yemen.

**Z**

Bank of Zambia, PO Box 80, Lusaka, Zambia

Chief Cashier, Reserve Bank, PO Box 1283, Harare, Zimbabwe

*Bank of England, 1845 — the Five Pound Bank Note Office.*

# Banknotes and
# The law

## Counterfeit Currency

A counterfeit is a forgery or imitation of a coin or banknote produced with the intention of defrauding the revenue of the State or deceiving members of the public. By the Coinage Offences Act (1861) it was a felony to counterfeit gold or silver coins. Lesser offences included the gilding of farthings and sixpences to pass them off as half-sovereigns, the possession of moulds, machines or tools clandestinely removed from the Royal Mint, the impairment or diminution of gold or silver coins by filing or clipping (or even the possession of such filings and clippings).

The Coinage Act of 1870 made provision for the counterfeiting of base-metal coins, or the stamping of letters or words on coins of any kind, or the forging of colonial coinage. The most celebrated prosecution under this Act occurred in 1930 when Martin Coles Harman was convicted and fined £5 for issuing bronze coins resembling the British penny and halfpenny for the island of Lundy of which he was then the proprietor. Interestingly, no attempt was made to prosecute the Birmingham Mint which actually struck the coins (prudently omitting the H mintmark).

The making of medals or coins resembling current coin became a misdemeanour under the Counterfeit Medal Act of 1883. This Act is invoked from time to time against manufacturers or distributors of medallic pieces or coin jewellery. Such pieces, often struck in 9 carat gold, are deemed to infringe the Act if, for example, they have a figure even vaguely resembling St George and the Dragon on one side. The use of the royal effigy, however, without due authorisation, is regarded as a misdemeanour punishable by an unlimited fine and the confiscation of tools, dies and instruments. At the present time it is a serious offence to make a counterfeit of a currency note or coin with the intention of passing it off or tendering it as genuine. This offence carries a maximum penalty of ten years' imprisonment or an unlimited fine, or both. Making a counterfeit of a currency note or coin without lawful authority incurs a penalty up to two years' imprisonment or an unlimited fine, or both.

Passing or tendering as genuine anything which is known or believed to be a counterfeit of a currency note or coin renders the criminal on conviction to a term of ten years' imprisonment or an unlimited fine, or both. The mere possession of any forged note or coin is itself a criminal offence. Possessing countertfeits without authority or permission so to do, and doing so knowingly, renders the possessor liable to two years' imprisonment or an unlimited fine, or both. The Act also stipulates that the reproduction of a current banknote—of the Bank of England or of the Scottish and Northern Irish banks is a serious offence. This clause covers even such apparently innocent acts as making a photocopy (whether in black and white or full colour) of a current banknote, the photography of such a note or the illustration of such a note in any book, magazine or newspaper. Strict regulations are laid down concerning the legitimate illustration of notes, whether current or not, in books and periodicals; such illustrations must be either greatly reduced or enlarged *and* must bear a prominent defacement, such as SPECIMEN or CANCELLED. It is also a serious offence to utilise a reproduction of a current British banknote in any medium. Theoretically this includes such things as tea-towels, T-shirts, mugs, plates and other souvenirs in glass or ceramics, but in practice the law seems to turn a blind eye to such practices. Imitations and parodies of notes and coins are also regarded as infringements of the law, but in these instances prosecution of the offender seldom proceeds; a warning is generally regarded as sufficient, provided that the offending article or articles are withdrawn and suppressed.

The advent of high-definition colour photo-copying in recent years has brought the offence of reproduction into prominence once more. The regulations have been tightened considerably and there have been several cases of successful prosecution. In each case, however, the intent deliberately to deceive the public by passing a colour photocopy as a genuine note was proved. Technically the offence takes place as soon as the photocopy is made, for whatever purpose, but as a rule only those cases in which an element of fraudulent deception subsequently arose were pursued with the full rigour of the law. The law is quite clear, however, and it is a criminal offence to make a colour photocopy or photograph of any current British note unless permission to do so has been obtained from the Treasury. The maximum penalty on conviction is an unlimited fine.

The note-issuing banks have, of course, taken steps in recent years to incorporate further security devices into their notes, notably the use of latent images and underprints in colours which are difficult, if not impossible to photocopy accurately. At the same time, the adoption of metal strips and more complex watermark devices has theoretically made the task of the forger much more difficult. If, by some unlucky chance, someone passes a dud note on to you, you must make no attempt to pass it in turn. To do so renders you liable to prosecution for uttering a forgery. Forged notes must be handed over to the police as soon as possible. If you receive a forged note in payment for goods or services you are entitled to claim its face value from the person who gave it to you. Even if the person giving you the note did not realise that it was counterfeit, it is assumed in law that he or she represented to you that the note was worth its face value at the time the note was passed. If the tenderer knew that the note was forged, he can be prosecuted; but at the end of the day he is still liable to you for the fraud and can be sued in the civil courts for the recovery of the sum involved. If, on the other hand, you received the money as a gift, you have no legal claim against the person who gave it to you. If you pay someone with a counterfeit note or coin unknowingly, you have committed no offence, but you must pay again. The degree of culpability is often difficult to prove or disprove, but it is unlikely that a prosecution would be initiated on the basis of a single note.

## Legal Tender

The dictionary defines this as currency which a creditor is bound by law to accept as payment of a money debt. Debts and purchases must be paid for in cash of legal tender unless the creditor or seller is willing to accept payment in another form, such as a postal order, money order, cheque or, nowadays, credit card. Bank of England notes of any denomination are legal tender in England and Wales. Formerly Bank of England pound notes (but no other) were legal tender in Scotland. Technically, since the demise of the pound note, no Bank of England notes are legal tender in Scotland, although in practice they circulate freely north of the Border. Even more surprisingly, Scottish banknotes are not legal tender anywhere, not even in Scotland! The subtle difference is reflected in the actual wording of the promise on English and Scottish banknotes. Thus English notes are inscribed "*I promise to pay the bearer on demand the sum of . . .*" without stipulating any specific place, the promise being made by the Chief Cashier. Scottish notes, on the other hand, have the promise in the third person. It is the bank itself which makes the promise "*to pay the bearer on demand . . . pounds sterling at their head office here in Edinburgh, by order of the Board*". In practice, however, Scottish banknotes are accepted without question, not only throughout Scotland but also in parts of England, and

are generally accepted in London, although there is no obligation on the part of a creditor so to do.

Apart from gold coins, the base-metal pound coin is legal tender for payment of any amounts. So, too, presumably, are the various two-pound and five-pound base-metal coins of recent years, even though they have been struck as commemoratives and not intended for general circulation in the ordinary sense. Smaller denominations are only legal tender up to a maximum value in each case. In the case of 50p coins, 25p crowns and 20p coins, they may be used alone, or in combination with each other, in payment of amounts up to £10. 10p and 5p coins, alone or in combination, may be used for sums up to £5. Bronze 1p and 2p coins, however, can only be used for payment of amounts up to 20p. In practice, of course, you can probably get away with making payment in larger quantities (within reason!) although strictly speaking there is no obligation on the part of your creditor to accept them.

## Value Added Tax

This is a matter which primarily concerns dealers, but it also applies to those who dabble in coins on a part-time basis, and has implications for collectors at all levels. Briefly, anyone conducting a business, or in self-employment, who has a turnover in excess of £43,000 per annum, must register with HM Customs and Excise for the collection and payment of Value Added Tax. Anyone whose turnover is less than £43,000 is exempt from the obligation to register, but is at liberty to register if he or she feels that this would be advantageous. It is nice to think that there is an element of choice in this, although one would be hard pressed to think why anyone would voluntarily register for VAT unless they absolutely had to! Incidentally, the government raised the VAT registration level by 40 per cent to £35,000 in March 1991 with the avowed intention of relieving a large number of businesses from this burden, at a time when the rate of tax was increased from 15 per cent to 17.5 per cent. Assuming that you are a dealer with a turnover above the magic limit, then you are committing a serious offence if you fail to register. Registration then lays you open to the full machinery of the system. You have to charge VAT on all goods and services, issuing VAT invoices and receipts and keeping detailed accounts which are liable to snap inspection at any time. You have to make quarterly returns to Customs and Excise of the amount of tax you have collected. From this you are allowed to deduct the VAT which you yourself have paid out in the course of your business, and you then have to remit the difference to the VAT collector. Of course, should the amount you have paid exceed the tax you have collected, you receive a repayment in due course. This arises in businesses which handle zero-rated goods and services, but coins and medals do not come within that category.

From January 1, 1995 the special margin scheme of accounting for VAT currently available for certain second-hand goods, such as cars, was extended to almost all second-hand goods. The scheme allows businesses buying and selling eligible goods to account for VAT only on the difference between the buying and selling prices of these items.

A special system of accounting has recently been introduced which enables some dealers to account for VAT without the need to keep a detailed record of every transaction. Certain works of art, antiques and collector's items, including "secondhand" coins, defined in Notice 712 *Second-hand goods*, were exempt from VAT at import. From January 1, 1996 these items became subject to VAT at import at an effective rate of 2.5 per cent.

## Importing Coins by Mail

Elsewhere in this volume will be found the names and addresses of mints, banks and numismatic bureaux around the world from whom it may be possible to obtain currency direct. It is a wise precaution to write to these bodies in the first instance for details of their sales and distribution. In some cases they appoint a dealer in Britain as an agent and this is a method of purchase that removes a great deal of the hassle and red tape. Nowadays, however, many mints and banks are quite happy to use the credit card system to make it easy to part you from your money. The problem arises, however, when the notes are despatched. As a rule, banks and mints stipulate quite clearly that they will not accept orders prepaid in cash, and it is an offence to send coins or banknotes out of the country as payment, except through banks authorised for this purpose. Cheques drawn on British banks should not be used. Indeed, this may be actively discouraged by the imposition of heavy clearance and handling charges at the other end. The converse is also true, although Americans seem to think that dollar cheques drawn on some obscure mid-West bank will be eagerly accepted here, and are consequently aggrieved when it is tactfully pointed out to them that this creates enormous problems—to say nothing of the swingeing bank charges incurred in converting such cheques to sterling. Other than credit cards, the Girobank system is probably the best method of remitting currency from one country to another; full details may be obtained from any post office. Details on the preferred method of sending remittances, or transferring cash to another country, as well as the transmission of coins by post to different countries, will be found in the *Royal Mail International Service Guide*.

The receipt of postal packets containing banknotes from abroad makes you liable for Value Added Tax on their importation. As a rule, the despatching mint or bank will have affixed a Customs declaration to the packet, listing the contents, their weight and value, and it is on that basis that VAT will be calculated. The position regarding the import and export of coins by post is more complicated, and applies also to goods sent on approval. In such cases you must consult your Customs and Excise office who will advise you on the correct procedure and what your liabilities will be to tax in either case. This also applies to dealers taking stock out of the country to a show and then re-importing the unsold stock afterwards, or importing material purchased at the show.

## Buying and Selling

When goods are sold, the seller and the buyer enter into a contract which confers rights and imposes obligations on both parties. The contract need not be in writing. There is no law governing the quality of goods sold by a private individual. If you purchase a coin from a fellow-collector as a result of an informal meeting at the local numismatic society it is incumbent on you to ensure that what you buy is what you think you are buying. If you purchase something from a dealer or shopkeeper, however, you are entitled under the Sale of Goods Act to goods of "merchantable quality" which means that they must be reasonably fit for their purpose. Items sold under a specific description, on the other hand, must correspond exactly with that description. If they do not, the seller *even a private individual* can be sued under the Sale of Goods Act. This is an important distinction because there is an erroneous notion that the Act does not apply to transactions between private individuals. If A sells a coin to B, purporting it to be a rare date, and B subsequently discovers that the date has been deliberately altered, then B can sue A. Even if A claims that he made the sale in good faith, believing the coin to be a genuine rare date, he will still be liable for restitution (giving B his money back) and may also face a claim for damages. The Sale of Goods Act thus overturns the traditional adage *caveat emptor* which, in its full formula, translates as "let the buyer beware for he ought not to be ignorant of the nature of the property which he is buying from another party". Traditionally this was the maxim applicable at auctions. Once the auctioneer's gavel had dropped, the successful bidder had, in effect, made a contract with the vendor and was bound to pay for the lot, even if he subsequently discovered that what he had purchased was not what he had imagined. The view was that it was up to the purchaser to ensure beforehand that what he purchased was genuine and answered the description in the sale catalogue.

Because of vexatious disputes arising from questions of authenticity, and with the Sale of Goods Act breathing down their necks, many auctioneers now have a safety net, in the form of extensions. These enable successful bidders to delay payment for two or three weeks while they seek expertisation of doubtful material. In other words, the law allows a cooling-off period, but only for he legitimate purpose of verifying the authenticity of items over which there may be some doubt. This is only operative in cases where a coin or medal is sold as genuine, and described and estimated in value accordingly. In many doubtful cases, however, an auctioneer will cover himself by adding the crucial words "as is" to the description of a lot. Then, indeed, it is a case of *caveat emptor*. The auctioneer has done everything humanly possible to draw attention to the controversial nature of the item, and it must then rest on the judgment of the purchaser.

On the subject of auctions there are legal aspects which are not always apparent, as well as subtle differences in law and practice between England and Scotland. These tend to arise in cases where coins and medals come up for sale at provincial general mixed auctions, rather than in the sales conducted by numismatic auctioneers. Goods up for auction may be subject to an upset price which is made public as the price at which the bidding will start. A reserve price, on the other hand, is known only to the auctioneer, and if it is not reached, the goods will not be sold. Upset prices are common in Scotland, reserve prices in England. If no upset price is specified and the goods are not subject to a reserve price then the highest bid secures them, even though it may not be as high as the vendor hoped for. If a seller notifies other bidders that he is bidding for his own goods, or that he has employed an agent to bid for him, the bidding is legal. If he does not give notice and bids himself, or gets someone to bid for him, thus forcing up the price, the sale is fraudulent, and the buyer can purchase the goods for the amount of the last bid he made before fraudulent bidding started.

One frequently hears dark, but usually apocryphal, tales of "the ring" in action to depress the bidding and secure items below the price commensurate with their actual value. This is a fraudulent practice and in law is regarded as a criminal conspiracy. In practice, however, it would be very difficult for a group of dealers or other individuals to keep the bidding down merely by sitting on their hands. This practice could only operate successfully in sales which were largely, if not entirely, frequented by dealers. But coin sales, like other specialist collector-orientated auctions, are characterised by a high proportion of private bidders in attendance. Any conspiracy by a ring would merely allow some private bidder to step in and secure the lot at a bargain price. Rings are illegal, but in practice prosecutions are very rare as it is extremely difficult to obtain proof of their operations. What is more likely to happen is that dealers have been known to act in concert to force up the bidding to frighten off some unwelcome interloper. Here again, such tales are legion, but astonishingly lacking in specific details. The golden rule in attending auctions is to know what you are going after, and to have a pretty precise idea of how much you are prepared to pay. Do not be stampeded in the heat of the moment into going way beyond your limit.

**Taxation of Profits on Disposal**

The Inland Revenue define an asset as "any form of property (other than sterling) wherever situated". A disposal includes a sale, exchange or gift of an asset, or the receipt of a capital sum in respect of them. In layman's terms you dispose of an asset when you sell it, give it away, exchange it or lose it. A transfer of assets between husband and wife doesn't count (unless they are legally separated), nor does the transfer of an asset you leave when you die. If a disposal results in a profit you could be liable to tax. Any profit made on the sale of certain assets, including coins, medals and other collectables, constitutes a capital gain and is subject to Capital Gains Tax (CGT) which is now charged at the same 25% and 40% rates as income tax. However the government allows you to make a total capital gain

in the current tax year of £5,500 before tax becomes chargeable. If this is the case, and the total proceeds from disposal do not exceed £10,000, then a simple declaration to this effect is all you need to make in the relevant section of your annual tax return.

Computing the actual capital gain is a complicated matter. Suppose you purchased a banknote in 1960 for £5,000 and sold it in 1993 for £12,000. On the face of it, you've made a capital gain of £7,000 and you might think that you were liable to CGT because the gain was over £5,500. However, the *length of time* you've held the asset also has to be taken into consideration. From April 6, 1988 the law was altered so that only gains made after March 31, 1982 are now taxable. In effect, you are taxed as if you acquired the coin on March 31, 1982. The initial value of the coin is deemed to be its market value at that date. If the gain from March 1982 to the time of disposal is greater than the overall gain from acquisition in 1960 to disposal in 1993, you take the lesser of the two figures. If this produces a gain, whereas the old method of working it out would have produced a loss, you will be regarded, for tax purposes, as having made neither a gain nor a loss on disposal. You have a choice of opting for computing from the time of actual acquisition or from March 1982, whichever seems the more advantageous; but once you've made your choice you cannot subsequently change your mind.

How do you establish what the coin was worth in March 1982? The Inland Revenue tend to regard Seaby, Krause or other relevant catalogues as their yardstick. The difference between the nominal or catalogue value in 1982 and what you eventually got for the coin *assuming that the latter was greater,* might be regarded as the capital gain, but even then the position is complicated by inflation in the intervening years eroding the real value of the coin.

At this stage things get really complicated as you have to work out the indexation allowance. This is determined by the Retail Prices Index (RPI), and you need to know the RPI for (a) the month of disposal, and (b) the month in which you acquired the asset, or March 1982, if later. The RPI is announced each month by the Departmenrt of Employment and is published in its *Employment Gazette* which ought to be available in your local public library. Take the RPI for the month of the disposal and subtract the RPI for the month when indexation commenced. Then divide the result by the RPI for the month when indexation began, and work out this figure to the nearest third decimal place. This is known as the indexation factor, which you then multiply by the initial value of your coin. Simple isn't it? In most cases, however, I expect you will have made a capital loss in real terms, so these sums, though necessary to satisfy the Inland Revenue, are largely academic.

# INDEX TO ADVERTISERS